70°

THE WEST INDIES

Area enclosed by dotted line comprises the West Indies as a faunal region

25°

Scale of Miles

| 0 | 50 | 100 | 200 | 300 | 400 |

(dor I.
ing)

Mayaguana I.

Caicos Is.

Turks Is.

Great Inagua

Tortue I.

20°

A N T I L L E S

St. Thomas

San Juan

Anegada

Anguilla

St Martin I.

St Bartholomew

HAITI   DOMINICAN
REPUBLIC

Mona

PUERTO
RICO

St Croix

Saba

Barbuda

Cauo
rince

Santo Domingo

St Eustatius
St Christopher
(St Kitts)

Nevis

Antigua

Montserrat

I S P A N I O L A

Désirade

Guadeloupe

Marie Galante

LESSER
ANTILLES

Dominica

15°

Martinique

St Lucia

Barbados

S E A

St Vincent

Grenadines

Carriacou

Grenada I.

Aruba

Curaçao

Bonaire

Isla
Margarita

Tobago

Trinidad 10°

V E N E Z U E L A

70°

60°

A FIELD GUIDE TO THE
Butterflies
OF THE WEST INDIES

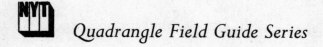
Quadrangle Field Guide Series

A FIELD GUIDE
TO THE
BUTTERFLIES
OF THE WEST INDIES

NORMAN D. RILEY

A Demeter Press Book

QUADRANGLE/THE NEW YORK TIMES BOOK CO.

Library of Congress Catalog Card Number: 74-25436

Distributed to the trade by Harper & Row

Contents

List of Plates

Plates 1-3, 9, 11, 12, 14, 15 and 18-20 were painted by Brian
  Hargreaves;
Plates 4-8, 10, 13, 16, 17 and 21-24 were painted by Gordon Riley.

List of Text Figures

Preface

When work on this guide was started the only publication available that could provide a means of identifying the butterflies of all the West Indian islands was the volume of Seitz's *Macrolepidoptera of the World* that dealt with the far richer faunas of North, Central and South America as well. Nor were there any really up-to-date books even on the larger islands. Although this latter gap has in the meantime been partly filled, the obvious need for a single comprehensive account of all the butterflies of all the islands remained. Indeed, in view of the growing interest in the butterflies of the area, it had become pressing. For the purposes of this guide the area of the West Indies is defined in the Introduction and delimited on the endpapers. Had it been extended more widely it would have encroached on other faunal areas at the risk of becoming too large and too superficial. The inclusion of Trinidad, for example, would have more than doubled the number of species to be listed.

It was surprising to find that, although the West Indies lie wholly within the Tropics, they mustered fewer species than the continent of Europe, 292 as against about 390; and disappointing that so little precise information existed about the biology of these species either in the literature or in the data attaching to collected specimens. One is inclined, mistakenly perhaps, to assume that in tropical islands most butterflies, due to the nature of the environment, would have a succession of broods throughout the year. Dated specimens were too few to permit more than a guess in most cases as to the number of annual broods any species had. Sometimes it seemed that 'rarity' reflected no more than the absence of collectors during a restricted flight period, especially during the summer months. Regular observations month by month throughout the year could fill in many gaps.

I have been at some pains to include, in abbreviated form, the available information about caterpillars and food plants, omitting reference to eggs and pupae because these stages are so seldom encountered. But a glance through the pages of this guide will show that nothing whatever is known about any stage in the life history of almost half of the species involved. Of other aspects of the lives of the West Indian butterflies I have been able to gather little but scraps. The one outstanding exception is in respect of the butterflies of Jamaica, the authors of *Jamaica and its Butterflies* having carefully brought together all that is known of the biology of that island. It is worth echoing the sentiments on this subject so well expressed by Dr A. B. Klots some years ago in his *Field Guide to the North American Butterflies*: those who successfully use this guide to identify their captures should realise that they have taken 'only the first step; those who pass beyond it and become interested in studying the life histories, habits, behaviour and environments of butterflies, will reap far greater rewards'.

Writing this guide, free from the pressures of 'full employment', has provided me with a welcome occupation rendered all the more enjoyable because it has brought me once again into close touch with fellow entomologists first met many years ago, and given me the opportunity to meet others also interested in the butterflies of the West Indies. First and foremost my thanks must go to Martin Brown, of Colorado Springs and known world-wide to lepidopterists as 'Brownie', for critically and most helpfully reading the whole of the manuscript, contributing the first account of the Lycaenidae, and reading a full set of the proofs, in spite of his many other pressing commitments. Not only that; only long after I had started work did I learn indirectly that he had quite spontaneously withdrawn and left to me the writing of this guide, which truly he was in many ways better qualified to do – a generous and yet so characteristic an act for which I shall ever be grateful. I think we first met, together with Dr Klots, mentioned above, at the International Entomological Congress at Ithaca in 1928. Dr J. F Gates Clarke, another friend of long standing, I have to thank for the loan of specimens from the United States National Museum, Washington; Dr F. H Rindge of the American Museum of Natural History, New York, Dr Kirby' Brown of the Peabody Museum of Natural History, Yale, and Dr J. M. Burns of the Museum of Comparative Zoology, Harvard, for the loan of important specimens from their respective institutes many of which are illustrated in colour for the first time in this guide, as listed below. Harry Clench of the Carnegie Museum, Pittsburgh, who as a 'G.I.' used to arrive on my doorstep at all hours of the day or night, I have to thank for far more information about the butterflies of the Bahamas than I was able to use; M. P. Viette of the Museum National d' Histoire Naturelle, Paris, and Mr E. C. Pelham-Clinton of the Royal Scottish Museum, Edinburgh, for help in elucidating the identity of species described by Godart; Mr J. G. Coutsis of Athens, for making available, through the University of Yale, a large part of the considerable collection of butterflies which he himself had made in Haiti; Mr T. J. G. Homer for the loan of a male of *Thereus bourkei*, a rare and very beautiful Jamaican Hairstreak; Dr T. J. Witt, of Munich, for giving me advance news of his work on the Antillean species of the genus *Anaea* and Dr Lee D. Miller for kindly comments on my treatment of the Hesperiidae. To all these I now have a welcome opportunity publicly to offer my thanks for friendships that have been such a pleasure, and sometimes an unrealised encouragement, over the years. Looking back, however, one cannot but regret that it is too late to do more than remember others who had special knowledge of the West Indian butterflies, and whom one knew. Such were F. D. Godman, W. J. Kaye, G. B. Longstaff, E. L. Bell, R. C. Williams Arthur Hall, G. D. Hale Carpenter, W. H. Evans, Karl Jordan, W. J. Holland and A. Avinoff.

To my two artists who have so expertly illustrated this guide, Brian Hargreaves and Gordon Riley especial thanks are due, not only for their pains-taking accuracy but also the brilliance of their colours, some of which would seem almost to flatter the originals did one not know how much more vivid most butterflies are in life than when pinned in a collection. To my thanks will undoubtedly be added those of many readers who will find the figures more helpful than my text.

Finally I must confess that without the continued and unrestricted access to the rich library and collections of the British Museum (Natural History), which I have enjoyed for so long, I could never have written this book. To the Trustees of that Museum therefore, and to their staff, I owe an especial debt of gratitude.

A Note on the Figured Specimens

All the specimens figured in this guide are in the British Museum (Natural History), London, and are utilised* by permission of the Trustees of that Museum, with the following exceptions:

SPECIMENS IN THE AMERICAN MUSEUM OF NATURAL HISTORY

Calisto lyceius, Plate 3 figure 5
Calisto hysius, Plate 3 figure 7a
Calisto eleleus, Plate 3 figure 11
Calisto chrysaoros, Plate 3 figure 14
Leptotes perkinsae, Plate 12 figure 14
Hemiargus dominica, Plate 12 figure 15
Pseudochrysops bornoi, Plate 12 figure 16
Burca stillmani, Plate 22 figure 5
Strymon christophei, text figure 12
Rhinthon bushi, text figure 23
Oarisma stillmani, text figure 24
Atalopedes nabokovi ♀, text figure 26
Choranthus borinconus, text figure 28

SPECIMENS IN THE MUSEUM OF COMPARATIVE ZOOLOGY, HARVARD

Calisto loxias, Plate 3 figures 2a and 2b
Calisto tragius, Plate 3 figure 6
Calisto montana, Plate 3 figure 8
Calisto grannus, Plate 3 figure 12
Calisto micheneri, Plate 3 figure 13
Calisto arcas, text figure 6
Eurema euterpiformis, text figure 16
Atalopedes nabokovi ♂, text figure 26
Paratrytone batesi, text figure 29

SPECIMENS IN THE PEABODY MUSEUM OF NATURAL HISTORY, YALE

Calisto nubila, Plate 2 figure 5a
Calisto archebates, Plate 3 figures 1a and 1b
Calisto hysius, Plate 3 figure 7b
Papilio aristor, Plate 2 figure 2

IN THE COLLECTION OF MR T. J. G. HOMER

Thereus bourkei, Plate 11 figure 3

Introduction

The purpose of this guide is to enable the butterflies of the West Indies to be identified with a minimum of difficulty. In most cases a simple comparison with the coloured figures will achieve this, for by far the greater number of species are so distinctive as to be unmistakable. However, as a further aid, key characters are printed in italics in the text, and repeated on the legends to the plates, when desirable. This applies especially to such difficult groups as the Hairstreaks and Blues (Plates 11 and 12), the Sulphurs (Plates 14 and 15) and the Skippers (Plates 21 to 24). It is particularly important to examine the markings on the underside of the wings, for nearly always it is there that the best specific characters are to be found.

Illustrations. All illustrations are life size, unless otherwise indicated, and the left half of each represents the upperside, the right half the underside.

The **area** covered is delimited on the endpapers. It is the whole of the West Indies, with the exception of the islands of Trinidad and Tobago, which faunistically belong to the mainland of South America.

It falls into two very distinct halves, the geologically older Greater Antilles which extend from Cuba to the Virgin Islands and include Hispaniola, Jamaica and Porto Rico on the one hand, and on the other hand the more recent volcanic Lesser Antilles which run from Anguilla and Montserrat to Grenada. The coverage is less detailed than in the Bird Guide to the same area as from many of the smaller islands there are no records of butterflies at all.

The **range** of each species as a whole, and its type locality, are given at the end of the paragraphs on **distribution**.

On page 199 will be found a combined **Check List** and **Distribution Table.** The latter should aid identification because it shows at a glance which species are to be found in each of the Greater Antilles or groups of smaller islands, and because very many species and subspecies are confined to a single island or a limited group. Besides being a guide to identification, however, the Check List and Distribution Table provide a rich fund of information for anyone interested in zoogeography. The fascination of this study of the geographical distribution of animals lies in finding the answers to such questions as: how did they get where they are now? How is it that *Papilio homerus* is unique to Jamaica, *Parides gundlachianus* is found only in Cuba, *Papilio aristor* only in Haiti? Where did they come from, when and how? These same questions can be asked of more than sixty species of West Indian butterflies. How did fourteen species of *Calisto* develop in Hispaniola whilst Cuba has at most three and Jamaica and Porto Rico only one each; and the whole genus is without a close representative anywhere on the mainland?

Questions of this kind, interesting as they are, are outside the scope of this guide. Papers listed under Zoogeography in the **Bibliography** (p. 209) will provide an introduction to the subject. There are, however, a few generalised conclusions of some interest that can be drawn from the Distribution Table. As a whole the Caribbean butterfly fauna is poor, considering that the entire area is within the tropics; it is smaller by nearly 25% than the European fauna for example, and not much more than one seventh the size of that of Central America. It consists of 'samples' derived from the mainland which, over an immense period of time, have succeeded in establishing themselves on the islands.

These samples fall into two groups, those that reached the islands before the emergence of the Lesser Antilles, including all the 'old' species of the Greater Antilles; and the geologically more recent arrivals that used the Lesser Antilles as stepping stones in a northward movement, most of them species already having a wide continental distribution. This has been a continuous process uninterrupted by earth movement and geological changes. Relating these suppositions to the present position, and considering species only, it is not surprising to find that in the single island of Hispaniola out of a total of 151 species no less than 41 are endemics (not found in any other West Indian island or indeed anywhere else), and that to a lesser degree this applies also to Cuba with 28 endemic species, Jamaica with 18, Porto Rico with 4, and the Bahamas with one or two. It is surprising, however, that in the Lesser Antilles Dominica has 2, the other islands, none.

BUTTERFLY MORPHOLOGY

The gross anatomy of a butterfly (Fig. 1) is quite simple: head, thorax, abdomen, two pairs of wings and three pairs of legs. It is on the variations of these structures that the classification of butterflies depends. The *head* bears a pair of antennae (feelers), a pair of short three-jointed sensory organs (palpi) between which lies the coiled proboscis, and a pair of large compound eyes. In butterflies

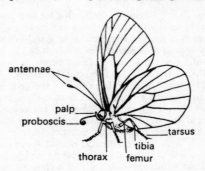

Fig. 1. Side view of a Pierid butterfly. Diagrammatic.

the *antennae* are always thickened distally (i.e. at the far end) to form clubs and these may, in Skippers only, sometimes end in a short bent point called the apiculus. Antennae are usually scaled; an area of the club that is free of scales is known as the nudum and is of importance in the classification of the Skippers. The relative lengths of the joints of the *palpi*, their clothing and direction are of classificatory value. The large compound *eyes* are roughly hemispherical, only in Lycaenidae is the circumference cut into due to the positioning of the antennal sockets. The *proboscis*, through which the butterfly sucks up water or nectar, is a hollow tube formed of the interlocking of two semi-cylindrical tubes derived from paired mouth parts called the maxillae.

The *thorax* is the butterfly's power plant containing the muscles that operate the wings and legs. A normal leg is made up of four parts, an immovable basal coxa, and three mobile parts, the femur (thigh), tibia (shin) and tarsus (foot), the last of which is typically five-jointed and ends in a claw or claws. Modifications of the legs provide most useful characters in distinguishing the families of the butterflies; for example in the Papilionidae, Pieridae and Hesperiidae all three pairs of legs are fully functional as legs in both sexes. In all the other families the forelegs are much altered, and often useless as legs, in one sex or even in both sexes, as described below under the various families. The *wings* are flattened bags between which run the veins that support them. The arrangements of these *veins* (Fig. 2) provide, as it were, map references that make it possible to locate on the surface of the wings, spots, lines and other markings that are important for identification purposes. They are more readily visible on the underside than on the upperside of the wing. A touch of benzine from a paint brush will show them up temporarily and do no damage to the wing. The veins all have names, indicating their homologies with the veins in other kinds of insects, but for the purposes of identification it is simpler to number them, 1 to 12 on the forewing, 1 to 8 on the hindwing, than to try to remember which they are. It is easiest to start counting at vein 2, which is the first vein arising from the lower

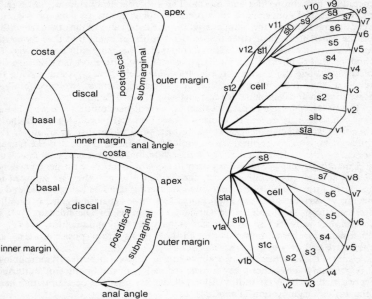

Fig. 2. The principal parts of a butterfly's wings. v = vein; s = space. The *anal angle* lies where the inner and outer margins meet. Diagrammatic.

edge of the cell, because vein 1 is sometimes duplicated. The spaces between the veins take their numbers from the veins below (i.e. behind) them. The pattern of the *markings* on the wings depends on the arrangement of the coloured scales that cover the wing surfaces and are fastened and overlap like tiles on a roof. The slightest touch will remove them. Their colour depends upon their contained pigment or, if metallic, on structural features that break up the light (interference colours), or sometimes on a combination of the two.

Compared with the head and thorax, the *abdomen* is simple. It contains the viscera, such as the alimentary canal (gut), a pulsating dorsal vessel (heart) which circulates the colourless 'blood' in which all the vessels are bathed, and central nerve cord, all of which extend forwards into the thorax. It also holds the reproductive organs, the chitinised 'external' parts of which are known as the *genitalia* and provide characters of great taxonomic significance at all levels of classification. Their examination is often essential for identification in critical groups, for example the Hesperiid genus *Ephyriades* (p. 174), and necessitates dissection.

CLASSIFICATION OF BUTTERFLIES

Scientifically butterflies are known as *Rhopalocera*, a term descriptive of their clubbed antennae. They are a division of the Lepidoptera, meaning scale-winged, which, in the hierarchy of classification, is an order of the class *Insecta* including both butterflies and moths. The suborder Rhopalocera, however, is more a term of convenience than precision for it covers two morphologically very different groups, the Skippers (on the one hand) and all the other butterflies on the other hand, their chief points of resemblance being that they fly by day and are, for the most part, brightly coloured. One can easily be forgiven for thinking that Skippers are day-flying moths. These differences have been recognised by placing the Skippers in a separate suborder, the Grypocera, leaving the others as the suborder Rhopalocera; or by treating them as two superfamilies, Hesperioidea and Papilionoidea respectively, of equal rank.

The prime objective of classification is convenience, putting like with like so that comparison is easier. If likeness is based on real morphological similarity then the resulting classification is said to be natural and to display affinities. The different kinds of butterflies, for example, the Monarch (Pl. I) and the Queen, are called *species*. If they are very similar, differing, for example, only in colours and markings, they are placed together in a *genus*, in this case the genus *Danaus*. *Genera* again display similarities to take account of which they are grouped together to form *Families*, the characters separating families being considered as having greater classificatory importance than those separating genera. Families are sometimes subdivided into subfamilies (e.g. as in Danaidae, p. 33); or several may be united to form a superfamily (as in Papilionoidea, above). It must be remembered, however, that all these terms, from species upwards, are subjective and denote concepts, not things.

Using the characters outlined above in the section on butterfly morphology it is possible to construct a key for the separation of the families of butterflies represented in the West Indies. All the characters used can be seen with a hand lens with a magnification of about × 10.

Key to Families of West Indian Butterflies
(not applicable in other areas)

1. All legs fully developed in both sexes, and with claws 2
1. Fore legs modified, often very small and without claws except in ♀ Lycaenidae and Riodinidae (Pls. 10–12) 4

2. All 12 forewing veins simple and unbranched, antennal sockets wide apart, club curved or with definite apiculus, head large, thorax stout, wings relatively short ....Hesperiidae
(Pls. 21–24)
2. At least some veins of forewing branched, antennae arise close together, antennal club straight and never with apiculus, wings relatively large 3

3. Hindwing with only one anal vein and usually tailed ....Papilionidae
(Pls. 18–20)
3. Hindwing with two anal veins, no tail ....Pieridae
(Pls. 13–17)

4. Palpi very prominent, much longer than thorax and projecting straight forward ....Libytheidae
(Pl. 10)
4. Palpi not as long as thorax, usually erect 5

5. One or two of the main veins of forewings much swollen at base of wing 6
5. Forewing veins not swollen basally 7

6. Dark brown species with at least one true eyespot on underside of forewing near apex ....Satyridae
(Pls. 2–3)
6. Brightly coloured species with no true eyespot on forewing underside near apex ....Nymphalidae*

7. Wings transparent ....Ithomiidae
(Pl. 2)
7. Wings not transparent..8

8. Antennae scaleless ....Danaidae
(Pl. 1)
8. Antennae, scaled, at least above..9

9. Forewing very long, twice as long as wide, or longer............Heliconiidae
(Pls.11–12)
9. Forewing not exceptionally elongate..10

10. Foreleg greatly reduced in both sexes, delicate and hairy in ♂, stouter in ♀ – brush-footed and clawless............................Nymphalidae
(Pls. 4–8)

*genera *Mestra, Eunica* and *Lucinia* (Plate 6)

LIFE CYCLE OF A BUTTERFLY

The cycle starts with the *egg* (ovum), a delicate object rarely as much as one millimetre in diameter and usually beautifully ribbed and sculptured in such variety as to be recognisably different in each species. Those of the Pieridae are tall and conical; Hesperiid eggs are for the most part hemispherical; those of the Lycaenidae characteristically disc-shaped. In between are the more rounded eggs of the other families. In all there are minute pores called micropyles at the top which allow the male sperm to penetrate the shell and fertilise the egg.

The most conspicuous feature of the newly hatched *caterpillar* (larva) is its seemingly disproportionately large head. Even at this stage each family displays characteristic anatomical features, especially in the nature and disposition of the hairs with which most caterpillars are covered. The head is chiefly remarkable for its jaws, but it does also have minute simple eyes and tiny antennae. The first three segments immediately behind the head each bear a pair of true legs, the next two have none, the next four and the last (again after a gap of apparently two but actually three) bear fleshy false legs. As the caterpillar grows a certain amount of expansion is taken up by the divisions between the segments, but as the skin, though flexible, cannot expand, it is sloughed from time to time. Each new skin disclosed by the moults, of which there are usually four or five, differs, sometimes very strikingly, from the previous one, and is adapted to the caterpillar's particular habits and needs at that stage of its growth.

The final moult reveals the *chrysalis* (pupa). At this stage the insect appears externally to be completely static; internally, however, the situation is very different, for the body tissues are being broken down and reformed in the shape of the butterfly that will eventually emerge. Pupae of most butterflies are attached to a foothold by means of a group of cremastral hooks at the extreme tip of the abdomen that are fastened to a pad of silk spun by the caterpillar before it pupates. Those of the Swallowtails and Whites are also held in position, upright, by means of a silken girdle. Others hang upside down suspended by the tail. Pupae of most of the Blues also have a girdle but lie flat on their support; and the Skippers mainly lie unattached within a rolled leaf of their food plant.

When the butterfly finally emerges as a 'perfect' insect or '*imago*', its wings hang limp on either side like tiny bags. They are expanded by fluid which is pumped through the veins until they dry and harden. This final moult, and the moult from caterpillar to chrysalis, are well worth watching, for they seem to be almost conjuring tricks. Once the butterfly has reached maturity it takes food, through its proboscis, only to maintain life and supply the needs of its reproductive system, all growth having taken place in the caterpillar stage.

The process of change through which a butterfly passes during its lifetime is sometimes called *metamorphosis*. Each moult is fraught with danger, for during it the insect can do nothing to protect itself from the attacks of the numerous predators and parasites that beset it throughout life.

How to tell the sexes. It will often be necessary to distinguish the sexes, especially if attempts are made to breed butterflies in captivity so as to obtain really perfect specimens. It is usual for males and females of any species to be rather different in appearance. In extreme cases, such as *Hypolimnas misippus* (p. 73), this dimorphism is so marked that the sexes were only linked originally by breeding experiments. Often resemblances between the sexes are much more obvious in the markings of the underside than the upperside, and association can be established by matching these, for instance in Lycaenidae. However, the difficulty arises most frequently when only one specimen is available. The first things to look for in this situation are secondary sexual characters such as patches of *androconia* (special scent scales only found on the wings of males), sex brands, etc., peculiar to males. Examples of these are the scent pockets on vein 2 of the hindwing in male *Danaus* (Pl. 1), the tufts of hair where the wings overlap in *Greta* (Pl. 2), the diffuse black patches of *androconia* (specialised scent scales) in *Calisto* (Pl. 3), the oval patch of androconia at the cell-end on the forewing of many Hairstreaks (Pls. 11 and 12), and the extensive areas of modified scales that give the wings a different texture in *Aphrissa* (Pl. 17) and *Ascia* (Pl. 13). In Skippers a short length of the forewing costa is often folded over (*costal fold*) to enclose androconia, or there is a bold dark *brand* on the disc of the forewing. None of these features is to be found in females. In most Nymphalidae the forelegs (p. 55) will provide a clue. If all else fails, the external *genitalia* must be examined. Brush away the hair and scales from the tip of the abdomen, then, looking at the exposed area from beneath, the paired claspers (one on either side, possibly with the tip of the penis showing in between) should be visible in the case of a male; the female again exhibits negative characters, the most that is likely to be seen is the tip of the ovipositor or, farther back on the ventral surface, the opening of the genital duct (*ostium bursae*).

Species, subspecies and varieties. Anyone sufficiently interested in butterflies to know something about their classification will sooner or later find himself in difficulties over the definition of a *species,* which is unfortunate, since species are the basic units (taxa) of classification. A good definition, applicable without difficulty to West Indian butterflies, would be: a group of inter-breeding natural populations which is reproductively isolated from other such groups. Clearly, butterflies like *Parides gundlachianus* (p. 139) and *Papilio homerus* (p. 150) are 'good' species, isolated geographically and with no similar closely related species with which they could interbreed even if they had contact with them. However, using this definition, what are we to call the numerous island races of *Battus polydamas* (p. 140) or *Dryas iulia* (p. 86)? Each of these species has developed a series of island populations which are in appearance (phenotypically) quite distinct and also geographically isolated, but we have no information as to whether they would interbreed, i.e. whether they are reproductively isolated. If they did not interbreed they would be species; if they did, they would be *subspecies,* which are, by definition, geographically isolated populations of a species that can interbreed when in contact, as for example, along the frontiers of their respective areas, and generally do. In this guide these races are called subspecies, on the assumption that they could interbreed given the opportunity. Sometimes these island races have evolved to the point at which the degree of difference between them would seem to be greater than that between subspecies. To meet this situation these 'advanced' subspecies are sometimes called *semispecies* which, collectively, form a *superspecies*, terms which are intended to indicate the evolutionary stage reached on the way from subspecies to species, and thence presumably to genera. Another form of variation that affects whole populations is the *cline*. This, to take a purely hypothetical case, would occur when a species with an unbroken distribution ranging from north to south, for example, was black in the north, white in the south, with every grade of grey in between. Gradual changes like this occur along the chain of islands forming the West Indies, or within the Bahamas, but they are not simple clines, being made of discontinuous series of isolated island populations.

Seasonal variation in tropical countries occurs only where there are marked seasonal changes in weather as between dry season and wet season. If dry and wet in this case are equated with temperature, then the dry season falls between November and March, which are the colder months, the wet season is May to September. It is not a conspicuous phenomenon in Caribbean butterflies; in fact it is only in the genus *Eurema* that it is at all noticeable. It is best seen in *Eurema daira* (Pl. 14). The reduction of the black markings and the change in underside coloration from white to reddish or sandy in this species is very characteristic of the difference between the 'summer' (wet) and 'winter' (dry) season broods throughout the Pieridae that exhibit any seasonal variation at all.

The range of *individual variation* observed in West Indian butterflies does not compare with that exhibited by butterflies of the temperate zones of North America or the Old World. This may be more apparent than real as they have been relatively much less studied. The Blues vary, as everywhere, in the size, disposition and shape of the spots on the undersides of the hindwings; some species of *Eurema*, notably *E. nise*, vary a good deal in the extent, though not the disposition of their wing markings, probably in relation to the seasons. Satyridae vary extensively in the development of their eye-spots, but in the other families individual variation is unusual, though in all groups the rare freak such as an albino or a black 'melanic' is liable to occur.

Names. Each species in this guide is given two names, an English name and a scientific name. The former is a national, the latter an international name. Most of the former have been invented during the writing of this guide, though almost all those already in existence have been used. The scientific (Latin) names will sometimes be found to differ from those current elsewhere for the same insect. Changes of this kind are mostly due to the applications of Rules formulated by the International Commission on Zoological Nomenclature, the guiding principle of which is that the *first* name given to any species, in or after 1758, shall be its valid name. The year 1758 is chosen, since it was in that year that Linnaeus published the 10th edition of his *Systema Naturae*, which is the foundation of modern zoological nomenclature. In most cases of change the displaced name is quoted as a synonym or homonym (see Glossary).

COLLECTING

Butterfly nets are available from dealers in natural history apparatus in a variety of shapes, sizes and prices, and most of them are made to fold up or take

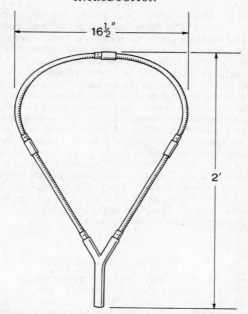

Fig. 3. Frame of balloon or kite net, showing the five detachable parts.

to pieces for easy packing. The one most favoured by experienced collectors is known as a kite or balloon net (**Fig. 3**). The four sections of this socket together and fit into the brass Y, into which a handle of convenient length can be fitted. The bag should be made of dark coloured tough but soft netting – for butterflies are very delicate things – not longer than the length of one's arm and tapering a little at the bottom so as to restrict the butterfly's movements when it is being coaxed into the killing bottle. In a recent improved form of this net the two straight sections are made of light metal and the two curved sections are replaced by a single length of pliable plastic rod, making the whole frame much lighter. It is advisable to have at least one spare bag.

Where to collect. Butterflies are true creatures of the sun. In dull weather they go to ground and the difficulty of finding them then at rest is an object lesson in natural camouflage: the colours and patterns that make them conspicuous when in flight serve the opposite purpose when they rest. In the West Indies different types of habitat have their characteristic species: Swallowtails, Whites and Sulphurs (Pieridae) and some kinds of Nymphalidae, are especially conspicuous around gardens where there is a profusion of flowers. It seems almost as if they have formed an association with man-made habitats, both his flowers and his crops. It is on this type of habitat, especially in the lowlands that wide-ranging species such as *Papilio polydamas* (p. 140), *Danaus plexippus* (p. 33)

Historis odius (p. 66), *Colobura dirce* (p. 63), *Junonia* (p. 74) and *Anartia* (p. 75), *Dryas iulia* (p. 86), *Dione vanillae* (p. 88) and many of the Blues, Hairstreaks and Skippers are to be found. At higher levels species of more restricted range, many of them confined to a single island, like *Papilio homerus*, the two species of *Greta*, *Atlantea*, most of the species of *Calisto* and several local Hairstreaks will occur, flying in upland glades and grasslands in forests that are much wetter than those of the lowlands. Places to search here, where by comparison with the lowlands flowers may be scarce, are the edges of forests and particularly muddy patches in runnels and stream beds especially if fouled at all by animal droppings, rotting fruit or sap exuding from wounded tree trunks. In such places butterflies, which otherwise may seem surprisingly scarce, may occasionally congregate in amazing numbers, almost all of them males, drinking whilst the females are busy egg-laying. Woodland paths and roadsides are always worth exploring, but intensely cultivated areas are generally decidedly barren of butterflies. Trees and plants that are particularly attractive include Logwood (*Haematoxylon*), Vervain (*Stachytarpheta*), Lantana, Christmas Bush and False Christmas Bush (*Eupatorium*), Goat Weed (*Ageratum*), Spanish Needle or Wild Daisy (*Bidens pilosa*), *Distreptus spicatus* (a small composite), *Poinsettia, Bauhinia, Bougainvillea*.

MAKING A COLLECTION

Killing. Most collectors of butterflies in the tropics practise the crude but very quick and effective *pinching* method for killing their catch. The butterfly's thorax is sharply nipped between finger and thumb whilst still in the net, breaking the integument but not the legs. It requires practice, as there is a certain knack in the operation. The rather leathery Danaidae (p. 33) require exceptionally firm treatment. In all cases pressure should be applied to the thorax only, not to the abdomen as well.

More civilised methods, which are also more cumbersome and therefore troublesome when the size of the load to be carried is a consideration, entail the use of a *killing bottle*. This should be a wide mouthed bottle some six inches deep and closed by a cork or rubber bung, which is quicker to operate than a screw-cap. The standard killing agent used in this way is *cyanide of potassium*, which is a deadly poison. Cyanide bottles should only be prepared by an experienced chemist. Three or four lumps of cyanide placed in the bottom of the bottle should first be covered with dry plaster of Paris. Wet plaster is then poured on top to a depth of about half an inch and allowed to harden. The bottle should then be left *uncorked* for 2 or 3 days to dry out before being taken into use. If not dried out it will sweat and eventually virtually deliquesce and become quite useless. A plastic bottle is safer than a glass one, but the risk of glass scatter on breakage can be minimised by winding adhesive tape round the outside. A good alternative to cyanide, and less deadly, is *ethyl acetate*. This is a volatile liquid, but should not be used in a plastic bottle because it tends to dissolve it. Allow about an inch of plaster of Paris to set in the bottom of a glass bottle. When thoroughly dry, pour in just as much ethyl acetate as the plaster will completely absorb, and renew it from time to time as necessary. Several other liquid killing agents can be used in the same way as ethyl acetate, *carbon tetrachloride* (which renders specimens very brittle), *chloroform* and *benzine*, *ammonia* (which may cause colour changes) or even in emergencies *ether* or *petrol*.

Whatever form of killing bottle is used, care must be taken to ensure that specimens do not damage themselves or become damaged before being removed from the bottle. It is often helpful to put some cellulose wadding or twisted paper in the bottle to provide footholds for the insects. It is also most important not to have too many in the bottle at the same time as they damage each other by rubbing the scales off the wings, or are 'rubbed' just by movement of the bottle. To prevent damage of this kind, especially to the smaller butterflies like Hairstreaks and Blues, many collectors remove the capture as soon as it is stupefied to another larger killing bottle 'papering' it (see below) in the process so that it is safe from further contacts that might damage it.

Some butterflies, especially Blues, have a regrettable habit of folding their wings together beneath them, instead of over their backs, as they die, which can make setting very troublesome. Watch for this and 'spring' them back again at once. Often this can be done by picking them up by their legs with a very fine-pointed forceps, and blowing gently on the wings; more often it will be necessary to insert the forceps along the sides of the thorax between the closed wings and then gently release pressure on the forceps.

At this stage, too, a decision should be made as to whether the capture is to be kept or released. If not wanted for the collection it should be set free at once, and will probably recover quite quickly if not left too long in the killing bottle, or not too severely pinched.

Preparing. Having decided to keep the specimen, it becomes necessary to decide how to proceed. It can be pinned and 'set' at once, kept relaxed to be set a few days later, or papered for indefinite storage and setting when convenient. Ordinary brass household pins should never be used; they are much too clumsy. Special steel *entomological pins*, which can be obtained from dealers in natural history supplies, are essential. These vary in length and thickness, but for the sake of appearances in a collection it is better to keep to one length and vary only the thickness to suit the size of the insect. For butterflies the preferred length is 38 mm, say just short of $1\frac{1}{2}$ inches. It is easier, and safer, to handle butterflies on pins that are 'too long' than 'too short'.

If it is not convenient to pin and set specimens at once, then they can either be kept temporarily in a relaxing tin that is only slightly damp and also contains some mould preventative, e.g. naphthalene or thymol (but not carbolic, which makes specimens brittle), till they can be set, or papered. Papers are folded triangles formed by cutting paper rectangles the sides of which measure in the proportion of about 3:5 inches and folding them as indicated in the diagram. The butterfly should not be inserted until after the data are written on the second folded side. Ordinary newspaper makes excellent envelopes because it is soft and somewhat absorbent. Hard, shiny paper and the transparent envelopes used by stamp collectors have their advantages during storage and handling, but can be troublesome when the need to relax the specimen arises. (**Fig. 4**).

A *relaxing tin* can be made of any flat container with a moderately well fitting lid. It is usual to fill this to a depth of about 1 inch with sterilised sand or other absorbent material that can be kept wet, and to cover this with a sheet of perforated zinc. This again is usually covered with a sheet of blotting paper on which the papers are laid. A constant high humidity must be maintained at a

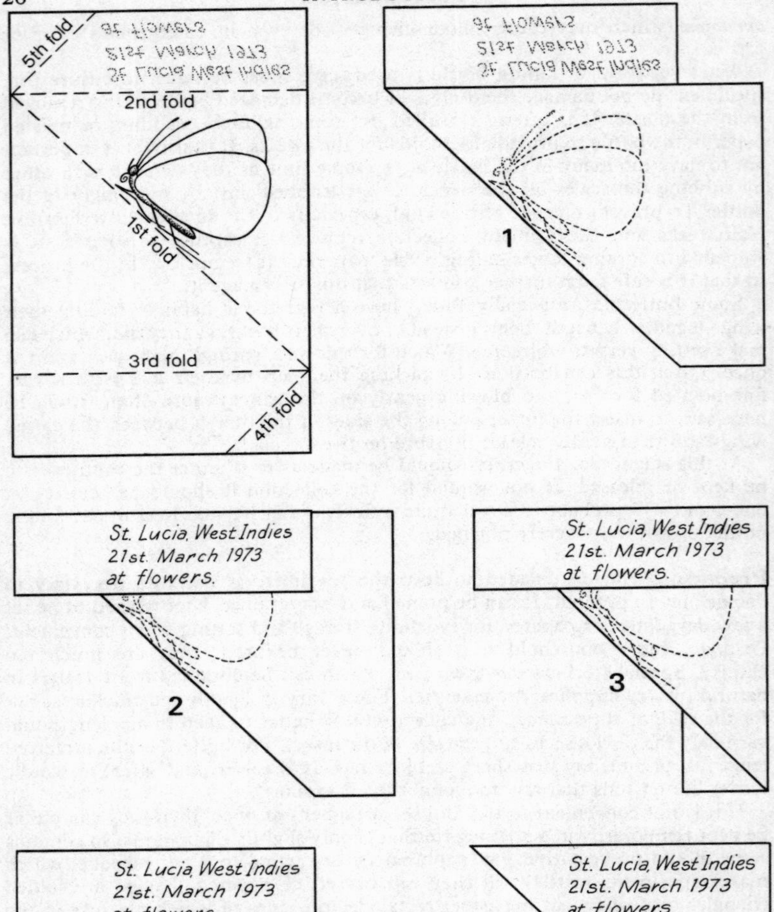

Fig. 4. Stages in 'papering' a butterfly.

temperature of at least 65°F. Specimens in hard non-absorbent paper or transparent envelopes are best fully exposed, and changes of temperature that could result in condensation within the container should be avoided. Mould can be discouraged by flaked naphthalene or thymol crystals.

Setting or spreading. This process involves opening and spreading the wings of the butterfly and then securing them in a position in which they will dry and 'set'. Apparatus needed consists of setting boards, tracing paper or tracing

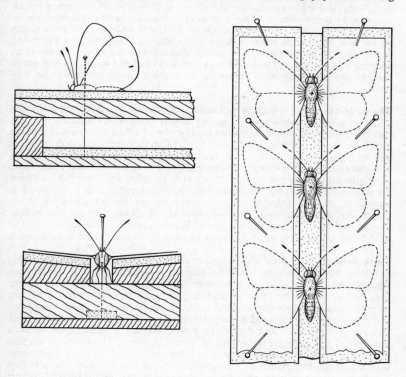

Fig. 5. How to pin and set a butterfly.

cloth, setting needles (ordinary needles stuck into pen holders) and quantities of pins ('baby' or glass-headed) that are easy to handle. The only other essential is that the butterfly should be properly relaxed, for if it is not it will be impossible to set it. Soon after death *rigor mortis* will set in, unless the killing agent used is ethyl acetate, and setting will not be possible until this has worn off, which may be overnight. Skippers present a special difficulty, for whether fresh or not their wings are always refractory; the only way to overcome this is by making a short cut in the side of the thorax just below the base of each wing, using a fine scalpel or broken piece of razor blade. (**Fig. 5**).

Setting boards are flat, cork covered boards, about 14 inches long as a rule, with a deep central groove in which the pinned body of the butterfly can rest. They can be bought ready made in various widths. The bottom of the central groove must be deep enough to accommodate about 1 inch of the pin and also cork to hold it. Pin the butterfly through the centre of the thorax at right angles to its body, and make sure that, when pinned in the groove of the setting board, it is exactly perpendicular. Take a strip of tracing paper that has been cut to slightly less than the width of one side of the board and lay it over the wings on one side. Move the wings into position, holding them with the paper and secure them by pinning the paper around the edges of the wings. Do the same with the other wings and leave for a week or so to dry and set. Be careful not to damage the specimen when removing the tracing paper, for it will be very brittle.

The collection. The first thing to do when a specimen is ready for the collection is to pin a proper label below it giving details as to where and when it was collected, and any other information likely to be of value. The date of capture should be recorded as day, month, year (31.1.74) in that order, not in the illogical and ambiguous month, day, year system used in certain misguided circles. Without these data a specimen, however perfect, has little scientific value. Cork lined airtight store boxes in which there is a 'camphor cell' or other provision for an insect deterrent are essential for permanent storage of the collection. For butterflies, in which many of the most important specific characters are on the undersides, glass-bottomed cabinet drawers are ideal, but they are very expensive. Name labels should also be pinned below specimens that have proved at all difficult to identify, for it is unwise to trust to memory alone in such cases.

Conservation. The West Indies are remarkably poor in nature reserves. Cuba has four largish Reserves totalling some 25000 hectares. The Dominican Republic has one of about 5000 hectares surrounding an important catchment area, and several others of rather uncertain status. There are none in Haiti nor even in Jamaica, where the Cockpit country and parts of the Blue Mountains should certainly be accorded some measure of protection. The Liquillo Forest Reserve in Porto Rico and the several forest reserves in Jamaica are valuable but they are not quite the same thing as Nature Reserves. There is no doubt that the intensive clearance of so many islands for agricultural purposes has already brought about the extinction of certain races of the handsome Swallowtail butterfly *Battus polydamas* peculiar to those islands, and almost certainly others as well. The establishment of strict reserves to safeguard what is left would seem to be an urgent necessity. In the meantime it behoves the butterfly collector constantly to bear in mind that the facet of nature that interests him, tiny as it may seem, is part of a much greater and unbelievably complicated natural system, no part of which can be upset without risk of disturbing the whole. In terms of collecting this means that he should exercise the greatest restraint, especially in respect of those rare and local species which are so much sought after. There is a critical minimum population size for any colony of a species, and if numbers drop below this, extinction follows: if a species is 'rare' it is fairly certain that it is not far from this danger point, and that unnatural risk at the hands of a collector, when added to the immense natural risks it runs, may well tip the scales. However, it is nevertheless true that the most massive threat to the survival of many butterflies as of other animals and plants is posed by the destruction of the habitat to which they are adapted. It is for the preservation of habitats that nature reserves need to be established: the rest will follow, given enlightened maintenance. One should always aim for the protection of a complete habitat, a whole ecological system, not just one element of it alone.

♂	male
♀	female
f	form, as in ♀-f, i.e. female form
fw	forewing. Fw length is measured from wing tip to point of attachment of wing to thorax
hw	hindwing
s	space
syn	synonym
ssp	subspecies
TL	type locality (see Glossary)
v	vein

Allopatric. Occupying different geographical areas.

Anal angle. The angle on either wing which lies nearest to the tip of the abdomen when the wings are closed; the angle formed by the meeting of the outer and inner margins.

Androconia. Scales of special form, peculiar to males and usually situate on the wings, which give off scent; sometimes scattered amongst the ordinary scales but often grouped together to form 'brands'.

Basad. Towards the base, e.g. of the wing.

Brand. *See* androconia.

Cell. The open area towards the base of either wing bounded by veins from which most of the other veins arise.

Chitinous. Made of chitin, the substance of which the hard outer covering of a butterfly (integument) is composed; more usually known nowadays as sclerotin.

Costa. The front edge of a wing (see Fig. 2).

Cremastral hooks. Hooks at the tip of the abdomen of a pupa by which it is attached to its support.

Dimorphic. Exhibiting dimorphism, i.e. occurring in two different forms. The brown and grey forms of the female of *Danaus plexippus* are dimorphs. *Hypolimnas misippus*, in which the male is blue, the female brown, is sexually dimorphic.

Discal. Related to the disc, or central area of a wing.

Distad. Away from the body, towards the outer margin (if of a wing marking).

Distal. Distant from the body or wing base.

Endemic. Native to and always present in a particular country; of insects, confined to that area and not found elsewhere.

Fauna. Collective name for all the living animals in a particular area.

Form. Any recognisably distinct variant of a species, e.g. a female form, a seasonal or local form, a variety or aberration; an indefinite term unless qualified.

Fulvous. Yellowish brown.

Fuscous. Grey-brown.

Genitalia. Sex organs; in insects especially the hard chitinous parts.

Holotype. The actual specimen on which the name of a species is based.

Homonym. Identical names given to different species are homonyms. Of two or more homonyms only the one first published can be valid.

Hyaline. Translucent.

Invalid. A scientific name is said to be invalid when it contravenes the Rules of Zoological Nomenclature. Such a name must not be used.
Irrorated. Sprinkled with minute coloured specks.

Ocellus. An eye-spot, i.e. a wing marking that resembles an eye; a simple single-lens eye (as in caterpillars).

Palpi. Paired sensory organs arising one on either side of the proboscis.
Paratype. One of a series of specimens on which an author based the original description of a species.
Postdiscal. The area of a wing beyond the central discal area and before the submarginal area. See Fig. 2.
Proximal. Near to the body; the opposite of distal.
Pupate. To turn into a chrysalis, or pupa.

Race. A recognisable local form; an incipient subspecies perhaps.

Setigerous. Bearing setae, or bristles.
Space. Part of the surface of a wing enclosed between veins.
Spiracular line. The line of openings (spiracles) along the side of a caterpillar through which it obtains its air supply.
Sympatric. Occupying the same geographical area; flying together.
Synonym. Different names given to one and the same species are synonyms. Of two or more synonyms the first to be published, provided that it satisfies the Rules of Zoological Nomenclature, is the valid name of the species to which it was given.

Type. A specimen on which an author based the name and description of a species. *See* also holotype and paratype.
Type locality. The type locality of a species is the locality where the first named and described specimen of that species was captured. This information is of particular importance in the study of geographical variation. Many early authors did not state where their specimens came from. In such cases, if no subsequent author has selected a type locality in the meantime, one is suggested in this guide, if desirable.

Valid name. The correct name of a species according to the Rules of Zoological Nomenclature.
Veins. The tubular supports of the wings.

Zoogeography. The study of the geographical distribution of animals.

The Danaidae are a cosmopolitan family of strong-flying, tough, conspicuous, rather 'leathery' butterflies which most insectivorous animals avoid because of their unpleasant taste. They are essentially tropical in distribution. Their caterpillars feed on milkweeds and nightshades, plants that have acrid milky poisonous juices from which the protection of both caterpillar and butterfly is derived. The hairless, smooth and often conspicuously coloured cater-pillars of the Monarchs make no attempt to hide; the two or three pairs of fleshy tentacles that most of them have are very characteristic of the family. The chrysalis is squat, stubby and smooth, usually green and flecked with metallic markings. It hangs suspended by its cremastral hooks.

The Danaidae form a very distinct family which can be recognised 'at sight' after a little experience. The combination of the following anatomical features will usually serve to distinguish them: the forelegs are greatly atrophied in both sexes – very small and delicate in the males, larger and ending in a kind of spiked knobkerrie in the female – the antennae are scaleless and the discal cell is 'closed' in both wings. Three subfamilies are represented in the West Indies. The Danainae, represented by the genus *Danaus*, have a conspicuous pocket on vein 2 of the hindwing of the males which can be swept by a pencil of hair at the tip of the abdomen, apparently to disperse scent. In the long-winged Ituninae, represented by the genus *Lycorea*, this scent apparatus is lacking and the arrangement of the veins closing the hindwing cell differs greatly from that of the Danainae. The third subfamily, the Anetiinae, formerly known as the Clothildinae, contains the single genus *Anetia* and is confined to Central America and the Greater Antilles. It is a true Danaid though often placed in the Nymphalidae because of its superficial resemblance to a Fritillary.

DANAUS PLEXIPPUS Linnaeus 1758   *The Monarch*   **Pl. 1**
Description. Fw ♂ and ♀ 45–50 mm. Upperside warm brown, veins black. *Forewing costa, apex, outer margin and inner margin broadly black;* hindwing outer margin black; numerous white apical and marginal spots. Underside paler, white spots larger. Male has a small oval sex-brand on vein 2 of the hindwing.
Distribution. Throughout the West Indies. The Bahamas and Cuba are populated by the migratory North American subspecies *plexippus*. In His-paniola, Porto Rico, Jamaica, the Cayman Islands and the Lesser Antilles, though with a good deal of overlapping, the sedentary subspecies *megalippe* Huebner 1819 replaces it. This has a less pointed forewing and much less heavily white-spotted borders, the veins, especially of the male, are less heavily blackened, and the pale spots on the forewing immediately beyond the end of the cell are always small, often absent. The Jamaican population is typical of this subspecies. In Porto Rico these characteristics are intensified in a proportion of the population (subspecies *portoricensis* Clark 1941); and in the Lesser Antilles females often have a grey-brown or pale grey upperside ground colour (♀-f. *leucogyne* Butler 1884) though the males are indistinguishable from normal

B.W.I.   C *megalippe*. Size and the black forewing inner margin will always distinguish *D. plexippus* from the other species of *Danaus* present in the islands. RANGE: Canada to Argentina; Australia, New Zealand, E. Indies; Canary Islands; W. Europe as vagrant. TL: Pennsylvania, U.S.A.

Early stages. The conspicuous fleshy caterpillar is bright yellow or greenish yellow, banded with shining black. It has a pair of prominent fleshy processes (tentacles) behind the head and another pair near the tail. It feeds on various milkweeds, especially *Asclepias curassavica*, also sometimes on *Calotropis procera*. The green chrysalis is flecked with gold.

DANAUS ERESIMUS Cramer 1779   *The Soldier*   **Pl. 1**

Description. Fw ♂ and ♀ 40–45 mm. The upperside in both sexes is so deceptively similar to *D. gilippus cleothera* as readily to cause confusion. *D. eresimus* however is slightly larger and more richly coloured, has a pale postdiscal spot in space 2 of the forewing on both surfaces, and a *postdiscal series of faint spots only slightly paler than the ground colour on the underside of the hindwings*. This last feature distinguishes it at once from all the other West Indian species of *Danaus*. The upperside ground colour varies, individually rather than locally, from light brown to chestnut and the intensity of the pale spots on the underside is also subject to considerable variation.

Distribution. Cuba, Haiti, Jamaica and Cayman Islands – resident but apparently rare or local. Not recorded from Porto Rico. Grenada – probably vagrants from north or south, probably the latter. Because these island populations all have rather heavier black borders on the underside of the hindwing than is typical of *D. eresimus* from Surinam they are sometimes treated as a distinct subspecies, *tethys* Forbes 1943. RANGE: southern U.S.A. to Brazil and Peru. TL: Surinam.

Early stages. Fully grown caterpillar basically black but every segment with several irregular transverse yellow-green stripes, about ten pairs of conjoined white diamond-shaped spots at intervals across the back, lateral area above the spiracles black but with irregular yellow-green markings; a pair of long black 'tentacles' close behind the head, another pair a little farther back and a third pair near the hind end.

DANAUS GILIPPUS Cramer 1775   *The Queen*   **Pl. 1**

Danaus gilippus ranges from the southern U.S.A. to Argentina (TL: Rio de Janeiro and coast of Brazil). It occurs in the West Indies in three subspecies which are sometimes treated as distinct species:

1 **D. gilippus berenice** Cramer 1779

Description. Fw ♂ and ♀ 36–43 mm. Upperside rather dark coffee-brown; *forewing upperside with prominent white postdiscal spots in spaces 1b, 2 and 3*, the ground colour extending fully to the apex and along the inner margin. Hindwing underside without postdiscal spots, veins broadly black, edged white. Abdomen with a narrow white stripe underneath. In form *strigosa* Bates 1864 the veins on the upperside of the hindwing are white-edged.

Distribution. Widespread in Cuba, the Bahamas and Cayman Islands. TL: 'Jamaica', probably Georgia.

2 **D. gilippus jamaicensis** Bates 1864

Description. ♂ and ♀ smaller than *D. g. berenice* on average, with a forewing length seldom exceeding 39 mm. Upperside ground colour pale coffee-coloured, the borders tending to be brown rather than black, but all markings similar.

Distribution. Known only from Jamaica where it is a common and widespread butterfly of the lowlands. TL: Jamaica.

3 D. gilippus cleothera Godart 1819
syn *Danaus kaempfferi* Hall 1925

Description. Fw ♂ and ♀ 36–42 mm. Upperside warm brown, darker towards costa and apex of forewing; all pale spots white above and below; forewing upperside with no postdiscal spots in spaces 1b or 2; hindwing underside with no trace of postdiscal spots; abdomen with a white stripe underneath.

D. gilippus cleothera looks as if it should be the Haitian subspecies of *D. cleophile* or *D. eresimus* rather than of *D. gilippus*, but it is separated from the former by the absence of the dark stripe along the inner margin of the forewing and the whiteness of the pale spots, and from the latter by having no postdiscal spots on the underside of the hindwing. The white stripe along the body underneath also allies it to *D. gilippus*.

Distribution. Dominican Republic and Haiti (e.g. near Puerto Plata). TL: 'Timor', *recte* Haiti.

Early stages. The caterpillar of this species when full grown is almost black, with a white band across the front of each segment and sometimes traces of black and yellow markings. It has three pairs of fleshy tentacles. The underneath of the body is red or reddish brown. Food plant *Asclepias curassavica* and other Milkweeds, especially *Vincetoxicum*.

Note. The occasional *D. gilippus* that reach the Lesser Antilles at times are referable to subspecies *xanthippus* Felder 1860, and probably originate in Trinidad or Venezuela. They are characterised by having a white postdiscal spot in space 2 on the upperside of the forewing.

DANAUS CLEOPHILE Godart 1819 *Jamaican Monarch* Pl. 1
Description. Fw ♂ and ♀ 33–38 mm, female usually rather smaller than male. Very like *D. plexippus* but readily distinguished by the following characters: smaller, *upperside spots always yellow*, never white or buff; on the forewing there is always a pale spot in space 3 (very rare in *D. plexippus*); on the underside the apex of the forewing and the whole of the hindwing are uniformly brown, and on the hindwing the extent of the ground colour is much reduced by the broad pinkish shading along the veins.

Distribution. Rare and local in Hispaniola and Jamaica from about 1500 ft upwards, e.g. Mt Diablo, July (Jamaica), Mt Isabella, June (Dominican Republic). Reported from Porto Rico. RANGE: confined to these islands. TL (not stated by Godart): Hispaniola.

Early stages. The caterpillar is very similar to that of *D. plexippus*, but very much darker when full-fed, the segments being black, separated by narrow bands of yellow, and with faint traces of paler transverse bands obscurely indicated here and there. Food plant *Asclepias curassavica*.

ANETIA BRIAREA Huebner 1823 *Lesser False Fritillary* Pl. 1
Confined to the West Indies in two subspecies:

1 A. briarea numidia Huebner 1823
Description. Fw ♂ and ♀ 36–46 mm, female rather larger than male. The light

Plate 1   **DANAIDAE**   *Scale:* × $\frac{2}{3}$

1. **Danaus plexippus**   *The Monarch*   p. 33
   ♂ Portsmouth, Dominica. October. Forewing apex broadly black.

2. **Danaus eresimus**   *The Soldier*   34
   ♂ Grand Cayman. July. Hindwing underside with postdiscal
   series of faint pale spots.

3. **Danaus gilippus**   *The Queen*   34
   Forewing apex not broadly darkened.
   3a *D. g. cleothera* ♂ Puerto Plata, Dominican Republic. June.
       No postdiscal spots on hindwing underside, veins prominent.
   3b *D. g. jamaicensis* ♂ Fish River, Portland, Jamaica. Hindwing
       pale coffee coloured, dark borders 2 to 3 mm wide.
   3c *D. g. berenice* ♂ Grand Cayman. June. Hindwing dark coffee
       coloured, dark borders 4 to 5 mm wide.

4. **Danaus cleophile**   *Jamaican Monarch*   35
   ♀ Mt Isabella, Dominican Republic, 1000 ft. June. Upperside
   pale spots all yellow.

5. **Anetia briarea**   *Lesser False Fritillary*   35
   A. b. briarea ♂ Haiti. Upperside both wings with three rows of
   well separated dark spots.

6. **Anetia pantherata**   *False Fritillary*   35
   A. p. pantherata ♂ Haiti. Upperside of hindwing with only two
   rows of dark spots.

7. **Anetia jaegeri**   *Jaeger's Anetia*   38
   ♂ Haiti. Hindwing upperside unspotted.

8. **Anetia cubana**   *Salvin's Anetia*   39
   ♂ Cuba. Forewing upperside with line of bold white postdiscal
   spots.

1. Lycorea ceres   *The Large Tiger*
   L. c. demeter ♂ Cuba. Forewing upperside with bold band of connected spots.

p. 39

ITHOMIIDAE

2. Greta diaphana   *Jamaican Clearwing*
   G. d. diaphana ♂ Jamaica. Forewing white spots well separated.

41

3. Greta cubana   *Cuban Clearwing*
   ♂ Cuba. Forewing white spots joined to form a band beyond the cell.

42

SATYRIDAE

4. Calisto zangis   *Jamaican Ringlet*
   4a ♂ Jamaica. Forewing with large circular grey sex brand.
   4b ♀ Gordon Town, Jamaica. February.

43

5. Calisto nubila   *Porto Rican Ringlet*
   Both sexes with round dark anal eye-spot.
   5a ♂ El Yunque, Porto Rico. July.
   5b ♀ Porto Rico.

46

6. Calisto pulchella   *Orange Ringlet*
   Hindwing underside with large rust-red area.
   6a ♂ Haiti.
   6b ♀ Dominican Republic.

46

brown heavily spotted upperside is very suggestive of a large North American Fritillary, but the delicate tracery of the underside of the hindwing, best appreciated from the illustration, at once denies the affinity. Both wings have *three rows of well separated black spots* on the upperside, and the pale marginal spots between the veins are taller than broad and light brown.

Distribution. Said to be common and widespread on Cuba, to have a slow flight and when visiting flowers to settle with the wings only half open. Frequents the edges of woods, meadows and gardens. TL: Cuba.

2 A. briarea briarea   Godart 1819

Description. Male and female differ from *A. b. numidia* as follows: upperside ground colour duller, more uniform; forewing rather more falcate; twin marginal spots and also the pale spots on the forewing costa white and generally rather larger; hindwing underside ground colour darker and also especially the outermost row of dark spots, which are also much larger.

Distribution. Haiti and Dominican Republic. Not rare. TL (not stated): Haiti.

Early stages. The caterpillar feeds on a species of *Jacquinia* known locally as Espuela de Caballero. Its head is black and large, the body white and smooth with darker transverse lines but none of the fleshy tentacles characteristic of the genus *Danaus*. Pupa like that of *Danaus*.

ANETIA PANTHERATA   Martyn 1797   *False Fritillary*   Pl. 1
Confined to the West Indies in two subspecies:

1 A. pantherata pantherata   Martyn

Description. Fw ♂ and ♀ 46–58 mm. Confusingly similar to the last species (*A. briarea*) but easily distinguished, apart from size, by there being on the upperside of the hindwing *only two concentric rows of black spots* instead of three, with the inner row composed usually of only four spots (the middle (fifth) spot being very small or absent) as against six spots in the corresponding (middle) row in *A. briarea*. Comparison of the illustrations will show many other small differences, notably the more falcate forewing.

Distribution. Confined to Hispaniola but widespread and much commoner than *A. briarea*: Port au Prince, La Cumbre, Puerto Plata, etc. TL: Port au Prince, Haiti.

2 A. pantherata clarescens   Hall 1925

Description. Slightly smaller, paler but brighter on the upperside than *A. p. pantherata*, the twin marginal spots on the upperside of the hindwing darker and tending to disappear. Hindwing underside ground colour darker, the markings less well developed, especially towards the outer margin, the white tracery fainter and duller.

Distribution. Confined to Cuba, but widespread and commoner than *A. briarea*. TL: Cuba.

Early stages. Not known.

ANETIA JAEGERI   Ménétriés 1832   *Jaeger's Anetia*   Pl. 1
Description. Fw ♂ and ♀ 40–43 mm. Upperside very dark brown; forewing upperside tinged reddish in basal half and with a pattern of spots arranged as in *A. briarea*, those in the basal half of the wing black, the others pale buff to whitish, marginal twin spots similar; *hindwing upperside unspotted* except for the series of much larger twin marginal spots. Underside of forewing much as on

upperside, but basal area brighter purplish; hindwing underside silver-washed and patterned much as in *A. cubana*.

Distribution. Known only from Haiti and the Dominican Republic. Exceedingly rare, only some half-dozen specimens known. Habitat and life history unknown. RANGE: Hispaniola. TL: Haiti.

Note. *A. jaegeri* is sometimes regarded as a subspecies of *A. cubana*. This seems quite unjustified. It appears to be a very distinct species.

ANETIA CUBANA Salvin 1869 *Salvin's Anetia* Pl. 1

Description. Fw ♂ 50 mm, ♀ 55 mm. Upperside black; forewing upperside crossed by a *bracelet of bold white spots beyond the cell* bent almost at right angles at vein 4; hindwing with a postdiscal buff band narrowly cut by black along the veins. The underside of the forewing is enlivened by a few crimson discal markings; the hindwing is feebly silver-washed and also has hints of the white tracery of *A. pantherata* and *A. briarea*.

Distribution. Confined to Cuba. Known best from the mountains near Guantanamo from November to February. Flies slowly. RANGE and TL: Cuba.

Early stages. Not known.

Note. A closely related species is believed to exist in Jamaica.

LYCOREA CERES Cramer 1779 *The Large Tiger* Pl. 2

Lycorea ceres ranges from Mexico to Argentina. It occurs in the West Indies in two subspecies:

1 **L. ceres demeter** Felder 1867

Description. Fw ♂ and ♀ 45–52 mm., the female usually slightly larger than the male. Black, with a *band of connected spots* across the forewing and a few small subapical spots *all yellow*, and two long brown basal stripes; hindwing with a band across cell to inner margin and another running in a circle from costa to inner margin, both brown. Underside similar but darker, the white spots near the margin more conspicuous than on the upperside.

Distribution. Cuba only. A widespread forest insect. *Eueides melphis cleobaea* (see p. 86) is sometimes confused with *L. ceres* but it is a very much smaller insect. TL: Cuba.

2 **L. ceres cleobaea** Godart 1819

Description. Male and female very slightly smaller than *L. c. demeter*, the fulvous areas on both wings much paler, the yellow forewing band broken into well separated spots, the central (discal) band of hindwing also yellow instead of fulvous. Underside the same.

Distribution. Haiti and the Dominican Republic. Not uncommon in mountain forest. Porto Rico: rather rare. Found in Jamaica in 1974. TL: 'Antilles'.

Early stages. The caterpillar is said to feed on figs (which seems unlikely), but has not been described.

Note. *L. ceres* has been taken at times in the Lesser Antilles, e.g. on St Lucia in 1913, no doubt as a wanderer from Trinidad or the neighbouring mainland where it occurs as *L. ceres atergatis* Doubleday 1847. This is very similar to *L. c. cleobaea* except that the yellow spots across the forewing beyond the cell are much larger and united, and the discal band on the hindwing is light brown, not yellow.

The Ithomiidae are an easily recognised family of rather long-winged butterflies peculiar, except for the single Old World genus *Tellervo*, to the New World tropics, where they form a large and highly characteristic element of the butterfly fauna. Their frequent association with the Danaidae, as a separate subfamily, is not really justifiable on morphological grounds. It is a curious fact that although some four hundred different species of Ithomiidae are known from the American mainland no more than two occur in the West Indies. These two are at once distinguished from all the other butterflies of the Antilles by their transparent wings.

Male Ithomiidae can always be recognised by the patch of rather long hairs that arises from the front edge of the hindwings close against the cell. This is a constant secondary sexual character of the males. Females lack it. The tarsus of the male foreleg is aborted, that of the female 4- or 5-jointed. Separation of the genera of Ithomiidae rests very largely on characters of the wing venation, which fortunately are unusually easy to see because of the transparency of the wings in so many species.

The few caterpillars that are known are slender and tapering, smooth and devoid of tentacles, usually pale in colour and inconspicuously striped. All those known feed on Solanaceae.

GRETA DIAPHANA Drury 1773   *Jamaican Clearwing*   **Pl. 2**
syn. *Hymenitis diaphanus*
Confined to the West Indies in two subspecies:

1 G. diaphana diaphana Drury 1773
Description. Fw ♂ and ♀ 25–26 mm. Both wings completely transparent except for the narrowly black margins, the black veins and, on the forewing, a black bar across the end of the cell; *forewing with four or five opaque white spots,* hindwing usually with a single minute apical spot; all spots rather larger in female than in male. On the underside the black markings are as on the upperside but rust-red in colour.
Distribution: Apparently, but improbably, almost confined to the Blue Mountains of Jamaica, where it would seem to occur in two broods, one in February to April, the other in July to September. Prefers the shade of humid forest. TL: Jamaica.

2 G. diaphana quisqueya Fox 1963
Description. Both sexes differ from *G. d. diaphana* in three obvious particulars: the black marginal edging is narrower; the three white spots in line just beyond the end of the cell have a tendency, realised in the female but seldom in the male, to link up and form a narrow chain; and the outer margin of the forewing is bluntly angled between the extremities of veins 2 and 3. On the underside the markings are paler, ochreous rather than rust-red.
Distribution. At 3–4000 ft in the mountains of north western Dominican

Republic in July – the only precisely recorded locality. No doubt elsewhere in suitable forest country. TL: Dominican Republic, Mt Diego de Ocampa.

Early stages. Not known.

GRETA CUBANA Herrich-Schaeffer 1862 *Cuban Clearwing* **Pl. 2**
syn. *Hymenitis cubana*

Description. Fw ♂ and ♀ 25–29 mm. Transparent. Black cell-bar on forewing twice as wide as in *G. diaphana*; forewing apex and anal angle rather broadly black, separated by a marginal white spot in space 2 which is joined to the white patch beyond the end of the cell so as to form a *continuous transverse white band* which, like the apical black patch, is much wider in the female than in the male. On the underside the pattern is repeated, the black areas becoming rust-red.

Distribution. Confined to the mountains of eastern, central and western Cuba from about 1000 ft upwards. Flies very slowly and is almost invisible on the wing in the rather shady situations it favours. RANGE and TL: Cuba.

Early stages. The caterpillar is reported to feed on Galan, a species of *Cestrum* (Solanaceae) but has not been described.

It is curious that of this cosmopolitan family, so strongly represented in South and Central America, only a single genus has penetrated the Caribbean sub-region. This is the genus *Calisto* which, besides being the only Satyrid genus to occur in the Caribbean area, is not found anywhere else in the world. Its affinities are thought to lie with some of the High Andean genera of South America, but could almost equally well be with the African fauna. The nineteen species recognised below are confined to the Greater Antilles, and more than half of them to Hispaniola alone, where many are to be found only at compara-tively high altitudes, and most are quite rare. Ringlets are decidedly sedentary butterflies, closely tied to their birth places and little given to wandering. This may explain why not one of the numerous small and delicate species of Satyridae that occur plentifully in neighbouring Central America, Venezuela, Guiana, Trinidad or Tobago, has established a foothold on any of the islands. The main strongholds of the family are in open country, especially temperate grasslands, as their caterpillars' food plants are almost exclusively grasses. Tropical and subtropical regions seem only to have been invaded by them where additional monocotyledons such as bamboos, cane, rice, maize, etc., provide them with suitable food plants. Like the Hesperiinae, which also are restricted to mono-cotyledons, they would seem to be a geologically old family.

Morphologically the Satyridae are an easily recognised family on account of both wing markings and anatomical features. The 'eye-spots' or ocelli that are almost invariably to be found, at least on the underside of the hindwing, provide one clue; the minute forelegs and especially the swollen veins at the base of the forewings provide others. Caterpillars are spindle-shaped rather than cylindrical, smooth, the head sometimes slightly lobed, the tail always forked. The cater-pillars of only two species of *Calisto* are known.

CALISTO ZANGIS Fabricus 1775   *Jamaican Ringlet*   **Pl. 2**
Description. Fw ♂ and ♀ 20–23 mm. Male upperside very dark silky brown, forewing with a large *shiny circular dark grey sex brand*; female upperside with cell-end darkened, both wings faintly washed ferrugineous. Underside ground colour lighter brown; forewing with a single very large subapical ocellus; hindwing with a much smaller oval ocellus in space 2, a few white specks above it, and two parallel wavy darker lines nearer the margin, the postdiscal area faintly lilac tinted.
Distribution. Confined to Jamaica, where it is widespread from sea level to about 6000 ft. Prefers rough shady places and does not wander afield. The only species of *Calisto* known to occur on Jamaica. RANGE: Jamaica. TL: 'Carolina', *recte* Jamaica.
Early stages. The caterpillar has the forked tail characteristic of all Satyrid larvae. Head with two short stout horns. Green at first, the caterpillar turns brown as it grows. When full-fed it is variegated light and dark brown with a row of lozenge-shaped brown dorsal marks on a paler brown background, traces

Plate 3   **SATYRIDAE**

1. **Calisto archebates**   *Yellow-barred Ringlet*   p. 46
Hindwing underside with broad pale band.
1a ♂, 1b ♀, Furcy, Haiti. July.

2. **Calisto loxias**   *Bates's Ringlet*   47
Forewing ocellus with a single central pupil.
2a ♂, 2b ♀, Roche Croix, Haiti, 5000 ft. October.

3. **Calisto confusa**   *Confused Ringlet*   50
Both sexes with signs of an ocellus at anal angle, which is slightly
lobed; discal lines bright. 3a ♂, 3b ♀, Haiti.

4. **Calisto obscura**   *Obscure Ringlet*   50
Hindwing underside without anal eye-spot; discal lines dull.
4a ♂, 4b ♀, Haiti.

5. **Calisto lyceius**   *Saona Ringlet*   50
♂ near Monte Christi, Dominican Republic. Fw underside reddish.

6. **Calisto tragius**   *La Selle Ringlet*   51
♀ La Selle Range, Haiti, 5-7000 ft. Sept. Upperside distally paler.

7. **Calisto hysius**   *Rusty Ringlet*   51
Hindwing underside pale transverse lines dull.
7a ♂ Velle de Polo, Dominican Republic, 2500 ft. August.
7b ♀ La Boulle, Haiti. July.

8. **Calisto montana**   *Mountain Ringlet*   51
♂ Mt Basil, Haiti, 4500 ft. September. Forewing underside with
cell wholly red.

9. **Calisto herophile**   *Common Ringlet*   52
Hw underside twin submarginal lines parallel. 9a ♂, 9b ♀, Cuba.

10. **Calisto sibylla**   *Cuban Ringlet*   52
♂ *C. s. smintheus,* Cuba. Inner submarginal line on hindwing
underside obscured towards apex, outer line faint.

11. **Calisto eleleus**   *Dingy Ringlet*   53
♂ Kenscoff, Haiti, 4800 ft. March. No sex brand.

12. **Calisto grannus**   *Darlington's Ringlet*   53
♂ S.E. Cordillera, Dominican Republic, 7000 ft. August. Hindwing
underside with two ocelli.

13. **Calisto micheneri**   *Michener's Ringlet*   53
♂ C. Cordillera, Dominican Republic. June.

14. **Calisto chrysaoros**   *White Y Ringlet*   46
♂ Monteada Nueva, Dominican Republic. February. Hindwing
underside in male with two white bands.

3

4

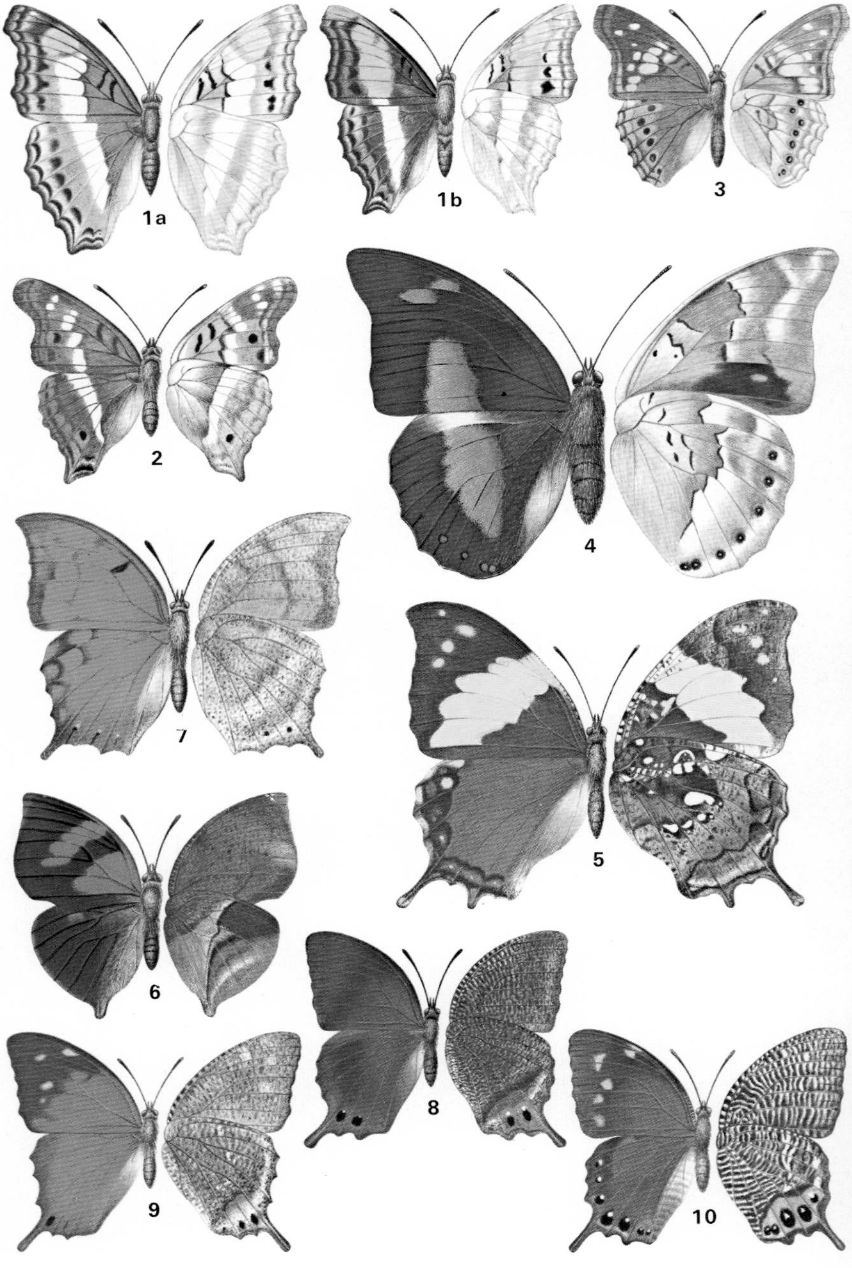

1. Doxocopa laure   *Cuban Emperor*   p. 55
1a ♀ Guantanamo, Cuba. Forewing band white.
1b ♂ Holguin, Cuba. Forewing band yellow, disc of hindwing with brilliant blue gloss.

2. Doxocopa thoe   *Purple Emperor*   56
♂ Haiti. Both wings with deep blue gloss.

3. Asterocampa idyia   *Dusky Emperor*   56
♂ Holguin, Cuba. Forewing discal spots pale fawn; hindwing postdiscal spots black.

4. Prepona amphitoe   *Silver King*   56
♂ Haiti. The discal line on hindwing underside is shaped like the profile of a human head.

5. Hypna iphigenia   *Iphigenia*   57
♂ Cuba. Spangles on hindwing underside are silver.

6. Siderone galanthis   *Scarlet Emperor*   57
♂ Cuba. The forewing scarlet bands are quite specific.

7. Anaea troglodyta   *The Troglodyte*   57
♂ Haiti. Upperside usually with a faint purple flush.

8. Anaea echemus   *Chestnut Leaf Butterfly*   59
♂ Grand Cayman. April. Forewing upperside with no yellow spots.

9. Anaea dominicana   *Godman's Leaf Butterfly*   61
♂ *A. d. luciana,* St Lucia. Forewing upperside with four yellow spots in subapical area.

10. Anaea intermedia   *Turk Island Leaf Butterfly*   60
♂ Grand Turk Island. December, January. Forewing upperside with five yellow spots.

of a white lateral line along the sides, the underneath dark brown. Food plants grasses, especially Bahama grass. Feeds at night.

CALISTO NUBILA Lathy 1899   *Porto Rican Ringlet*   **Pl. 2**
Description. Fw ♂ 21 mm, ♀ 22 mm. Rather similar to *Calisto zangis* but forewing apex less pointed. Male upperside very dark, almost black, androconia present but not forming a recognisable patch; female upperside dark brown, the hindwing with faintly darker submarginal line; both sexes with *prominent dark round ocellar anal spot*. Underside with at most two white specks above the oval hindwing ocellus, and inner margin faintly but rather broadly ferrugineous; forewing with ferrugineous area below the ocellus in female only.
Distribution. Confined to Porto Rico, and the only *Calisto* known there. Flies throughout the year, commonest in the mountains but also found in the coastal foothills to 2000 ft. RANGE and TL: Porto Rico.
Early stages. Not known.

CALISTO PULCHELLA Lathy 1899   *Orange Ringlet*   **Pl. 2**
Description. Fw ♂ 20–24 mm, ♀ 23–26 mm. The largest species in the genus and at once recognised by the *large ferrugineous area* that extends broadly *across the underside of the hindwing* from the inner margin, except in ♀-form *tenebrosa* Lathy, which lacks it. The upperside of the male is uniformly dark brown, with a large black ill-defined rounded androconical patch in spaces 1b, 2 and 3; female upperside forewing apical half paler than basal half and with a marginal band; hindwing outer half largely suffused orange (except in ♀-form *tenebrosa*); in both sexes the anal ocellar spots are very imperfectly represented on both surfaces.
Distribution. Confined to Haiti and the Dominican Republic, from sea level to at least 2500 ft. Form *darlingtoni* Clench 1943 occurs at higher elevations in the central Cordilleras and is smaller and more brightly coloured beneath. RANGE: Hispaniola. TL: Haiti.
Early stages. The caterpillar has not been described in spite of the fact that it is at times a pest of sugar cane, even at sea level, where the butterfly sometimes occurs in swarms.

CALISTO ARCHEBATES Ménétriés 1832   *Yellow-barred Ringlet*
Pl. 3
Description. Fw ♂ 20 mm, ♀ larger. Upperside very dark brown; forewing in the male with large black androconial patch occupying most of the basal two-thirds of the wing. Underside at once distinguished from all other known species of *Calisto* by the *broad transverse pale band on the hindwing*, which expands broadly as it approaches the inner margin and is yellow or orange in the male, usually white in the female. Ocelli and other markings as usual in the genus but without ferrugineous areas.
Distribution. Confined to Hispaniola: La Selle Range at 5–7000 ft in S. Haiti; Puerto Plata in Dominican Republic. RANGE: Hispaniola. TL: Haiti.
Early stages. Not known.

CALISTO CHRYSAOROS Bates 1935   *White Y Ringlet*   **Pl. 3**
Description. Fw 17–20 mm. Upperside fuscous; hindwing with diffuse brown anal patch and some discal brown shading. Underside fuscous; forewing un-

marked except for the yellow-ringed apical ocellus which has a single central dot; *hindwing in the male with two white bands*, a long narrow one that runs from costa near the apex across to the middle of the inner margin, expanded and bent at the cell-end, and a second shorter zig-zag band from near base of space 3 to end of vein 1b; in the female these bands are absent and there is instead a confused pattern of brown shadings; in both sexes there is a small or minute anal ocellus and some postdiscal white dots. The sex brand of the male occupies the basal halves of spaces 1b, 2 and 3 without entering the cell or space 1a.

Distribution. Only known from the La Hotte – La Selle complex in southern Haiti at 3–7000 ft in September and October. RANGE: Hispaniola. TL: Roche Croix, 5000 ft.

Early stages. Not known.

CALISTO LOXIAS Bates 1935 *Bates's Ringlet* Pl. 3

Description. Fw ♂ and ♀ 22–23 mm. Upperside dark brown. Male with basal two-thirds of forewing largely covered by a diffuse patch of black androconial scales. Underside warm brown; *forewing* with a faint diffuse rusty red area in the cell towards the upper outer angle, a round *black ocellus* narrowly ringed with ochreous and *with a single central pupil*, and a faint submarginal line; hindwing warmer brown, basal third darker than rest of wing, the broad and slightly paler discal band shaped somewhat as in *Calisto archebates* but much wider towards the costa and delineated on either side by a delicate line of pale grey scales; ocellus black and with a single central white pupil; postdiscal area lighter and with a faint scattering of pale grey scales. In the female the rusty red area in the cell of the forewing on the underside may be more extensive, and the hindwing band better defined.

Distribution. Known only from the Type Locality (Roche Croix, La Hotte Mts, Haiti), where it was taken at an altitude of about 5000 ft in October. RANGE: Haiti.

Early stages. Not known.

CALISTO ARCAS Bates 1939 *Fulvous Ringlet*

Description. Fw 24–27 mm. Upperside dark fuscous; forewing with a *row of large ill-defined fulvous submarginal spots* from inner margin to vein 5; *hindwing with distal half fulvous* and a narrow submarginal orange line. Underside of forewing dark red-brown to just beyond cell-end, but inner margin black;

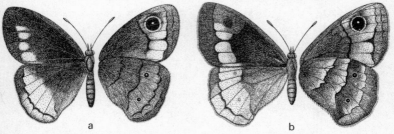

Fig. 6. *Calisto arcas. Left,* ♂; *right,* ♀. Valle Nuevo, S.E. Constanza, Dominican Republic, 7,000 ft., August.

Plate 5 NYMPHALIDAE *Scale:* × ⅔

1. Marpesia petreus *Southern Dagger Tail* p. 61
♂ Dominica. July. Discal line on forewing upperside straight almost to costa.

2. Marpesia eleuchea *Cuban Dagger Tail* 62
♂ Holguin, Cuba. Discal line on forewing upperside sharply angled at vein 4.

3. Marpesia chiron *Common Dagger Tail* 62
♂ Holguin, Cuba. Sooty brown with three pale stripes across both wings.

4. Myscelia antholia *The Royal Blue* 63
♂ Haiti. The contrast of vivid blue and dead white is almost startling.

5. Colobura dirce *The Mosaic* 63
♂ Haiti. Underside with very complicated pattern of dark lines.

6. Historis acheronta *Cadmus* 66
♂ *H. a. semele,* Holguin, Cuba Forewing with five or six pure white subapical spots.

7. Historis odius *Orion* 66
♂ *H. o. odius,* Bayate, Santiago de Cuba. Forewing with a single small white spot towards apex.

8. Hamadryas feronia *The Cracker* 67
♂ *H. f. insularis,* Trinidad. Postdiscal ocelli on hindwing upperside blue-ringed.

9. Hamadryas februa *Haitian Cracker* 67
♂ *H. f. diasia,* Port au Prince, Haiti. Ocelli ringed buff and black, not blue.

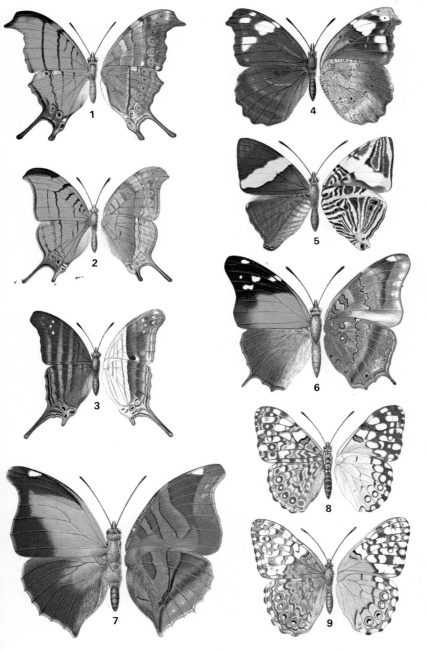

6

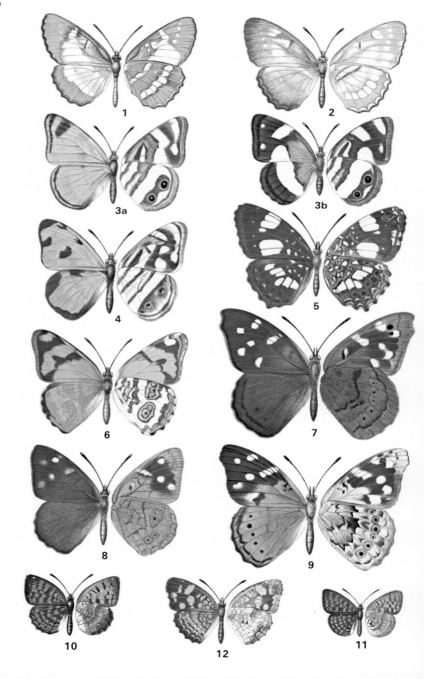

1. **Mestra dorcas** *Jamaican Mestra* p. 68
   ♂ Jamaica. Underside mainly ochreous.

2. **Mestra cana** *St Lucia Mestra* 68
   ♀ St Lucia. Underside pale orange, almost lemon yellow.

3. **Dynamine egaea** *Bronze Wing* 69
   D. e. calais. Upperside yellowish green.
   3a ♂, 3b ♀, Cuba.

4. **Dynamine mylitta** *Emerald Wing* 69
   ♂ Mexico. Upperside bluish green.

5. **Archimestra teleboas** *False Neptis* 70
   ♂ Haiti. Broad white bands are accompanied by very numerous
   small white spots, as in Old World *Neptis.*

6. **Lucinia sida** *Cuban Lucinia* 70
   ♂ *L. s. torrebia,* Dominican Republic. Forewing cellbar not joined
   to subapical bar.

7. **Eunica tatila** *Purple Eunica* 71
   ♂ *E. t. tatilista,* Holguin, Cuba. Forewing spots clear white.

8. **Eunica monima** *Dingy Purple Wing* 71
   ♂ Haiti. Forewing spots mostly dull and indistinct.

9. **Eunica heraclitus** *Poey's Eunica* 72
   ♂ Cuba. Forewing ground colour dull greyish brown.

10. **Antillea proclea** *Jamaican Pygmy Fritillary* 79
    ♂ Kingston, Jamaica. Forewing with minute white apical dot.

11. **Antillea pelops** *Pygmy Fritillary* 78
    ♂ *A. p. pelops,* Dominican Republic. Forewing without white apical
    dot.

12. **Phyciodes frisia** *Cuban Crescent Spot* 79
    ♂ Havana, Cuba. Fulvous areas of upperside uniform in colour.
    For *Phyciodes phaon* see Plate 12.

fulvous postdiscal area marked off by narrow brown lines, the usual subapical ocellus present; hindwing rich brown, basal half suffused yellowish, distal half reddish; two ocelli of about equal size, one in space 2, the other in space 5; a white dot in space 4. Androconia present in spaces 1a–2 in male but not forming a defined patch.

Distribution. Known only from Hispaniola. A large and striking species at once distinguished by the extensive fulvous areas on the upperside and by having two large ocelli on the underside of the hindwing. RANGE: Hispaniola. TL: near Constanza, 7000 ft, in Central Cordillera.

Early stages. Not known.

CALISTO CONFUSA Lathy 1899   *Confused Ringlet*   **Pl. 3**
Description. Fw ♂ 14–16 mm, ♀ 15–17 mm. Very similar to, but slightly larger than *C. obscura*. Both sexes with *indications of an ocellus (lacking in* C. obscura) *on both surfaces at the slightly lobed anal angle.* Upperside black forewing androconial patch outwardly rounded, or only very slightly jagged, and not extending into base of space 4; female with no trace of a dark submarginal line, though margin often dark. Underside smooth dark brown, forewing basal patch dark rusty red; lower pupil in apical ocellus much closer than upper pupil to the yellow circumference; hindwing proximal transverse white line clear-cut and almost straight; distal line also sharp, white, and broadest from just above ocellus to inner margin.

Distribution. Common throughout Haiti and the Dominican Republic, from sea level to 5000 ft. Flies alongside *C. obscura* with which it is often confused. Form *debarriera* Clench 1943 is a high altitude form in which the whitish transverse lines on the underside are wholly or almost entirely obscured, so that virtually only the line before the ocellus on the hindwing and the narrow submarginal band beyond it are visible. RANGE: Hispaniola. TL: Haiti.

Early stages. Not known.

CALISTO OBSCURA Michener 1943   *Obscure Ringlet*   **Pl. 3**
Description. Fw ♂ 14 mm, ♀ 15 mm. Upperside dark rather silky brown; male with black androconial patch extending from inner margin into space 4, its outer edge rather jagged; female with faint indications of a darker submarginal line. Underside grey-brown, with a faintly roughened appearance; forewing *cell with light red patch not reaching the transverse pale line* at cell-end and only very rarely extending below the cell; apical ocellus with two blue pupils equidistant from circumference; hindwing with strongly curved proximal transverse line very indistinct; distal line also faint and best defined just above the ocellus in space 2, which is round if small, slightly oval if large, submarginal area paler and with two roughly parallel generally ill-defined darker lines.

Distribution. Haiti and Dominican Republic only, widespread and seemingly common, from sea level to 3000 ft, throughout the year except perhaps from August to November. RANGE: Hispaniola. TL: Pétionville, Haiti.

Early stages. Not known.

CALISTO LYCEIUS Bates 1935   *Saona Ringlet*   **Pl. 3**
Description. Fw 15–16 mm. Upperside dull grey-brown, the androconial patch in the male black, sharply defined, the veins that cross it grey. *Underside of forewing rusty red, except the apex* beyond the ocellus *and the margins*; hindwing

darker, faintly tinged with red-brown; transverse lines on both wings not white-edged, on the forewing positioned as in *C. confusa*, on the hindwing with the discal line starting about mid-costa so that a wide gap exists between it and the first submarginal line; a short creamy narrow band from anal angle to vein 3; white dots in spaces 3, 4, 5 and 6 far removed from the discal line (in *C. confusa* they almost touch it); the oval black ocellus enclosing a blue pupil and 2 or 3 additional blue points.

Distribution. *Calisto lyceius* has been taken in northern Hispaniola as well as on the island of Saona, which lies off the S.E. coast of the Dominican Republic. It is easily distinguished by the wide extent of the red area on the underside of the forewing. RANGE: Hispaniola. TL: Saona Island, Dominican Republic.

Early stages. Not known.

CALISTO TRAGIUS Bates 1935   *La Selle Ringlet*   **Pl. 3**
Description Fw ♂ and ♀ 18–21 mm. Upperside *shining fuscous, distally paler*. Underside also fuscous, forewing cell and discal area faintly reddish; apical ocellus small and with two white pupils; postdiscal line faint; underside pattern very faint in male, better developed in female, consisting of a pale transverse discal and a post-discal line, two zig-zag submarginal lines, a small *round* ocellus with a single *central* pupil and a single minute postdiscal white dot in space 3. Androconial patch as in *Calisto hysius*.

Distribution. So far known only from the La Selle Mountains of southern Haiti at 5–7000 ft. RANGE: Haiti. TL: La Visite.

Early stages. Not known.

CALISTO HYSIUS Godart 1819   *Rusty Ringlet*   **Pl. 3**
Description. Fw ♂ and ♀ 13–15 mm. Upperside dull dark brown; male with large androconial patch occupying the bases of areas 1a, 1b, 2, 3 and 4; female with faint reddish flush in postdiscal area of both wings. On the underside of the forewing the outer edge of the basal orange-red cell-patch is sharply defined, there is a red area present below the apical ocellus, and the two postdiscal (or submarginal) lines are edged with pale scales and more or less prominent. Hindwing underside grey-brown, the two *transverse pale lines duller and less well defined* than in *Calisto confusa*.

Distribution. Hispaniola only. La Selle Mts at 4500 to 7000 ft, also possibly in the Cap Haitien region. In the central and north-eastern Cordillera *C. hysius hysius* (described above) is replaced by *C. hysius batesi* Michener 1943, which is a larger insect (fw 15–18 mm.) with the red patch on the underside of the forewing very much darker in colour. A smaller race, with markings less well defined, occurs at Samana in the Dominican Republic. RANGE: Hispaniola. TL: Haiti.

Early stages. Not known.

CALISTO MONTANA Clench 1943   *Mountain Ringlet*   **Pl. 3**
Description. Fw ♂ 15 mm.; ♀ not known. Upperside blackish brown, forewing sex brand little darker, occupying basal halves of spaces 2 and 3 and part of cell, hindwing with ruddy patch near anal angle. Underside also blackish brown: *forewing cell wholly red*, the red spilling into neighbouring spaces but not present below the ocellus; a faint discal line and two faint submarginal lines; ocellus black, ringed yellow and with two pupils: hindwing dusted with grey

scales, the two submarginal lines more prominent than on the forewing; ocellus in space 2 circular, with a single central pupil; postdiscal area obscurely purple and enclosing single white spots (in spaces 3, 4 and 5) as well as the ocellus.
Distribution. Known only from Mt Basil, Haiti, at 4500 ft (TL), where it was taken in September. RANGE: Haiti.
Early stages. Not known.

CALISTO HEROPHILE Huebner 1823   *Common Ringlet*   **Pl. 3**
Description. Fw ♂ 15–17 mm, ♀ 17–19 mm. Upperside dark brown; male with basal two-thirds of forewing blackened by a large androconial area; female slightly darker in the same area. Underside lighter greyish brown, *both wings with twin wavy submarginal lines extending from anal angle to apex unobscured*, and a single marginal line; forewing basal red patch bounded distally by a brown line; prominent white dots in both ocelli, and in spaces 3 to 6 of hindwing, the last set against a faintly lilac ground colour.
Distribution. Throughout Cuba and also in the Isle of Pines, sea level to 3000 ft, common. Rather variable. A somewhat larger darker form that flies in the Trinidad Mountains has been named *parsonsi* Clench 1943; and in the subspecies *bruneri* Michener 1949, from Moa in the Orient Province, the red patch on the underside of the forewing towards the base is relatively longer, often longer than broad, but the hindwing postdiscal lines have the pattern of typical *herophile*. In the Bahamas the barely distinguishable subspecies *apollinis* Bates 1934 replaces typical *herophile* but appears now to be extremely rare. RANGE: Bahamas to Isle of Pines. TL: Havana, Cuba.
Early stages. The caterpillar when full grown is basically green, with wide dorsal and narrow paradorsal dark brown lines outlined in lighter brown, dark brown supraspiracular and spiracular lines, and a blue line below the spiracles; body yellowish beneath, head grey-green and rugose, legs dirty white. Food plants grasses, especially lawn grass, maize and sugar cane.

CALISTO SIBYLLA Bates 1934   *Cuban Ringlet*   **Pl. 3**
Description. Fw ♂ and ♀ 18–25 mm. Upperside dark velvety brown, darker than in *C. herophile*, outer area of forewing slightly paler. Underside also darker, rich chocolate brown, *submarginal line single and usually heavily obscured towards the apex on hindwing*; marginal line double on both wings; forewing red cell-mark deeper in colour and less well defined than in *C. herophile*, sometimes absent; hindwing postdiscal area lilac, sharply bounded inwardly by pale grey-brown edging of dark basal area; white speck in space 3 displaced inwardly.
Distribution. *C. sibylla* is largely but not exclusively a mountain species. It differs from *C. herophile*, with which it sometimes flies, not only in the characters mentioned above, but also in anatomical details and habitat. Whereas *C. herophile* seems to prefer more open, only slightly shaded areas around fields, hedgerows and roadsides, *C. sibylla* is found only in deep shady forest. This is particularly true of subspecies *smintheus* Bates 1935, first found in the Sierra del Cobre, Oriente, at about 3000 ft. On the neighbouring Pico Turquino at 4–6000 ft there occurs the rather larger, darker, subspecies *delos* Bates 1935, which has a dark red oval cell-patch on the forewing underside. *C. sibylla muripetens* Bates 1939 inhabits the Sierra de Escambray at 3000 ft in the Buenos Aires region and is like subspecies *smintheus* but paler in colour. A fourth mountain race is *C. sibylla bradleyi* Munro 1950 from the Sierra Rangel, Pinar

del Rio province in March, with a well developed red patch, more prominent dark androconial area and more olivaceous postdiscal areas beneath. Typical *sibylla* is known only from a single female and is barely distinguishable from subspecies *smintheus*. (See also *C. biocellatus*, below). RANGE: Bahamas to Isle of Pines. TL: Nassau, Bahamas.
Early stages. Not known.

CALISTO BIOCELLATUS de la Torre 1968 *de la Torre's Ringlet*
Description. Fw ♂ 25 mm, ♀ 26 mm. Very similar to *Calisto sibylla delos* but larger and darker, especially towards the wing bases, and with the narrow yellowish submarginal line on the hindwing underside more prominent; at once distinguished, however, by the presence of a small *additional ocellus on the underside of the forewing in space* 2.
Distribution. Known only from the type locality in Cuba, where two specimens only were taken in June 1963. The occurrence of extra ocelli is very frequent in Satyridae; this may be but yet another mountain race of *C. sibylla*. RANGE: Cuba. TL: Pico Cuba, Sierra Maestra.

CALISTO ELELEUS Bates 1935 *Dingy Ringlet* **Pl. 3**
Description. Fw 21–23 mm. Upperside *uniformly fuscous. Male without sexbrand,* female with a little postdiscal brown shading. On the underside of the forewing the cell is very dark crimson brown, there are almost invisible postdiscal and submarginal lines, and the ocellus is small, very dark, narrowly ringed with dark ochreous and enclosing two minute white pupils; *hindwing almost featureless,* the discal and postdiscal lines barely discernible, the ocellus in space 2 minute, black, oval and with its white pupil placed towards the basal edge, two zig-zag wavy submarginal lines, no postdiscal white dots. Chiefly characterised by large size and absence of clear characters.
Distribution. Port au Prince area only, in Haiti, at 2–5000 ft. RANGE: Haiti. TL: Mt Bourette.
Early stages. Not known.

CALISTO GRANNUS Bates 1939 *Darlington's Ringlet* **Pl. 3**
Description. Fw ♂ 16–18 mm. Upperside dark fuscous, the disc below vein 4 darkened by the presence of black androconia. On the underside the forewing is fuscous, with a dark postdiscal line from costa to inner margin, two wavy submarginal lines, the usual apical ocellus, but no red or orange markings; *hindwing* also fuscous, *with* red-brown discal and postdiscal lines, two irregular submarginal lines and *two symmetrical ocelli* each with a white central dot, one in space 2, the other in space 5 (slightly the smaller); a prominent white dot also in spaces 3 and 4. Androconia as in *Calisto hysius* (p. 51).
Distribution. All known specimens have been taken in the Central Cordillera at 7–8000 ft (TL). The small size, absence of red markings on the underside of the forewing and especially the presence of a second large ocellus on the underside of the hindwing easily distinguish this species, which in other respects is rather close to *Calisto hysius*. RANGE: Hispaniola only.
Early stages. Not known.

CALISTO MICHENERI Clench 1943 *Michener's Ringlet* **Pl. 3**
Description. Fw ♂ 14 mm, ♀ not known. Upperside blackish brown, forewing

with jet black androconial area occupying basal two-thirds of wing; hindwing distally paler. Underside grey-brown; forewing cell red almost to cell-end; apical ocellus with two white pupils; one discal and two submarginal lines all dark brown; hindwing with discal, postdiscal and two submarginal lines, the last much dislocated at the veins, a *very small black ocellus in space 2 with a single central pupil*; single white dots in spaces 3 and 4.

Distribution. Only a single male is known and was taken at Loma del Toro, south of Santiago, at about 5000 ft in June, in the Dominican Republic. RANGE: Dominican Republic. TL: Loma del Toro.

Early stages. Not known.

There is no single morphological character or simple combination of characters by which to distinguish this very large and cosmopolitan family. In so far as the fauna of the West Indies is concerned it comprises the whole of the 'brush-footed butterflies' that are not Satyridae, Danaidae, Ithomiidae or Heliconiidae; in other words practically all the larger and more conspicuous butterflies except these, the Swallowtails and Whites. They are called 'brush-footed' because of the condition of the fore-feet, which are useless for walking and reduced in the male to a brush-like object formed of long hair-scales borne on what remains of the tarsus. The female tarsus is larger, less hairy and usually ends in a rounded comb-like tip. The antennae are generally well developed and have a distinct club. On the hindwing the short humeral (precostal) vein near the base of the costa is well formed and usually branched, and the cell in most species is open, i.e. not closed by a tubular cross vein.

The family divides easily into two major subfamilies, the Apaturinae (Emperors) and the Nymphalinae, on characters of the larvae; those of the actual butterflies are less easy. All the Apaturid caterpillars are smooth skinned, without spines except on the head and these are horns rather than spines; also they have forked tails. In the Nymphaline caterpillar all the body segments (with one or two exceptions) bear branching spines but there are no horns, though there may be spines on the head, the spines being arranged in anything from one to nine parallel rows; and the last segment is not forked. Both these subfamilies break down into groups that become recognisable as one becomes familiar with the species but are not at all easy to define, such as the Fritillaries, e.g. *Euptoieta* (Argynnini) and *Phyciodes* (Melitaeini), the Tortoiseshells (Nymphalini) and the Admirals (Limenitidini).

DOXOCOPA LAURE Drury 1773   *Cuban Emperor*   **Pl. 4**
Description. Fw ♂ 27–28 mm, ♀ 31–36 mm. Upperside dark brown, crossed by a white band that runs from near the anal angle of hindwing and in the male extends barely to vein 1 and in the female to vein 5 of the forewing; in the male this band changes to dull yellow at vein 2 and continues to the costa though often divided just beyond the cell end; in the female the continuation of the band is limited to an isolated round yellow subapical spot. In certain lights the *disc of the hindwing and part of the basal area of the forewing reflect a brilliant blue gloss.* The pearly underside reproduces the pattern of the upperside.
Distribution. *D. laure fabricii* Hall 1925 is the Jamaican subspecies and is found chiefly in the Cockpit country, but is rare. It differs little from the mainland *D. l. laure* though on the whole it has narrower and duller yellow markings. In Cuba it is replaced by the very distinct *D. l. druryi* Huebner 1823. In this subspecies the male has a wider and paler yellow band and the female is very much paler, all the dark brown areas being replaced by pale grey or light brown. Said to be a common woodland butterfly. RANGE: Mexico to Venezuela. TL: 'Gulf of Honduras'.
Early stages. The fully grown caterpillar is rather dark green covered in

minute yellow spots that give it a shagreened look, tapering behind to a single narrow pointed tail and bearing a pair of widely separated delicate green horns on the head each with a few short branches; on the middle of the back are two small round red spots one on either side of the mid-dorsal line; a rather indefinite yellow lateral line runs just above the legs. Food plant in Cuba is Jia (*Casearia*).

DOXOCOPA THOE Godart 1823   *Purple Emperor*   **Pl. 4**
Description. Fw ♂ 30 mm, ♀ 36 mm. Dimorphic. Male upperside black, *both wings with brilliant deep blue reflections* that extend almost to the margins; a narrow white discal band on the hindwing is continued as a series of white spots on the forewing, where there are also a pair of white subapical spots; a small red submarginal spot in space 2 on both wings; underside pattern as on upperside but ground colour silvery. Female upperside ochreous brown, without purple reflections, the pattern of markings as in the male but the only white markings are the subapical spots on the forewing and a costal mark on the hindwing. Underside like the male.
Distribution. Known only from Hispaniola, where it is very rare. Nothing is known of its habitats or early stages. RANGE: Hispaniola. TL: 'America'.

ASTEROCAMPA IDYIA Huebner 1828   *Dusky Emperor*   **Pl. 4**
Description. Fw ♂ 29–30 mm, ♀ 35–38 mm. Female consistently much larger than the male and with much less elongate forewings. Upperside dusky brown in both sexes, the forewing disc crossed by a transverse band of confused pale brown spots, which are best defined in the male, and with a pair of similar subapical spots; *hindwing* with a prominent row of *six solid black submarginal spots*. Underside much paler, the hindwing ocellar spots pupilled with blue. A variety of the female which is almost uniformly ochreous brown has been named ♀-f. *padola* Fruhstorfer 1912.
Distribution. Cuba and Isle of Pines, widespread in woodland country. Rare in Hispaniola and Porto Rico. RANGE: Greater Antilles only. TL: Cuba.
Early stages. The full grown caterpillar is greenish white with a shagreened effect, a subdorsal and a dorso-lateral line are darker green edged with orange, and there is an orange spiracular line; head black, a white line near the mouth and two branched black and white horns. Food plant in Cuba *Ardisia cubana*. The normal food plant of other species of *Asterocampa* is *Celtis*, the butterflies being known as the Hackberry Butterflies.

PREPONA AMPHITOE Godart 1823   *Silver King*   **Pl. 4**
    syn. *insulicola* Fruhstorfer 1897
Description. Fw ♂ 50 mm, ♀ 55 mm. Upperside black; *forewing blue band not extending above vein* 3, its outer edge straight, *width along vein* 1 *only* 10 *mm*; hindwing band a little wider in the middle, occupying less than half of space 2 in the male, barely entering space 2 in the female. On the underside, in the words of Godart 'the sinuosities of the transverse black discal line [on the hindwing] form a sort of human profile', an excellent character not found in any other *Prepona*.
Distribution. Haiti: Port au Prince; Dominican Republic: La Vega, La Cumbre, Mt Isabella; not uncommon. *P. a. amphitoe* of these islands is replaced on Cuba by the rather smaller and darker subspecies *P. a. crassina* Fruhstorfer

1904, which seems to be local and rather scarce: Holguin, Baracoa, Tanamo, Rio Cano, etc. The species is not known from Jamaica, but it might well turn up still in the Cockpit Country. RANGE: Greater Antilles. TL: 'S. America', *recte* Haiti.

Early stages. Not known. Known caterpillars of closely related species (e.g. *P. antimache*) are very similar to the caterpillar of *Siderone* (below). The head has a pair of short widely separated knobs (not spines) and is joined to the body by a narrow rather flattened neck formed of the thoracic segments, the first abdominal segments are then greatly expanded, the remainder tapering to a bifurcate tail-like anal segment. The body is without spines. Food plants of *Prepona* include *Nectandra, Mollinedia, Inga, Duguetia* and *Melicocea* (Spanish Lime).

HYPNA IPHIGENIA Herrich-Schaeffer 1862 *Iphigenia* Pl. 4

Description. Fw 40–48 mm. Upperside light coffee brown; forewing basal third darker, disc crossed by broad yellow band from mid-costa to anal angle, apical third black and enclosing three or four small yellow spots; hindwing with a watery black marginal band that encloses a few pale spots. Underside mottled grey, brown and purplish and with *silver spangles in cell of forewing and basal half of hindwing*.

Distribution. Restricted to Cuba where it is a coastal species seldom seen inland and not common. It is frequently treated as a subspecies of the wide-ranging continental *Hypna clytemnestra*, which is smaller and has a white fore-wing band. It is abundantly distinct. RANGE and TL: Cuba.

Early stages. Not known.

SIDERONE GALANTHIS Cramer 1775 *Scarlet Emperor* Pl. 4

Description. Fw 33 mm ♂ to 40 mm ♀. A very handsome black butterfly, the *forewing crossed by a scarlet discal band* and with a triangular basal patch of the same colour, the extreme apex, and the outer margins of both wings, also flushed red; one or two minute white spots are often present near the forewing apex, especially in females; hindwing with a red patch against the costa. The under-side dead leaf pattern in purples and browns is exceptionally beautiful.

Distribution: Cuba: Holguin, Oriente, Baracoa, Sta Clara, etc. Isle of Pines. Hispaniola: La Vega, Puerto Plata. Porto Rico: Manati and Isabella. Apparently rather scarce. The Antillean population is subspecies *S. g. nemesis* Illiger 1802 (TL: S. Domingo) and differs from *S. g. galanthis* of the mainland in that the red discal band of the hindwing is reduced to a small square patch. RANGE: C. America to S. Brazil; Cuba. TL: Surinam.

Early stages. The fully grown dark brown caterpillar has a row of five large contiguous diamond-shaped dark marks along the back and is peculiarly shaped. The two or three segments immediately behind the head, which bears a pair of short knob-shaped horns, are narrow and flattened; the next segment greatly expanded and forming a somewhat hood-like structure directed forwards and tapering away backwards to end in a shovel-like final segment. Food plant, in Cuba, *Casearia aculeata*.

ANAEA TROGLODYTA Fabricius 1775 *The Troglodyte* Pl. 4

Description. Fw ♂ 35 mm, ♀ 40 mm. Upperside tawny red, the *male usually with a light purplish flush*, the *female with* the area beyond the *jagged discal band* (which the male usually lacks) dull orange. Underside grey (yellow-greenish in female) and cryptically patterned in minute striae, the leaf-like effect enhanced by the short hindwing tail and slightly falcate forewing, the latter better developed in the winter (dry season) form than in the summer form.

Distribution. Haiti and the Dominican Republic, widespread and seemingly common. RANGE: West Indies only. TL: 'America'.

Other islands are inhabited by the following distinct populations which are variously regarded as subspecies of *Anaea troglodyta* or as distinct species:

1 **Anaea portia** Fabricius 1775. Smaller, 32–36 mm, forewing more falcate, hindwing tail a little longer, black borders more sharply defined, purplish flush weaker, the underside ground colour almost the same in both sexes. Jamaica. A forest butterfly widespread and sometimes abundant from sea level to one or two thousand feet.

2 **Anaea borinquenalis** Johnson and Comstock 1941, from Porto Rico, is about the same size as *A. portia*, the black markings a little less well defined, and the crooked discal line joined to the marginal border by a dark shade along vein 4 in most males and all females.

3 **Anaea minor** Hall 1936, from St Kitts and Antigua, is the smallest, with a forewing length that rarely exceeds 31 mm in either sex. The forewing discal and marginal bands are united by a dark shadow along vein 4 and the underside is very uniformly purplish grey.

4 **Anaea cubana** Druce 1905, with a forewing length of 35–37 mm in the male and 40–45 mm in the female, is by far the largest member of the group. Upperside black markings strong and sharply defined, the outer half of the hindwing yellowish on both surfaces, not dusky as in the related smaller species. Widespread in Cuba throughout the year.

All five members of this group seem to prefer rather dry open lowland forest habitats, resting on twigs and stems, like the related oriental Leaf Butterflies of the genus *Kallima*.

Early stages. The caterpillar of *A. cubana* has been found on *Romero cimarron* (*Pectis*) but has not been described. Nothing is known of the early stages of the other species. The caterpillar of *Anaea floridalis*, a very close relative of *A. cubana*, is green, with many scattered white points and a pair of yellow stripes along the side; head light green, with black and orange tubercles. Food plant *Croton linearis*.

ANAEA JOHNSONI Avinoff and Shoumatoff 1941
Johnson's Leaf Butterfly

Description. Fw ♂ 27–30 mm, ♀ 31–33 mm. Upperside bright russet brown. Forewing with jagged black bar from mid-costa across cell-end usually ending in space 3 without joining the marginal border (male), or joining it (female), apex very dark brown. Hindwing generally uniformly russet brown except for three very small ocelli between the tail and the anal angle, and a faint dark bar from costa towards cell-end. In the female the upperside may be more yellowish and have darker brown shadows between the cell and inner margin on forewing and towards costa on hindwing. Underside markings as in *A. troglodyta*.

Distribution. Confined to Jamaica. Widely distributed but decidedly rare.

Fig. 7. *Anaea glycerium.* ♂ Corumba, Brazil, April.

Easily confused with *Anaea glycerium* of the mainland, which it no doubt represents. The black forewing bar and darker ground colour easily distinguish it from *Anaea portia* (above), which also flies in Jamaica. RANGE and TL: Jamaica.
Early stages. Not known.
Note. Since the above description was written a single male *Anaea,* thought at first to be *Anaea glycerium* Doubleday 1850, and taken at Boufillier, Haiti, by Mr John Coutsis, has been seen. It is an *Anaea johnsoni*, with the black subapical bar well separated from the marginal border, as is often the case in *A. glycerium*. It is almost certainly a chance vagrant, from Jamaica.

ANAEA ECHEMUS Doubleday and Hewitson 1850
Chestnut Leaf Butterfly   **Pl. 4**
Description. Fw ♂ 25–28 mm, ♀ 28–33 mm. Upperside chestnut brown, *forewing without yellow spots*, heavily suffused black except in basal areas; hindwing tail and adjacent area also chestnut, the latter enclosing two or more black spots usually tipped with white, the largest spot lying in space 3. Underside general coloration warmer brown than in the related Caribbean species of *Anaea*, the pattern consisting either of irregular short transverse striae, or of similar striae overlaid by a variegated pattern of light and dark brown shades; a wide area above the tail is free of markings other than the ocellar spots in spaces 2 and 3. In the dry (winter) form the forewing is more falcate and lighter brown and the underside of both wings is much less patterned, f. *aguayoi* de la Torre 1951.
Distribution. Widespread and common in Cuba and flying throughout the year, especially in coastal regions, less common in the interior: Santiago, Holguin, Matanzas, Habana, etc. In the Bahamas on New Providence Island there occurs a form that is lighter brown than the Cuban form and has 4 to 6 ocellar spots on the upperside of the hindwing – subsp. *bahamae* Witt. In the Cayman Islands *A. echemus* is one of the commonest and most widely distributed butterflies, flying everywhere except on open meadows and beaches –

a handsome dark race, the ocellar spots large and white-tipped, subsp. *danieliana* Witt. RANGE: Cayman Isles to Bahamas. TL: 'Honduras', *recte* Cuba.

Early stages. Not known. Food plant in Cuba *Croton lucidus*.

ANAEA INTERMEDIA Witt 1972

Turk Island Leaf Butterfly   **Pl. 4**

Description. Fw ♂ 29 mm, ♀ 32 mm. Upperside rich chestnut brown intermediate in colour between *Anaea verticordia* and *Anaea echemus*, the black borders of both wings only slightly less extensive than in the former; forewing yellow spots in spaces 2, 3, 5 and 6 triangular and clear cut; a fifth spot distally in space 1b is diffuse; hindwing *submarginal row of white ocellar spots conspicuous from anal angle to space 6*. Underside pattern of short striae as in *A. verticordia* and *A. echemus* but boldly black and white, not brown as in those species.

Distribution. Known only from Grand Turk Island (TL) at the south-eastern extremity of the Bahamas, flying in December and January. RANGE: Turk Islands.

Early stages. Not known.

ANAEA VERTICORDIA Huebner 1824

Yellow-spotted Leaf Butterfly

Description. Fw ♂ 30–34 mm, ♀ 34–39 mm. Upperside light brown; forewing broadly suffused dark brown apically and along outer margin, this area enclosing an irregular row of five yellow spots; *hindwing with* dusky outer margin

Fig. 8. *Anaea verticordia.* ♀ Port au Prince, Haiti.

and a *row of three, sometimes four, very small ocellar spots* from anal angle to (or beyond) the base of the tail. The cryptic underside varies in colour from almost plain brown to a variety of shades and patterns in grey and brownish grey.

Distribution. Confined to Hispaniola: La Cumbre, Port au Prince, Fond Parisien, Cabral, etc. Apparently rather rare. RANGE: Hispaniola. TL (not stated): Haiti.

Early stages. Not known, but probably very similar to those of *Anaea dominicana* (p. 61).

ANAEA DOMINICANA Godman and Salvin 1884
Godman's Leaf Butterfly **Pl. 4**

Description. Fw ♂ 28–30 mm, ♀ 29–32 mm. Smaller than *Anaea verticordia*, lighter brown, the pale spots on the upperside of the forewing in spaces 2 and 3 equal in size, not well defined, fused together and little paler than the ground colour; spot in space 1a barely differentiated from ground colour; *only the two subapical spots at all well defined* and markedly paler. The cryptic underside pattern varies from an even pattern of very short irregular transverse striae to a typical variegated 'dead leaf' pattern in brownish grey, but with the area above the ocellar spots on the hindwing always quite free of pattern.

Fig. 9. *Anaea dominicana dominicana.* ♂ Dominica.

Distribution. Confined to Dominica. Not rare and, though strong on the wing, easily caught when drinking the sap of wounded logwood trees. *A. d. dominicana* is replaced on St Lucia and Martinique by *A. d. luciana* Hall 1929 in which the upperside ground colour is rather darker and the spots in spaces 2 and 3, though equal in size, are not joined together. RANGE: Leeward Islands. TL: Dominica.

Early stages. A painting made by Miss M. E. Fountaine at Castries on St Lucia shows a fully grown caterpillar which is olive green on the back with numerous scattered white specks, lighter green below, with a whitish lateral line separating the two colours, and white prolegs, the head variegated green, reddish and cream. Food plant *Croton astroites*.

MARPESIA PETREUS Cramer 1779
Southern Dagger Tail **Pl. 5**
syn. *peleus* Sulzer 1776 (invalid homonym)

Description. Fw ♂ and ♀ 35–40 mm. Upperside bright orange-brown, the three thin straight transverse lines all black on both wings and well defined. Purple flush on underside strong and dark in most specimens. Similar to *M. eleuchea* but easily distinguished by the characters given under that species, *the discal line on forewing being straight almost to the costa.*

Distribution. Only on the Windward and Leeward Islands, e.g. St Lucia, Dominica, Guadeloupe and St Kitts and very rarely on Porto Rico, almost certainly as migrants from farther south, for their appearance is sporadic. The capture of a single specimen in the Bahamas supports this view. The butterfly tends to visit the same flowers as *Dryas iulia* and *Dione juno* from which it is very difficult to distinguish it when on the wing. All are referable to the typical subspecies *M. petreus petreus*. The Central American subspecies *thetys* Fabricius is paler and has fainter, browner transverse lines on the upperside. RANGE: Mexico to Brazil. TL: Surinam.

Early stages. Full grown caterpillar purplish, white beneath, and with the abdominal segments sulphur yellow above; head with two horns, segments 5, 7, 9 and 11 each bearing a weak upright thread-like appendage. Food plant Cachou (*Anacardium occidentale*) and fig.

MARPESIA ELEUCHEA Huebner 1818
Cuban Dagger Tail
Pl. 5

Description. Fw ♂ 30–35 mm, ♀ 33–38 mm. Upperside bright reddish brown in male, a little duller in female, the tail at vein 4 of hindwing edged rather darker brown; both wings crossed by black lines of varying intensity; the *discal line on forewing sharply angled at vein* 4, the postdiscal line strongly curved between vein 4 and the costa. Both these lines are straight in *Marpesia petreus* with which *M. eleuchea* has often been confused. Underside pattern the same, but merged into a leaf-like background of grey-brown, grey-green and purplish.

Distribution. Widespread in all the Greater Antilles except Porto Rico, but not particularly common anywhere, in four well-marked island races. *M. e. bahamensis* Munroe 1971 is the most heavily marked subspecies and has the two ocellar spots on the hindwing upperside equally well developed and both capped with relatively conspicuous white crescents. Typical *M. eleuchea* comes from Cuba; it is paler, the dark lines are less heavy and the upper ocellar spot on the hindwing is less well formed than the lower one. In *M. e. dospassosi* Munroe 1971 from Hispaniola and *M. e. pellenis* Godart 1819 from Jamaica, the forewing discal line has virtually disappeared; the male of the former however has a solid black border to the outer margin of the forewing, the latter has this border reduced to a thin line separated from the margin. RANGE: Confined to the Antilles. TL: Cuba.

Early stages: Not known.

MARPESIA CHIRON Fabricius 1775   *Common Dagger Tail* **Pl. 5**

Description. Fw ♂ and ♀ 29–32 mm. Upperside rather *sooty dark brown, with three paler stripes* across the wings; forewing with three to six small pale subapical spots; hindwing with long tail at vein 4, a much shorter one at vein 2, and grey or black anal marks. Underside, both wings basally mother-of-pearl, the darker outer half separated by a straight narrow band of white.

Distribution. A woodland butterfly with a gliding flight, moisture-seeking and frequenting open sunlit glades. Commonest in Cuba where in the female the whole underside is often distinctly greenish with little colour contrast between the basal and distal halves of the wings, whereas the contrast between these two areas in the males is very strong. This Cuban population is unusually variable in underside coloration and sometimes lacks the small subapical spots on the forewing. Should the Cuban population be a subspecies distinct from the Jamaican *M. c. chiron*, of which very few specimens are known, Staudinger's name *chironides* is available for it. The Hispaniolan population is very similar and fairly common. The butterfly has a strong tendency to migrate, and this perhaps accounts for the absence of recognisable island races. RANGE: Texas to Brazil. TL: Jamaica.

Early stages. Full grown caterpillar yellowish along the back and with two black longitudinal lines and reddish transverse streaks, sides greenish yellow with very dark red longitudinal lines, last segment streaked with green; head very pale yellow and with a pair of 'horns'; spines on the back large and black. Food plants Moraceae, e.g. *Artocarpus, Ficus, Morus, Chlorophora tinctoria,* etc.

MYSCELIA ANTHOLIA Godart 1823   *The Royal Blue*   **Pl. 5**
Description. Fw ♂ 35–38 mm, ♀ 38–41 mm. Upperside black, *brilliantly shot with violet or blue*, and with large white markings in the outer half of the forewing. Male iridescence violet-blue, extending on forewing to within a few millimetres of the outer margin, on hindwing a little beyond the disc. In the female the iridescence is pure blue and confined to the forewing, where it hardly extends beyond the white markings. Underside mottled light grey-brown, the white forewing markings repeated. The wing shape strongly suggests a species of *Vanessa* (p. 82) or even *Hypanartia* and the cryptic underside markings accentuate this impression.
Distribution. Although Godart in his original description stated that *M. antholia* came 'particularly from Martinique' there is no evidence to support this statement. All known specimens come from the Dominican Republic or Haiti. Some come from Port au Prince, but there is no real information about the habits or habitat of this startlingly beautiful butterfly. RANGE: Hispaniola. TL: Haiti.
Early stages. Not known.

COLOBURA DIRCE Linnaeus 1758   *The Mosaic*   **Pl. 5**
Description. Fw ♂ and ♀ 33–36 mm. Upperside dark brown; forewing with broad yellow band that does not quite reach anal angle and, sometimes, an indistinct yellow spot against the costa near apex; hindwing costa narrowly yellow. *Underside cream, with a complicated zebra-like pattern of dark lines.*
Distribution. Cuba, Jamaica, Hispaniola and Porto Rico. A shy butterfly but apparently not really rare and much attracted to rotting fruit. Typical *Colobura dirce* of the American mainland is much paler on the underside than are Caribbean specimens. The populations of the Greater Antilles have been separately named, but the characters said to separate them are so imprecise that it seems best to treat them all as a single Caribbean subspecies, namely *C. d. wolcotti* Comstock 1942 (Porto Rico and Hispaniola), and to regard *avinoffi* Comstock 1942 (Jamaica) and *clementi* Comstock 1942 (Cuba) as synonyms. RANGE: Mexico to Paraguay. TL: 'The Tropics'.
Early stages. The caterpillars of *C. dirce* are gregarious when young, sheltering by day under a protective tent formed of a leaf of *Cecropia*. When full grown the caterpillar is black, but has a row of short transverse yellow stripes low down on each side. The head bears a pair of long stout cream-coloured horns; along the body run six rows of formidable pale spines, those along the back longest and ending in a rosette of branching spines, the next row smaller, the third smallest; not all the rows of spines are complete.

Plate 7 NYMPHALIDAE *Scale:* × $\frac{2}{3}$

1. **Adelpha abyla** *Jamaican Admiral* p. 72
♂ Blue Mts, Jamaica, 1200 ft. July. Uppermost spot of white band less than 5 mm wide.

2. **Adelpha gelania** *Haitian Admiral* 72
♂ *A. g. gelania*, Port au Prince, Haiti. Band creamy, narrow.

3. **Adelpha iphicla** *Cuban Admiral* 73
♂ *A. i. iphimedia*, Holguin, Cuba. Uppermost spot of white band more than 6 mm wide.

4. **Hypolimnas misippus** *The Mimic* 73
4a ♂ Dominica. Upperside with wide white areas and blue reflections.
4b ♀ Dominica. Brown with black markings suggesting a species of *Danaus* (Plate 1).

5. **Anartia jatrophae** *White Peacock* 75
♂ *A. j. saturata*, Haiti. A jet black spot in space 2 of forewing.

6. **Anartia amathea** *Red Anartia* 75
♂ Grenada. Forewing with about twelve white spots beyond the rose-red basal area.

7. **Anartia lytrea** *Godart's Anartia* 76
♂ Dominican Republic. White bands narrow, not sharply defined.

8. **Anartia chrysopelea** *Huebner's Anartia* 76
♂ Cuba. White bands sharp-edged, wider.

9. **Biblis hyperia** *The Red Rim* 76
♂ St Kitts. The red-rimmed hindwing is unique.

10. **Atlantea pantoni** *Jamaican Harlequin* 77
♀ Cockpit Mts, Jamaica. March. Forewing with single row of yellow submarginal spots. In the male these spots are red-brown.

11. **Atlantea perezi** *Cuban Harlequin* 78
♂ Santiago, Cuba. April. Forewing with single row of white submarginal spots.

12. **Atlantea tulita** *Porto Rican Harlequin* 78
♂ Tallaboa, near Poncea, Porto Rico. July. Forewing with double row of red-brown submarginal spots.

13. **Siproeta stelenes** *The Malachite* 77
♂ Holguin, Cuba. Pale green spot in forewing cell small and round.

8

1. **Vanessa cardui** *Painted Lady*   p. 82
   ♂ St Helena. The red markings on the forewing do not form an
   even band, and quickly fade to pink.

2. **Vanessa virginiensis** *American Painted Lady*   82
   ♂ Holguin, Cuba. Hindwing underside has only two ocelli, both
   rather large.

3. **Vanessa atalanta**   *Red Admiral*   83
   ♂ Canada. The broad band on the forewing is not interrupted.

4. **Junonia coenia**   *The Buckeye*   74
   ♂ *J. c. bergi*, Bermuda. The eye-spot in space 2 of the forewing is
   surrounded by yellow or grey.

5. **Junonia evarete** *Caribbean Buckeye*   74
   ♂ *J. e. michaelesi*, Nevis. February. Forewing eye-spot red-ringed.

6. **Hypanartia paullus** *Sword-tailed Tortoiseshell*   83
   ♂ Cuba. Hindwing tail at vein 4 much longer than tail at vein 2.

7. **Euptoieta hegesia** *Mexican Fritillary*   83
   ♂ *E. h. hegesia*, Holguin, Cuba. Hindwing underside markings
   obscure, ground colour rather uniform.

8. **Euptoieta claudia** *Variegated Fritillary*   84
   ♂ Vera Cruz. Underside markings on hindwing boldly contrasting.

HISTORIS ACHERONTA Fabricius 1775   *Cadmus*   **Pl. 5**
Description. Fw ♂ 38–46 mm, ♀ 47–55 mm. Upperside chestnut brown; outer half of forewing black and enclosing 5 *or 6 small pure white subapical spots*; hindwing shading to burnt umber, the veins rather conspicuous. Underside greenish or purplish dark brown with a postdiscal darker transverse shadow and delicate lines and spots in the discal and basal areas.
Distribution. Greater Antilles only, in two fairly well-marked subspecies both of which differ from the continental races. In *H. acheronta cadmus* Cramer 1775 from Jamaica, and possibly Porto Rico, the black outer margin of the forewing extends at least one third of the way towards the base in spaces 2 and 3, the underside ground colour is rather dark brown with a heavy steel-blue flush, and in the male the spot in the centre of the hindwing cell is the same colour as the rest of the cell. In *H. a. semele* D. M. Bates 1939, which is found in Hispaniola and Cuba, the forewing outer black margin only reaches at most one quarter of the way to the base in spaces 2 and 3, the underside is lighter brown, the blue flush not extensive and (in the male only) the central spot in the cell is white or pale grey. RANGE: Mexico to Brazil. TL: Brazil.
Early stages. Not known. It is possible that a caterpillar found on *Cecropia* in Porto Rico may have been that of *H. acheronta*, though thought to be *H. odius*. It was medium grey with a white or grey saddle on middle of back, and had two spiny horns on the head.

HISTORIS ODIUS Fabricius 1775   *Orion*   **Pl. 5**
Description. Fw ♂ 53–56 mm, ♀ 60–65 mm. Forewing markedly falcate. Upperside velvety dark brown; forewing base and disc (almost to outer margin) rich bright ochreous brown, *a single small white costal spot towards the apex*; hindwing basal area slightly suffused ochreous brown, outer margin narrowly white or cream. Underside cryptically patterned in narrow bold black lines on a silky green-tinted purplish brown background.
Distribution. Two subspecies occur in the islands. Cuba, Hispaniola, Porto Rico and Jamaica are inhabited by typical *odius*, the Leeward and Windward Isles (Guadaloupe, Dominica, Martinique, St Lucia and Grenada) by subspecies *orion*, which has·no doubt reached them from the American mainland via Trinidad and Tobago. In the male of the latter subspecies the light brown area on the forewing juts out narrowly from the disc towards the outer margin like two fingers: in *H. o. odius* this light brown area is much wider from back to front and fills a large part of space 5 and some of space 6, areas which in *H. o. orion* are almost wholly black. In the females, both of which have more extensive light brown areas, the differences are comparable. *Orion* is a very strong flyer, much attracted to rotting fruit and fond of resting on tree trunks where its cryptic underside markings make it very difficult to see. On the wing all the year round and moderately common. RANGE: southern U.S.A. to Argentina. TL: West Indies.
Early stages. The fully grown caterpillar is about three inches long, light green with light brown transverse markings. The row of spines along the middle of the back black, lateral spines white, not all spines branched but, if branched, the branches arise very low down; three rows of spines on each side, but the rows not all complete. Head whitish marked with bold black cross and bearing a pair of short black spiky horns. Food plant *Cecropia peltata*.

HAMADRYAS FERONIA Linnaeus 1758 *The Cracker* **Pl. 5**

Description. Fw ♂ 29–32 mm, ♀ 33–36 mm. Upperside very similar to that of *Hamadryas februa*, but with a markedly blue tint and a coarser marbled pattern. The *postdiscal ocellar spots on the hindwing upperside* provide a sure guide to identification: in *H. feronia* they *are simple black spots with a white central spot and a narrow blue rim*; in *H. februa* the pupil is halved black and white and there are three concentric rings, the innermost buff or pinkish, the next black, the outermost grey. The closely similar undersides are again distinguished by the same ocelli, quite simple in *feronia*, rather complex in *februa*.

Distribution. The species is represented in the West Indies by subspecies *insularis* Fruhstorfer 1916, which is native to Trinidad. It has occurred on St Lucia and on Haiti, and probably on other islands, but very rarely, and almost certainly as a vagrant. RANGE: Mexico to Paraguay. TL: 'India', *recte* S. America.

Early stages. The fully grown caterpillar (in Brazil) is dirty grey-green with a shagreened effect, and has a narrow interrupted pale line low down on the side. The head has a pair of long horns ending in a small knob and bearing a few branching spines near the base; the thoracic and anal segments bear stout spines with many horizontal branches, like a flue-brush, the spines on the other segments branching in normal fashion. Food plant *Dalechampia*.

HAMADRYAS FEBRUA Huebner 1823 *Haitian Cracker* **Pl. 5**
syn. *ferentina* Godart 1824

Description. Fw ♂ 35–37 mm, ♀ 38–42 mm. Upperside intricately patterned in white, grey and brownish, but *not blue*, with a postdiscal series of *eye-spots best developed on the hindwing*, the whole producing a marbled mosaic effect; the outer two-thirds of the forewing very much paler than the base or the hindwing, especially in the male. Underside markings reduced to bold dark lines on the outer areas of the wings, the delicate tracery of the upperside quite lost.

Distribution. Hispaniola, fairly common; rare in Cuba, Jamaica and Porto Rico, where it would seem to occur as a wandering vagrant rather than a resident; always as subspecies *diasia* Fruhstorfer 1916 (TL: Haiti: syn. *antillana* Hall 1925), which is described above and is the only race to occur in the West Indies. RANGE: Mexico to Brazil. TL: not stated.

Early stages. The fully grown caterpillar is black, with several much interrupted narrow yellow lines along the back and some ill-defined reddish transverse colouring at the intersegmental folds. Head with a pair of long curved horns ending in small knobs. Body with nine rows of spines, not every row complete, and most of the spines with five or six branches. Food plant *Dalechampia*. The pupae are remarkable for the relatively very large leaf-like expansions that arise from the head.

Note. The species of the genus *Hamadryas* are called Crackers because of the crackling or clicking noise that they make when in flight. How this sound is produced is not certainly known.

HAMADRYAS AMPHINOME Linnaeus 1767 *King Cracker*

Description. Fw ♂ 35 mm, ♀ 40 mm. Upperside black, both wings with numerous wavy blue lines, *forewing with broad creamy band from mid-costa to outer margin in space 2*. Underside black, forewing white band as above, hindwing with black replaced by brick-red except on veins and near outer margin.

Fig. 10. *Hamadryas amphinome*. ♂ Rio Hondo, British Honduras.

Distribution. Has been taken once at Sabicú, Cuba. Almost certainly a stray from the mainland as the solitary male was of the subspecies *mexicana* Lucas. RANGE: Mexico to Paraguay. TL: not stated.

Early stages. The fully grown caterpillar (in Brazil) is very striking. Head, thoracic and anal segments black, with white spots, other segments black but densely covered with black-centred yellow rings, all segments with much branched moderately long spines, head with a pair of long horns ending in a round white club. Food plant *Dalechampia*.

MESTRA DORCAS Fabricius 1775   *Jamaican Mestra*   **Pl. 6**
Description. Fw ♂ 19–21 mm, ♀ 20–24 mm. Very fragile. Upperside, both sexes, white, the distal third of each wing bright yellow ochre; forewing broadly grey along costa, markings of underside showing through. *Underside greyish ochreous*, forewing with disc below vein 5 white and small scattered white spots; hindwing with two transverse white bands.
Distribution. A common butterfly of the lowlands, especially favouring moist pasture land with long grass. A weak flyer easily netted. RANGE: confined to Jamaica. TL: Jamaica.
Early stages. The spiny caterpillar when fully grown is brown, with seven bright green diamond-shaped dorsal patches, the head red, with black patches; head spiny and bearing a pair of long horns that end in a rosette of spines, the body with eight rows of delicately branching spines which are large on the last two segments but small elsewhere. Food plant *Tragia volubilis*, Cow-itch.

MESTRA CANA Erichson 1848   *St Lucia Mestra*   **Pl. 6**
Description. Fw ♂ and ♀ 20–24 mm. Male upperside evenly light dusty grey, relieved at times with a paler grey mark at cell-end and some shadowy paler discal stripes and postdiscal spots. Female similar, but the ground colour usually orange-tinted, especially on hindwings, and the pale markings (almost white at times) much better defined. Underside pattern as on upperside but much better defined, pale markings white, *dark markings pale orange*.

Distribution. Confined to the Lesser Antilles but reported only from Dominica, St Lucia, St Vincent, Grenada and Barbados. No doubt an arrival from South America via Trinidad and Tobago where it is very common, especially in hilly country during the rainy season. RANGE: Lesser Antilles and northern S. America. TL: Br. Guiana.

Early stages. In Trinidad the caterpillar feeds on *Dalechampia scandens,* but it has not been described. Presumably it is similar to that of *Mestra dorcas.*

DYNAMINE EGAEA Fabricius 1775   *The Bronzewing*   **Pl. 6**
Description. Fw ♂ 22 mm, ♀ 20 mm. Dimorphic. *Male upperside bronze-green, female black, with wide white band,* base with blue-green reflections. Underside, both sexes patterned as on female upperside, with the addition of transverse white basal markings and a pair of ocelli in the hindwing postdiscal area, one in space 2, the other in space 5.

Distribution. Jamaica, Hispaniola and Cuba. In Jamaica it occurs principally in the north, local and not common, frequenting the margins of woods, open plantations and similar places. In Cuba widespread in Santa Clara and Oriente provinces. Rare in Hispaniola. RANGE: Mexico to Colombia. TL: Jamaica.

The populations of the three islands differ somewhat. In *D. egaea egaea* of Jamaica the male has no subapical black band, only a dark patch against the outer margin in spaces 3 and 4 along vein 4, and the blue reflections on the upperside in the female extend undiminished to the white discal bands. In both *D. egaea zetes* Ménétriés 1834 from Haiti and *D. egaea calais* Bates 1936 from Cuba there is a triangular subapical black bar from costa to, but not always reaching, the outer margin at vein 4. On the underside of the hindwing the two ocelli are united by a broad chocolate band in *D. e. calais*; in *D. e. zetes* this band is slender and may even be broken. These last two subspecies may well represent a species distinct from *D. egaea.*

Early stages. In Jamaica the caterpillar feeds on *Tragia volubilis.* It is flattened, tapering and rather slug-like, green or yellowish brown, with a broad olive green dorsal stripe down the centre of which run two fine white lines; it has a collar of fine white hair and seven rows of branching spines, one of which is mid-dorsal.

DYNAMINE MYLITTA Cramer 1782   *Emerald Wing*   **Pl. 6**
Description. Fw ♂ and ♀ 20–22 mm. Dimorphic. *Male upperside metallic bluish green,* both wings with apex and outer margin black bordered, forewing with angular spot towards base of space 2 and all smaller spots all black. *Female upperside black, forewing with six white spots in outer half and a white bar* from just below cell that extends across the base of the hindwing; the hindwing also with a rather narrow transverse discal white line, a small anal ocellus and a wavy white submarginal line. The complicated underside markings are the same in both sexes, with the hindwing ocelli set in a purplish grey field bounded inwardly by a chocolate-coloured bar. Ab. *bipupillata* Roeber is a rare individual variety in which the 'blue spot behind the hindwing anal ocellus' is missing.

Distribution. Reported only from Cuba, where it was said to be common about a hundred years ago in the neighbourhood of Santa Cruz, San Diego de los Baños and Viñales, possibly due to a temporary invasion from the mainland, as there are no recent records. RANGE: Mexico to Argentina. TL: Surinam.

Early stages. The caterpillar (in Brazil) is green or yellowish brown when fully grown, with faint black transverse lines, oblique white lateral markings and a wide white or pinkish dorsal band, the prothoracic segment with black warts, the others with seven rows of branching spines which are white on the back, greenish or brown on the sides. Food plant in Cuba Pringa-moza (*Platygyne hexandra*).

ARCHIMESTRA TELEBOAS Ménétriés 1832
False Neptis   **Pl. 6**

Description. Fw ♂ 22–25 mm, ♀ 25–26 mm. Upperside black with white markings; forewing with a large white patch mid-costa and another on inner margin; hindwing with transverse discal band of smaller spots; *both wings with scattered very small white spots.* Underside slightly brownish grey, white markings as on upperside, hindwing with conspicuous postdiscal row of round black spots.

Distribution. Confined to Hispaniola. Common in pine forests, e.g. above La Vega. Flies among small bushes close to the ground. Though very unlike *Mestra dorcas* in appearance it is nevertheless closely allied to that species morphologically. RANGE: Hispaniola. TL: Haiti.

Early stages. Not known.

LUCINIA SIDA Huebner 1823 *Cuban Lucinia*   **Pl. 6**

Description. Fw 21 mm (♂) to 25 mm (♀). Very similar to *Lucinia cadma* but upperside ground colour paler, often with a slight pinkish flush, and black markings reduced in extent and more sharply defined, *cell-bar not reaching subapical bar.* On the underside the basal grey area on hindwing is much more broken up by white markings, and the included pupils in the ocellus nearest the costa are all light blue – in *L. cadma* the lowest one is very dark blue or black.

Distribution. *Lucinia sida sida* is known only from Cuba, where it appears to be widespread and not uncommon in woodlands, e.g. Habana, Matanzas, Holguin, St Christobal, Santiago, etc. In Hispaniola it is replaced by *L. sida torrebia* Ménétriés 1832, which is a little more heavily marked on the upperside, especially in respect of the black bar across the end of the cell of the forewing; on the underside of the hindwing on the other hand the ocellar spots are smaller and more delicate, especially the upper one, which is oval rather than round. *L. sida albomaculata* Rindge 1955 from the Bahamas differs most obviously in the much more dentate outer margin of the hindwing, less so in the more extended white areas on the underside. RANGE: Cuba and Hispaniola. TL: Havana.

Early stages. In Cuba the caterpillar has been found feeding on 'Angarilla or Clavelita' (*Echites* – Apocynaceae), but has not been described.

LUCINIA CADMA Drury 1773 *Jamaican Lucinia*

Description. Fw 23 mm (♂) to 27 mm (♀). Hindwing markedly scalloped. Upperside chestnut brown in male, slightly paler in female. Forewing markings not sharply defined; the *black bar across the end of the cell turns to meet or almost meet the transverse subapical bar,* and the rather square black anal spot almost fills the angle; hindwing with narrow black border much more pronounced in male than female. Underside of forewing like the upperside except the apical area, which matches the hindwing; underside of hindwing with broad white

Fig. 11. *Lucinia cadma*. ♂ Blue Mountains, Jamaica, 1,700 ft., July.

discal band enclosing two large ocellate spots each with at least two pupils; base and outer margin grey and bounded by wavy chocolate lines.

Distribution. Jamaica only. A rare butterfly of the highlands but not restricted to any particular season. It has been suggested that there is a mimetic association between this species and *Dynamine egaea*, based on the similarity of the markings of the underside of the hindwings. These patterns, however, could only be of protective significance when the insects are at rest, whereas mimetic resemblances in the generally accepted sense depend upon deceptive similarities between insects in flight. As there is no evidence that either of the species is in any way distasteful or 'protected' the suggestion does not seem to be very well based. RANGE and TL: Jamaica.

Early stages. Not known.

EUNICA TATILA Herrich-Schaeffer 1853 *Purple Eunica* **Pl. 6**
Description. Fw ♂ and ♀ 26–29 mm. Upperside basically *very dark brown, but shot brilliant purple in male, blue in female* and less extensive; forewing with seven white spots. Underside grey-brown, darker in male than in female, forewing markings patterned as on upperside; hindwing in male rather uniform, the postdiscal ocellar spots obscure, in female light brownish grey, the ocellar spots conspicuous but their black pupils (as in the male) without white centres; in either sex there may be a bold pale streak on the hindwing from the base to the outer margin in space 4, possibly a seasonal character.

Distribution. Cuba, Haiti and the Dominican Republic, Jamaica (very rare) and Porto Rico (one record only). Said to be widespread in Cuba. Records from the other islands could well be based on odd vagrants. Typical *Eunica tatila* differs from the West Indian subspecies *tatilista* Kaye 1926 (described above, TL: Jamaica) in having minute white specks in the pupils of the ocellar spots on the underside of the hindwings, and is confined to Central America. RANGE: Central America and Greater Antilles. TL: 'S. America'.

Early stages. Not known.

EUNICA MONIMA Cramer 1782 *Dingy Eunica* **Pl. 6**
Description. Fw ♂ and ♀ 21–25 mm. Upperside very dark brown with *dull purplish flush* in male and sometimes in female; smaller than *Eunica tatila* and with forewing outer margin more evenly rounded; forewing outer half darker

than inner half and enclosing five rather small isolated spots of which the spot in space 6 in the male and those in spaces 3 and 6 and just beyond the cell in the female are white, the others dusky. Underside faintly purplish grey-brown with a simple pattern of fine lines, the postdiscal ocelli arranged in two groups. What appears to be a dwarf or seasonal form, with a forewing length of only 15 mm and a single white subapical spot, has been named form *fairchildi* Bates 1935.
Distribution. Cuba, Haiti, Dominican Republic, Jamaica and Porto Rico. In Jamaica and Porto Rico occurrence seems to be sporadic. The insect has a strong tendency to migrate and has been taken at sea far from land. This may well account for the fact that it has not developed any island races. RANGE: Southern U.S.A. to Venezuela. TL: 'Côte de Guinée', *recte* Guiana.
Early stages. In Mexico the caterpillar is dull orange with a lateral black band, squat black tubercles with short branches on segments 3 and 12, the surface elsewhere roughened with small black setigerous tubercles. Food plant *Zanthoxylum pentamon*, a tropical Prickly Ash.

EUNICA HERACLITUS Poey 1847   *Poey's Eunica*   **Pl. 6**
Description. Fw ♂ and ♀ 25–26 mm. Upperside *silky pale grey* with a faint bronze flush. The dark distal half of forewing includes the usual pale spots, all rather small, and the hindwing bears a postdiscal row of five small but prominent black spots. Underside rather dusky purplish grey, the basal and discal lines very jagged and the postdiscal ocelli small and widely separated from the discal line.
Distribution. Known only from Cuba where, at one time, it was common near Habana, Vuelta-Abajo, Trinidad and south of Bayamo. There seem to be no recent records. *Eunica heraclitus* is often treated as a subspecies of the continental *Eunica macris* Godart, but is abundantly distinct. RANGE and TL: Cuba.
Early stages. Not known.

ADELPHA ABYLA Hewitson 1850   *Jamaican Admiral*   **Pl. 7**
Description. Fw ♂ 26–27 mm, ♀ 28–30 mm. Easily confused with *Adelpha iphicla* but distinguished by the following characters: *white band narrower (about 4 mm)* and faintly bluish, forewing apical patch a misshapen square rather than oblong, hindwing anal orange patch extending to vein 2 and often enclosing both black anal spots. General tone of underside darker, more reddish than in *A. iphicla*. For a useful character on underside of forewing see *A. iphicla*.
Distribution. Jamaica only. Widespread in foothills and mountains in open sunny forest glades, but by no means common. Not easily caught as it is fast on the wing and tends to fly high. Easily confused with *Doxocopa laure* (p. 55) when in flight. RANGE and TL: Jamaica.
Early stages. The fully grown caterpillar is dull dark brown, mixed with grey; head darker, with numerous short reddish spines; on first segment two brown horns bent forwards, then a silvery area followed by a pair of much smaller horns bent backwards, further similar horns on ninth and tenth segments, minute lateral spines on other segments. Food plant not recorded.

ADELPHA GELANIA Godart 1819   *Haitian Admiral*   **Pl. 7**
Description. Fw ♂ 28–29 mm, ♀ 30–34 mm. Upperside very dark brown, *the cream-coloured band* broken into well separated spots on the forewing above

vein 3, uninterrupted on the hindwing, *nowhere much in excess of 2 mm wide*; forewing cell with three deep crimson transverse bars; hindwing orange anal spot enclosing two black spots but not reaching vein 2. Underside light silky grey-brown, only two red bars in forewing cell, outer margin of both wings with fine red line enclosed between parallel white lines.

Distribution. Typical *A. gelania* only occurs in Haiti and the Dominican Republic, where it is undoubtedly rare and presumably an insect of the mountain forests. It is replaced in Porto Rico by *A. gelania arecosa* Hewitson 1847, a rather larger insect with a wider white band (up to 4 mm wide on the disc of the hindwing), the orange anal area of hindwing expanded to reach vein 3 and enclosing three black spots; underside darker, the pattern of markings much less sharply defined. RANGE: Hispaniola and Porto Rico. TL: 'Equinoctial America'.

Early stages. Not known.

ADELPHA IPHICLA Linnaeus 1758   *Cuban Admiral*   Pl. 7
Adelpha iphicla impimedia Fruhstorfer 1915

Description. Fw ♂ 25–27 mm, ♀ 28–31 mm. Upperside striped in shades of dark brown, with a broad pure *white band about 6 mm* wide from space 3 of forewing to anal angle of hindwing; forewing apex with orange patch twice as long as wide; hindwing with small orange anal patch that does not reach vein 2. Underside pattern as upperside, but dark areas variegated various shades of brown, grey and whitish; in space 2 of forewing the pair of parallel dark lines are not continued as a prolongation of the similar pair in the cell, as is the case in *A. abyla.*

Distribution. Cuba and the Isle of Pines. Widespread but not common. A forest insect of solitary habits, swift and direct in flight. It is surprising that *A. iphicla* should not have spread farther in the West Indies as it has spread far and wide on the mainland and formed many local races. RANGE: Mexico to Paraguay. TL: 'in Indiis'.

Early stages. The caterpillar has been found in Cuba feeding on 'Digame' (*Calycophyllum candidissimum*), elsewhere on *Gonzala spicata*. In Brazil the caterpillar is dull medium brown, the head and a series of dorso-lateral patches black; head very spiky, four large much-branched spines sloping forward from a little behind the head, another pair after a short interval and two pairs near tail of equal size, four pairs of much smaller spines between along the back. It is not clear whether there are any lateral spines. Larval characters are of great importance in this genus as species that seem almost identical often have quite different caterpillars.

HYPOLIMNAS MISIPPUS Linnaeus 1764   *The Mimic*   Pl. 7
Description. Fw ♂ 25–38 mm, ♀ 38–42 mm. Dimorphic. *Male upperside velvety black with strong blue reflections* especially *around the large white discal areas. Female upperside light brown*, forewing apex broadly black and enclosing a transverse band of white spots, outer margins narrowly black but with numerous enclosed small white spots. Underside patterns the same, but black largely replaced by greenish brown and male hindwing underside with broad unbroken white band. In the very rare ♀-form *inaria* Cramer the forewing is uniformly light brown, the band of white spots and the black apical area being lost. Both female forms are mimics of varieties of the Old World *Danaus chrysippus.*

Distribution. Somewhat sporadic. Very rare in Cuba and Jamaica. Not reported from Hispaniola. Occasionally common on Porto Rico. More regular in the Lesser Antilles: St Lucia, Antigua, Dominica, Guadeloupe, Martinique and Barbados. Thought to have reached America from Africa via the slave trade. RANGE: Old World Tropics and Subtropics; New World range erratic. TL: America.

Early stages. The caterpillars are gregarious. When fully grown they are black or very dark grey, with grey bands. The head is reddish and has two long stout stubbily branched horns. The numerous spines on the body bear very fine branches and are light grey or whitish. The principal food plants are *Ipomaea* and *Portulaca*.

JUNONIA COENIA Huebner 1822   *The Buckeye*   **Pl. 8**

Description. Fw ♂ 20–23 mm, ♀ 20–25 mm. Two simple characters of the upperside distinguish this species from *Junonia evarete* (see below). On the forewing the *larger ocellus is inwardly bordered by a white crescent* that runs from the inner margin at least as far as vein 3; on the hindwing the larger anterior ocellus outwardly is black, which changes to blue, and then to orange or red inwardly. On the underside the ocelli are small, very small, or absent, and the general appearance is usually that of a sandy dry season form.

Distribution. Bermuda, western Cuba and Isle of Pines, at altitudes below 1000 ft. The Bermudan population has been named subspecies *bergi* by Avinoff. RANGE: southern Canada to tropical America. TL: Cuba.

Early stages. Caterpillar (in U.S.A.) dark olive grey with yellow or orange stripes and spots. The numerous branched spines are only about 2 mm long, when the caterpillar is full grown, and yellow. Food plants include *Plantago, Gerardia, Linaria, Antirrhinum* and *Ludvigia*.

JUNONIA EVARETE Cramer 1775   *Caribbean Buckeye*   **Pl. 8**

Description. Fw ♂ 24–28 mm, ♀ 26–32 mm. Upperside ground colour rather velvety brown, often with faint greenish tinge, especially on hindwing. The *large ocellus on forewing upperside* always *ringed* completely with *red or reddish brown*, never white-edged; the transverse subapical band usually for the most part white, but often tinged pink or even wholly pink; the anterior ocellus on the hindwing very occasionally with a few blue scales centrally in the male; in the female more often with a certain amount of blue scaling in the basal half, i.e. eccentrically, but no red scaling in either sex. The underside is very variable as to ground colour, but on the whole the dry season type, in which the ocelli are very small indeed, or absent, is rare.

Distribution. Three subspecies are generally recognised in the islands though their definition has not yet been achieved to everyone's satisfaction. In the north the large subspecies *J. evarete zonalis* Felder extends from the Bahamas to the Cayman Islands, Jamaica and Hispaniola, overlapping *Junonia coenia* in Cuba; the name is based on a wet season form so that *genoveva* is available for the rare dry season form. It is replaced from Porto Rico southwards through the Lesser Antilles by the smaller and brighter subspecies *michaelesi* Munro 1951. In Barbados, however, typical *evarete* appears, probably introduced from mainland S. America by human agency. RANGE: W. Indies and S. America. TL: Surinam.

Junonia evarete presents a considerable puzzle from the point of view of classification. On top of local and seasonal variations of great amplitude it appears now that, at least on Jamaica, a pair of sibling species co-exist which at present cannot be distinguished by external characters.

Early stages. Fully grown caterpillar black, the head sometimes yellowish above, a fine dark mid-dorsal line is indicated by its delicate yellow edging; head and body sprinkled with minute white points, sometimes a double row of orange lateral spots above the pale supraspiracular line. Head with a pair of short stout branched 'horns', body with a dorsal line of branching spines and a further four rows of similar spines either black or yellow along each side decreasing in size towards the tail. (*Junonia coenia* does not seem to have so many spines.) Food plants *Stachytarpheta* (Blue Vervain), *Lippia*, *Valerianoides*, etc.

ANARTIA JATROPHAE Johansson 1763   *White Peacock*   **Pl. 7**
Description. Fw ♂ 16–20 mm, ♀ 20–24 mm. Upperside light grey with a complex pattern in dark grey and fulvous, the latter especially along the outer margins; a *jet black spot in space 2 of forewing* and others in spaces 2 and 5 of hindwing. Underside the same, but much paler and faintly lustrous. A good species in which to note the sexual differences in the forelegs characteristic of Nymphalidae: thin frail and hair-tipped in the male, stouter and ending in a kind of knobkerrie in the female.

Distribution. A common butterfly of open country, roadsides, beaches and waste land, often in association with the Buckeye. Very 'aggressive'. On the wing throughout the year and present on all the islands. Several recognisable but not easily defined subspecies occur in the West Indies. *A. jatrophae jatrophae* extends from the mainland of S. America via Trinidad and Tobago through the Lesser Antilles as far north as St Kitts. It is easily distinguished by being much the palest race, the marginal fulvous suffusion faint and rarely extending beyond the dark antemarginal line, except on the hindwing. The largest and brightest race is *E. j. saturata* Staudinger (1884) of Haiti and the Dominican Republic; the forewings are almost wholly smoky and both wings have a double row of well-developed yellow lunules, the inner row especially large. In this subspecies as in the others, the summer forms are duskier than those of the drier winter months. *A. j. jamaicensis* Moeschler (1886) is very similar but always a little smaller, the orange lunules not quite so large or bright. In *A. j. guantanamo* Munroe (1942) from Cuba and the Cayman Islands size and pattern are as in the Jamaican race but the dark markings are noticeably deeper in tone. *A. j. semifusca* Munroe (1942), from Porto Rico and St Thomas, and *A. j. intermedia* Munroe (1942) from St Cruz (St Croix) form connecting links with continental *A. j. jatrophae*. RANGE: southern U.S.A. to Argentina. TL: Surinam.

Early stages. Fully grown caterpillar black, spotted with silver, especially along the back, two branched spines on the head, warts on the first thoracic segment, and branching spines on the other segments arranged in seven rows. Food plant Water Hyssop, *Bacopa monniera*. *Lippia* (Fog Fruit) is also sometimes given as a foodplant, possibly due to confusion of the caterpillar with that of the Buckeye, which feeds on *Lippia* as well as many other plants.

ANARTIA AMATHEA Linnaeus 1758   *Red Anartia*   **Pl. 7**
syn. *Anartia amalthea* (misspelling)
Description. Fw ♂ 25 mm, ♀ 27 mm, more evenly rounded than in *A. jatrophae*. Male upperside black with a broad blood-red discal band from anal angle of

hindwing to forewing cell where it divides to form two narrower lines; *forewing apex with twelve white spots* arranged in three short transverse rows or 3, 4 and 5 spots. Underside pattern the same but with innumerable short darker striae on an ochreous background. Female upperside dark brown, the discal band light reddish brown, underside as in male.

Distribution. Antigua, Grenada and Barbados. Occurs sporadically, sometimes in great numbers, no doubt a vagrant from Trinidad or Tobago, where it is abundant; sometimes established for short periods. RANGE: Lesser Antilles to Argentina. TL: ' in Indiis'.

Early stages. The fully grown caterpillar is black and bears numerous moderately stout black branching spines. Food plants various species of Acanthaceae.

ANARTIA LYTREA   Godart   1819   *Godart's Anartia*   **Pl. 7**
syn. *A. dominicana* Skinner

Description. Fw 27 mm (♂) to 33 mm (♀). Male upperside warm dark brown, a slightly smoky white band of even width from mid-costa of forewing to the yellow-ringed eye spot in anal angle, and a similar short *dirty white median band on hindwing*; yellow submarginal lunules on both wings. Underside similar, but hindwing band continuous from costa to anal angle and only slightly expanded midway. Female lighter brown, the pale bands a little broader.

Distribution. Confined to Haiti and the Dominican Republic. Widespread and generally fairly common. Reports of *A. lytrea* in Antigua are in error being based on a misunderstanding of Fruhstorfer's original description of '*A. lytrea eurytis*' (see next species). RANGE: Hispaniola. TL: San Domingo.

Early stages. Not known.

ANARTIA CHRYSOPELEA   Huebner   1825
Huebner's Anartia   **Pl. 7**
syn. *Anartia lytrea eurytis* Fruhstorfer 1907

Description. Fw ♂ 24–26 mm, ♀ 25–28 mm, much squarer than in *A. lytrea*. Male upperside black, female dark brown, both sexes with a pure white straight band on forewing from costa to vein 2, and a much wider but shorter broad *spindle-shaped pure white hindwing band*; submarginal lunules delicate and shallow. Underside greyish brown; hindwing discal band just reaching costa at a point, widely expanded midway; anal ocellus sharply defined and narrowly ringed orange on both wings. Often treated as a subspecies of *A. lytrea*, but very distinct.

Distribution. Cuba: Sta Clara, Habana, Holguin, St Christobal, Matanzas, Tagua, Baracoa, San Luis, Guantanamo, etc., mostly during the winter months. Isle of Pines. Said to be common where it occurs. The solitary record from Jamaica needs confirmation. RANGE: Cuba and Isle of Pines. TL: Cuba.

Early stages. Not known.

BIBLIS HYPERIA   Cramer   1782   *The Red Rim*   **Pl. 7**
syn. *Didonis biblis* auctorum

Description. Fw ♂ and ♀ 28–36 mm. Upperside velvety dark brown, outer margin of forewing broadly paler, of hindwing bordered by a *broad red band cut into sections* by narrow black lines along the veins. Underside the same but colours all much paler and hindwing with three red basal spots.

Distribution. Not uncommon on Porto Rico and the Lesser Antilles, e.g. St

Croix, St Thomas, Dominica, St Kitts, Guadeloupe, Montserrat, St Lucia, Tortola and St Eustache. Rare in Hispaniola. Not reported from Cuba, Jamaica or Martinique. A lazy slow-flying rather sedentary butterfly, easily caught and preferring moist but fairly open ground and much attracted to rotting fruit. On the wing throughout the year in most places. RANGE: Mexico to Paraguay. TL: St Thomas.

Early stages. The caterpillar is spiny and grey-brown, with pale oblique lateral stripes, small green warts and a light coloured band on the seventh segment. When at rest it raises head and tail above its support to form an inverted arch. The food plant is Pine Nettle, *Tragia volubilis*.

SIPROETA STELENES Linnaeus 1758 *The Malachite* **Pl. 7**
Description. Fw 44 mm ($\male$) to 50 mm ($\female$). Upperside black with numerous large bold faintly translucent pale green markings. On the underside the black is replaced by light brown or cream, and there is a prominent white streak in the forewing cell. *Hindwing with short tail at vein* 4. Could only be confused with *Philaethria dido* (p. 89) a species of rather doubtful occurrence in the islands.
Distribution. *S. stelenes stelenes* is the subspecies found from St Kitts and St Croix westwards except in Cuba, the Cayman Isles and the Isle of Pines. It normally has only one green spot in the forewing cell, often none, and the orange anal spot on the hindwing upperside is relatively large and clear. The Cuban *S. stelenes insularis* Holland (1916) differs in having two pale green spots in the forewing cell and a smaller and partly suffused orange anal spot. On the underside the postdiscal pale spots on the hindwing, or rather the pale band in which they are set, is much narrower in subspecies *insularis* than in typical *stelenes* so that the brown marginal band is reduced from 4 or 5 mm in *insularis* to 2 or 3 mm in *stelenes*. The Malachite seems to be generally common and well distributed but solitary unless attracted to rotting fruit when it sometimes congregates in numbers. A forest insect. RANGE: southern U.S.A. to Brazil. TL: Jamaica.
Early stages. The fully grown caterpillar is about 1½ ins long, velvety black, the segmental divisions dark red or purple, the head shiny and the prolegs pink; head hairy and bearing two rather large spined horns, the three thoracic and last abdominal segments each with four warts or branched spines, the others with seven, black, pink, orange or red. Food plant *Blechum brownei*, more rarely *Ruellia coccinea* (Acanthaceae).

ATLANTEA PANTONI Kaye 1906 *Jamaican Harlequin* **Pl. 7**
Description. Fw $\male$ 28 mm, $\female$ 30 mm. Male upperside rather red-brown; forewing with confused black basal markings, a tapering black cell-bar that joins the broad black border in space 3, *the single row of round submarginal spots red-brown*; hindwing red-brown with a complete black border about 2 mm wide and two partial black bands extending from inner margin towards disc. Female upperside pattern the same but all pale markings clear light yellow, except the red-brown hindwing postdiscal band. Underside forewing like upperside in both sexes, hindwing in both sexes approximately like female upperside.
Distribution. Confined to Jamaica and restricted to the Cockpit Country. Rare and local. RANGE: Jamaica. TL: Manchester Mts.
Early stages. Not known.

ATLANTEA PEREZI Herrich-Schaeffer 1862
Cuban Harlequin   **Pl. 7**

Description. Fw ♂ 25–26 mm, ♀ 28–30 mm. Upperside a rather startling contrast in black and brilliant red-brown; forewing rather long and narrow, the wide black *outer margin containing a series of bold white spots*; male hindwing wide basal red-brown area unmarked except for a black triangle on inner margin, black border containing a series of red spots; female hindwing red basal area crossed by a broad black band. Forewing underside like upperside; hindwing black with basal and discal white or cream spots, narrow white marginal lunules and a series of red postdiscal spots.

Distribution. Cuba only: Santiago de Cuba, February to June; Baracoa. Said to be very slow on the wing which suggests, having regard to its bold colours, that it is distasteful and enjoys some immunity from the attacks of predators. RANGE: Confined to Cuba. TL: Cuba.

Early stages. Not known.

ATLANTEA TULITA Dewitz 1877
Porto Rican Harlequin   **Pl. 7**

Description. Fw ♂ 30 mm, ♀ 32 mm. Sexes alike. Forewing longer and narrower than in either of the other two species in the genus. Upperside red-brown, black markings as in *A. pantoni*, but forewing dark marginal band containing *two rows of red-brown spots*; hindwing border much wider, disc with two concentric black bands. Underside forewing as above, hindwing with broad discal band of white spots, some smaller white basal spots and a marginal row of fine white crescents.

Distribution. Quebradillas, October to January; Tallaboa, July; Arecibo, March. A hill country butterfly. There could well be a fourth species of *Atlantea*, in Hispaniola. It should be looked for in the mountains. RANGE: Porto Rico only. TL: Quebradillas.

Early stages. Not known.

ANTILLEA PELOPS Drury 1773   *Pygmy Fritillary*   **Pl. 6**

Description. Fw ♂ 9–11 mm, ♀ slightly larger. The smallest known Fritillary. Upperside very dark brown with a regular chequer-board pattern of square light brown spots, but *no white apical dot*. On the underside of the forewing the light brown spots are so enlarged as almost to displace the black, and the apex is mottled like the hindwing, the disc of which is crossed by a very irregular dark purplish band beyond which runs a row of small rather obscure ocelli. On the upperside of the hindwing close alongside the inner margin there is a fine pencil of long hairs in the male only.

Distribution. The typical subspecies occurs in St Kitts, Porto Rico and Hispaniola; it is the largest race, males sometimes having a forewing length of slightly more than 11 mm. The smallest race, with a forewing rarely more than 9 mm long, is *A. pelops pygmaea* Godart 1820 (syn. *aegon* Fabricius 1781 – an invalid homonym – *aedon* Godart 1823) which inhabits Jamaica. The Cuban subspecies, *anacaona* Herrich-Schaeffer 1864, is intermediate in size. The butterfly seems to be generally rare but locally common. RANGE: West Indies only. TL: St Kitts.

Early stages. Not known.

ANTILLEA PROCLEA Doubleday and Hewitson 1847

Jamaican Pygmy Fritillary   Pl. 6

Description. Fw 13 mm (♂) to 15 mm (♀). Upperside ground colour black, the fulvous spots of the several transverse bands more closely linked than in the rather smaller *A. pelops* and the pattern less regular; *forewing apex* rather broadly black and *enclosing a minute white spot* towards the costa (which at once distinguishes it from *A. pelops*). In the female the upperside fulvous areas are larger and brighter than in the male. Underside of hindwing cloudy purplish brown in male, strongly mottled in female.

Distribution. Widely distributed in woodland paths, forest edges, etc., attracted to flowers but often settling on the ground. John Crow and Blue Mts, Cockpit Country, from sea level to 3000 ft in January, March and April, June, July and August, October and December. RANGE: Jamaica only. TL: Jamaica.

Early stages. Not known.

PHYCIODES FRISIA Poey 1832   *Cuban Crescent Spot*   Pl. 6

Description. Fw ♂ 14–15 mm, ♀ 16–20 mm. Outer margin slightly concave between veins 2 and 4, hindwing margin gently crenulate. *Upperside light fulvous*, outer margins of both wings broadly black but enclosing pale lunules in spaces 2 and 3 on forewing; black markings of forewing very irregular, those of hindwing forming for the most part narrow concentric bands. Underside much paler, black markings confined to postdiscal area of forewing, pale marginal lunules in spaces 2 and 3 very conspicuous.

Distribution. Bahamas: Andros, Nassau, etc.; Cuba: Santiago, Matanzas, Holguin, St Christobal, etc.; Haiti: Port au Prince; Dominican Republic; Jamaica: Kingston, Montego Bay, etc. Apparently widespread but local throughout from sea level to about 1000 ft and at all seasons. The Jamaican population has been named subspecies *gyges* Hewitson (1864) but it is not visibly different from the populations of the other islands. RANGE: West Indies. TL: Cuba.

Early stages. The fully grown caterpillar is about one inch long, mottled yellow and grey, with nine rows of short stout branched spines, those near the head and low down on the sides yellow, the others black. Food plants not recorded. The closely related continental species, *Phyciodes tharos*, feeds on asters.

PHYCIODES PHAON Edwards 1864

Cayman Crescent Spot   Pl. 12

Description. Fw ♂ and ♀ 15–16 mm. Upperside ground colour blackish brown, fringes chequered grey; forewing cell crossed by four very dissimilar reddish-ochreous bands of the same colour as the postdiscal band that runs from space 5 to the inner margin; *an irregular yellow discal band* runs between the cell and the postdiscal band from costa to inner margin; hindwing disc broadly ochreous with a row of round black spots on its outer edge. On the underside of the forewing the upperside pattern is repeated but emphasised and brighter, and there is also some yellow at the apex and against the margin in space 3; hindwing entirely pale ochreous, with a pattern of delicate black lines, the round postdiscal spots smaller and bordering a dark marginal cloud.

Distribution. Cuba: Havana, rather rare. Cayman Isles: Grand Cayman,

Plate 9   **HELICONIIDAE**   *Scale:* × ⅔

1. Dryas iulia   *The Flambeau*   p. 86
The coloration of the upperside in the island races illustrated
varies roughly from golden in the north to fiery red in the south.
The shadowy underside markings and the characteristic white
streak at the base of the hindwing underside vary from island to
island, and will be best appreciated by a study of the figures.
All the specimens figured are males.
1a *Dryas iulia cillene* Holguin, Cuba.
1b *Dryas iulia carteri* Bahamas.
1c *Dryas iulia delila* Jamaica.
1d *Dryas iulia hispaniola* Haiti.
1e *Dryas iulia dominicana* Dominica.
1f *Dryas iulia framptoni* Grenada.
1g *Dryas iulia iulia* Tortola, Virgin Isles.
1h *Dryas iulia martinica* Martinique.
1i *Dryas iulia warneri* St Kitts.
1j *Dryas iulia lucia* St Lucia.

2. Dione juno   *Silver Spot*   88
♂ St Vincent. Forewing upperside with black bar across cell and
another parallel beyond.

3. Dione vanillae   *Gulf Fritillary*   88
♂ Grand Cayman. April, August. Forewing upperside with
numerous isolated black spots in discal area.

1a

1f

1b

1g

1c

1h

1d

1i

1e

1j

2

3

1. Eueides melphis   *Buff Zebra*   p. 86
♂ *E. m. melphis,* Haiti. Uniformly black and tan, the hindwing
divided horizontally by a black bar across the disc.

2. Heliconius charitonius   *The Zebra*   85
♂ *H. c. punctatus,* St Kitts. Black with bright yellow bands.

3. Philaethria dido   *Bamboo Page*   89
♂ Trinidad. Forewing cell almost wholly light green; hindwing
without a tail. See also *Siproeta stelenes,* Plate 7.

LIBYTHEIDAE

4. Libytheana motya   *Cuban Snout Butterfly*   91
♂ Cuba. Upperside grey, except forewing base; forewing subapical
spots white.

5. Libytheana terena   *Haitian Snout Butterfly*   91
♂ Haiti. Only the forewing spot in space 6 white, other markings
all fulvous.

6. Libytheana fulvescens   *Dominican Snout Butterfly*   92
♂ Dominica. All markings fulvous. *Holotype.*

RIODINIDAE

7. Apodemia carteri   *Carter's Metal Mark*   93
♂ *A. c. carteri,* Bahamas. A dark ocellus at anal angle on both wings.

April to July, common. The continuous discal and postdiscal bands at once distinguish *P. phaon* from *P. frisia* in which both these bands are much broken. RANGE: southern U.S.A. to Guatemala. TL: Georgia.

Early stages: In California the caterpillar is olive-green, marked with dark lines and mottled bands, and bears several rows of branching spines; head cream coloured and with large brown spots on vertex and sides. Food plants *Lippia lanceolata* and *L. nodiflora*. The butterfly has not been bred in the West Indies, but in the Cayman Islands it was associated with *Wedelia trilobata*, 'marigold', which might be its food plant though no larvae were found.

VANESSA CARDUI Linnaeus 1758   *Painted Lady*   **Pl. 8**
Description. Fw ♂ and ♀ 27–35 mm. Upperside *rosy-buff, bright pink when fresh*; forewing apical third black, with enclosed white spots, remainder and all hindwing with scattered irregular black markings. Underside light brownish grey with a pattern of delicate tracery and a series of five subequal postdiscal ocelli.

Distribution. The Painted Lady is a notable migrant, a greater wanderer even than *Danaus plexippus*, liable to occur almost anywhere except in arctic conditions. Any flowery place will attract it and it seems particularly fond of hill tops. It has been taken in Bermuda, the Bahamas, Cuba, Jamaica, Hispaniola, Porto Rico, St Lucia, Dominica, Martinique and Barbados and no doubt has occurred or will crop up on many other islands. RANGE: cosmopolitan. TL: Sweden.

Early stages. The fully grown caterpillar is velvety black with a chain of narrow yellow crescents along the side and a double pale line along the back, the numerous branching spines varying in colour between yellow and black. Food plants thistles and allied plants. The Painted Lady is not known for certain to breed anywhere in the islands.

VANESSA VIRGINIENSIS Drury 1770
American Painted Lady   **Pl. 8**
Description. Fw ♂ 20–25 mm, ♀ 25–35 mm. Upperside like *V. cardui* but black markings less heavy and forewing outer margin more deeply concave from vein 2 to vein 5. *Hindwing underside* greyer than in *V. cardui* and *with only two much larger ocelli*, in spaces 2 and 5.

Distribution. Cuba, Jamaica, Hispaniola and Porto Rico. The butterfly is a migrant like *V. cardui* and its occurrence in the West Indies is sporadic. Most records are of odd specimens taken in the mountains at some height above sea level. RANGE: Canada to C. America; Canary Islands and Hawaii. TL: New York.

Early stages. The fully grown caterpillar is velvety black, heavily spined and with white spots along the sides and narrow transverse yellow bands. It feeds on various species of Everlasting Flowers (*Gnaphalium, Antennaria*, etc.) and rests within a rolled-over leaf. It is doubtful whether it actually breeds on any of the islands regularly.

Note. This species, and *Vanessa cardui*, are sometimes placed in the genus *Cynthia* Fabricius 1807.

VANESSA ATALANTA Linnaeus 1758 *Red Admiral* **Pl. 8**
Description. Fw ♂ and ♀ 28–32 mm. Upperside black; forewing with white apical markings and a *vivid red band across cell to anal angle*; hindwing with broad red marginal border enclosing small black spots. Underside dark grey-brown cryptically mottled, except disc of forewing which is like the upperside. Quite unmistakable.
Distribution. Odd specimens have been taken in Bermuda, Cuba, Hispaniola and, quite recently, on Blue Mountain Peak in Jamaica. These are all referable to the N. American subspecies *V. a. rubria* Fruhstorfer 1909 (TL: Mexico), and no doubt all were vagrants. RANGE: Canada to Guatemala; Atlantic islands; N. Africa, Europe and W. Asia. TL: Sweden.
Early stages. The fully grown caterpillar is usually blackish in general coloration with rows of pale yellowish spots and many black branching spines that are orange basally. Solitary and very active. Food plants nettles, hops, etc. No breeding population is known in any of the islands.

HYPANARTIA PAULLUS Fabricius 1793
Sword-tailed Tortoiseshell **Pl. 8**
Description. Fw ♂ 30 mm, ♀ 32 mm. The warm golden brown upperside, angular forewing and *doubly tailed hindwing* at once distinguish this species. The female is generally lighter in colour, less heavily patterned in black than the male, and often lacks the small translucent spot in space 4 which is always present in the male. The boldly mottled underside must render the butterfly very difficult to see when at rest. The tails are very easily damaged.
Distribution. Cuba, Hispaniola, Jamaica and Porto Rico. A widespread butterfly recorded on the wing in every month except January and February, a fast flying, nectar seeking species especially partial to fairly open woodland. It has not developed any recognisable island races. RANGE: Greater Antilles only. TL: Jamaica.
Early stages. In Porto Rico the caterpillar is known as the Guacimilla caterpillar, guacimilla being the local name of the tree *Trema micrantha* on which it feeds and within the rolled-up leaves of which it commonly lives. When fully grown it is bright green, with a black or dark green head, which bears several protuberances ('cones') of various colours, the first thoracic segment bears warts, the second and third and ninth abdominal segments bear four spines each, the others seven each, all branched and black or dark red. In Cuba the caterpillar is duller green, the head cones less conspicuous, and the spines at most tipped with black; food plant a species of *Piper*.

EUPTOIETA HEGESIA Cramer 1779 *Mexican Fritillary* **Pl. 8**
Description. Fw ♂ and ♀ 25–33 mm. Very variable in size, female usually larger than male. Upperside rather bright clear fulvous; the base and disc of hindwing devoid of markings but outer margin widely dark brown preceded by a row of round black spots; forewing similar but with conspicuous narrow black markings in cell and on disc. *Underside mottled purplish brown*, the disc of forewing only marked in black as on upperside.
Distribution. Bahamas, Cuba, Cayman Islands, Haiti, Dominican Republic and Jamaica. A fairly common butterfly in open lowland areas freely visiting flowers. In Porto Rico *E. h. hegesia* is replaced by *E. hegesia watsoni* Comstock 1944, which differs from the typical subspecies only in that the four transverse

black lines in the cell of the forewing are fused to form two oval marks linked together by a black bar at their lower ends. RANGE: southern U.S.A. to Argentina. TL: Jamaica.

Early stages. The caterpillar when fully grown is red, shiny and armed with numerous short black spines arranged in parallel rows, with a long pair on the head, a silver dorsal line and a similar black-edged lateral line. Food plant 'wild yellow primrose', *Turnera ulmifolia*, and Passion Flower.

EUPTOIETA CLAUDIA Cramer 1779
Variegated Fritillary   **Pl. 8**

Description. Fw ♂ and ♀ 23–35 mm. Females usually much larger than males. Upperside rather dull greyish fulvous, somewhat variegated, numerous black linear markings and a short series of rounded black submarginal spots on both wings; hindwing basal area darker than discal area and separated from it by a black line, not devoid of markings as in *E. hegesia*. *Underside* much as in *E. hegesia*, but the *markings more strongly contrasting* and generally lighter in tone.

Distribution. Though originally described from Jamaican material by Cramer, *E. claudia* was either absent or overlooked there until found again in 1940 in one or two restricted areas. In Cuba very rare, first recorded in 1943. Flies at higher altitudes than *E. hegesia* and may have been overlooked through confusion with it. RANGE: eastern U.S.A. to Argentina. TL: Jamaica.

Early stages. Caterpillar when fully grown red, a pair of long rather blunt-ended spines immediately behind the head, two laterally on each of the next two segments, then three on either side much shorter than the first pair and rather blunt, a line of white dashes on the dorsal line, broken white flecks between the subdorsal spines and a lateral line of numerous smaller white spots. Food plants principally violets but reported also on Passion Flower, May Apple and numerous other plants.

The butterflies of this rather small family are confined to the tropics of the New World, of which they form an attractive and very characteristic faunal element. They are without exception brightly, sometimes startlingly coloured. In wing shape and markings they are only likely to be confused with the Ithomiidae, another family peculiar to the neotropics. Amongst the morphological characters that separate the Heliconiidae from the Nymphalidae, with which they have generally been associated as a subfamily, are the following: the long narrow forewing, the wide head and the simple unbranched humeral (precostal) vein on the hindwing.

The caterpillars, so far as is known, all feed on Passion Flowers – almost a family character. They are of simple cylindrical shape and rather conspicuously coloured, or at least not clothed in camouflage patterns and colours. Of the numerous branching spines they bear, one pair is on the head, one pair is placed laterally on each thoracic segment, three spines laterally on all the other segments. The chrysalis is greatly contorted, often armed with spines, and generally splashed with gold or silver.

Of the seven genera usually recognised in this family, *Heliconius* though by far the largest in terms of species, has but a single species in the whole of the West Indies. It is distinguished from the other genera by having the hindwing cell closed by a fully developed tubular vein. The other genera are separated by much less obvious morphological characters.

HELICONIUS CHARITONIUS Linnaeus 1767
The Zebra   **Pl. 10**

Description. Fw ♂ and ♀ 34–48 mm. Upperside *black, striped boldly with yellow*; underside paler, stripes paler and hindwing with a few red basal spots.

Distribution. This handsome butterfly, which is on the wing all the year round, is quite unmistakable. It occurs throughout the islands from Montserrat northwards as far as Andros Island in the Bahamas, in a series of subspecies which are just distinguishable statistically but only very uncertainly by eye. The differences are concerned mainly with wing length, breadth of yellow band and presence or absence of a yellow mark midway along vein 3 on the upperside of the forewing. Typical *H. charitonius charitonius* occurs in the Leeward Isles from Montserrat and Saba to Porto Rico and Mona Island; about 40% of them have the yellow dot on the forewing that is characteristic of *H. charitonius punctatus* Hall 1936, which inhabits St Kitts, Antigua and overlaps *H. c. charitonius* on Montserrat. Hispaniola is populated by *H. charitonius churchi* Comstock and Brown 1950, which is slightly larger; Jamaica by *H. charitonius simulator* Roeber 1921, with relatively broad yellow bands; and Cuba by *H. charitonius ramsdeni* Comstock and Brown 1950, a large broad-banded race. There is very little individual variation. RANGE: southern U.S.A. to Venezuela and Peru. TL: 'America', *recte* Virgin Isles.

Early stages. The very cylindrical caterpillar is creamy white, each segment encircled by three dark bands (which may be broken into spots) and with six

rows of very delicately branching spines. Head also white, marked with black.
It feeds on Passion Flower (Passiflora).

EUEIDES MELPHIS Godart 1819   *Buff Zebra*   **Pl. 10**
Eueides melphis ranges from Mexico to Panama and Greater Antilles. It occurs in
the West Indies in two subspecies:

1 E. melphis melphis Godart 1819
Description. Fw ♂ 23–36 mm. Upperside black with broad light brown
stripes. Forewing stripes uniform in colour. Of the spots forming the apical
transverse band, the longest, in space 5, is almost 10 mm long, that in space 4
nearly as long, the spot in space 3 less than twice as long as wide; apex usually
but not always with up to three very small white spots; black stripe in space 1b
just reaching, or just failing to reach the black margin at a point; *hindwing black
transverse median band much narrower than the fawn bands on either side of it.*
Underside similar but duller. Female not seen.
Distribution. Haiti and the Dominican Republic, possibly also in Porto Rico.
Very rare. Replaced in Cuba by *E. m. cleobaea* (below). TL: 'Antilles', *recte*
S. Domingo.

2 E. melphis cleobaea Geyer 1832
Description. Differs as follows: on the upperside of the forewing the apical
spots in spaces 4 and 5 are at most 5–6 mm long (sometimes larger in female),
and, like those of the median band, paler, sometimes quite yellow, and the black
stripe in space 1b is wider and almost always reaches the margin squarely (less
so in females at times); on the hindwing the transverse black median band is
about equal in width to the brown bands on either side of it.
Distribution. Throughout Cuba but very local. TL: Cuba.
Note. This rather rare insect is better known as *Eueides cleobaea*, Godart's
earlier name, *melphis*, having been completely overlooked.

Early stages. The caterpillar is said to feed on Passion Flower. It has not been
described.

DRYAS IULIA Fabricius 1775   *The Flambeau*   **Pl. 9**
syn. *juncta* Comstock 1944, Porto Rico
Description. Fw ♂ and ♀ 37–40 mm. Upperside silky golden orange, the red
tones quickly fading; forewing with uninterrupted black band 2–3 mm wide
along vein 4 from margin across cell-end to costa and thence tapering along
inner anterior edge of cell almost to wing base; a less sharply defined black apical
patch (enclosing some fulvous at extreme apex) extends along outer margin to
vein 4, with a prominent projection in space 5; veins 1, 2 and 3 very black, *fringes
white*; hindwing broadly paler along costa, outer black margin enclosing two
very narrow parallel pale lines, *fringes white*, a very small but conspicuous white
spot on the margin in space 1c touching vein 2. *Underside* much less brilliant,
markings rather cloudy, a prominent *white streak near the base of the hindwing*.
Distribution. The typical subspecies described above occurs in the Virgin
Islands and Porto Rico. The extremely similar subspecies, often regarded as
typical *iulia*, inhabiting most of northern and eastern South America, can be
distinguished by the solid black forewing apical patch and the dark fringes.
Fabricius specifically called attention to the white cilia in his original descrip-

tion. RANGE: southern U.S.A. to Brazil and Bolivia. TL: 'America', *recte* Virgin Isles, St. Croix.

Most of the West Indian islands have evolved their own endemic subspecies of *Dryas iulia*. *D. iulia warneri* Hall 1936 from St Kitts is a larger broader-winged insect with the forewing dark apical area separated from the outer margin by a tapering fulvous band that reaches to vein 4 in the male, less far in the female. In *D. iulia framptoni* Riley 1926, the subspecies from St Vincent and Grenada, the upperside is fiery red, like continental *iulia*, but the solid black bar on the forewing does not run basad along the front edge of the cell, and the cilia are white or chequered black and white. *D. iulia lucia* Riley 1926 from St Lucia is almost as brilliant but the black markings on the forewing upperside are much reduced, the black bar often consisting only of isolated spots, and the apex barely darkened. At the other extremity of its Caribbean range *D. iulia carteri* Riley 1926 occurs widely in the Bahamas and is best distinguished from the Cuban *D. iulia cillene* Cramer 1779 by its rather purplish underside and the roughly rectangular shape of the black mark at the cell-end on the forewing upperside; like *cillene* it is golden orange rather than red in colour and has a small black spot on vein 4 just beyond the cell-end. *D. i. carteri* also occurs in the Cayman Islands. In the Cuban *D. iulia cillene* the black cell-end spot on the forewing is characteristically triangular in shape with its apex produced to a fine point towards the wing base, and females are rather yellowish beneath. A very rare variety of the male, said to be quite devoid of upperside markings, has been named *nudeola* Stichel; it could have been mistakenly based on a specimen of the Jamaican *D. iulia delila* Fabricius 1775, which in the male has at most only a faint dark crescentic mark at the cell-end and is a lovely bright orange-yellow when fresh. The underside of *delila* is sandy in both sexes, the females not being pale yellow as in *D. iulia cillene* and *carteri*. *D. iulia hispaniola* Hall 1925, from Haiti and the Dominican Republic, with a forewing length of 45 mm or more is the largest of all the island races. The upperside has a slightly smoky look due to the presence of numerous scattered black scales; the cell bar starts broadly just below the middle of the costa and tapers rapidly towards the outer margin, which it usually just reaches along vein 4; the females are only slightly more heavily marked than the males; underside markings very ill-defined, ground colour faintly purplish. *D. iulia dominicana* Hall 1917, another large race, resembles *D. iulia warneri* in the shape and extent of the upperside markings but they are all more sharply defined and more intensely black. *D. iulia martinica* Pinchon and Enrico 1969, as its name implies, inhabits Martinique. It is very like *D. i. lucia* but the forewing apex is solid black, the marginal black 'teeth' are stronger and the underside markings paler and more contrasting.

D. iulia is a butterfly of the lowlands, very widespread and seemingly without any migratory tendencies, almost always to be seen in flowery gardens and similar places. It is sometimes placed in the genus *Agraulis* Boisduval and Leconte 1883.

Early stages. Caterpillar when full grown rather dark and very spiny. Dark coloration relieved principally by much paler blotches which run in roughly diagonal lateral bands. The finely branching spines are longest on the thoracic segments, half as long as those on the head, shorter and more delicate on abdominal segments, but increasing in length towards the rear, arranged approximately in three parallel rows on each side. Food plant Passion Flower, especially *Passiflora tuberosa*.

DIONE JUNO Cramer 1782   *Silver Spot*   **Pl. 9**
Description. Fw ♂ and ♀ 33–36 mm. Upperside fiery orange-red, when fresh, with black markings. Forewing apex rounded and outer margin concave between veins 3 and 5; margins narrowly black; a curved *black bar in cell and another across cell-end* to outer margin; hindwing border wider and divided lengthwise by a series of orange-red lunules. The bright silver spots on the underside give the butterfly its common name.
Distribution. In Lesser Antilles, from Martinique southwards, apparently a recent colonist from Trinidad and the S. American mainland, where it occurs widely but seldom in numbers. A butterfly of lowland flower gardens and such places, where it flies all the year round. The typical subspecies. Other subspecies occur on the mainland. RANGE: Lesser Antilles, C. and S. America. TL: Surinam.
Early stages. The caterpillars are gregarious, resting and even feeding together, on Passion Flower, especially *Passiflora serrato-digitata*. When fully grown they are reddish brown with six rows of spines as in *D. iulia* but all very short and none on the head, and marked with numerous pairs of small yellowish spots.

DIONE VANILLAE Linnaeus 1758   *Gulf Fritillary*   **Pl. 9**
The Gulf Fritillary occurs in a number of subspecies throughout its range, but only two of these are found in the West Indies. Its rather wider forewing and *spotty upperside markings* distinguish it from *D. juno*, the silver-spotted undersides of the two species being very similar.

1 **D. vanillae insularis** Maynard 1889 (TL: Bahamas) is the northern subspecies occurring from Bermuda and the Bahamas through Cuba, the Cayman Islands, Jamaica, Hispaniola and Porto Rico to Dominica. It is distinguished by heavier black upperside markings; a simple key character is the almost invariable presence of a round black spot centrally in space 1b on the forewing upperside.

2 **D. vanillae vanillae** is the less heavily marked southern mainland subspecies, in which the black spot in space 1b is almost always absent. It is found northwards from the Grenadines and Barbados to St Vincent and St Lucia. In Dominica, St Lucia and in Martinique and some of the small neighbouring islands the two subspecies meet, maintaining a good deal of independence but also hybridising to some extent.

Distribution. *D. vanillae* is very much a sun-loving species of the lowlands, strongly attracted to blossom and not difficult to catch. On the wing throughout the year. RANGE: U.S.A. to Argentina. TL: 'Americas'.

Early stages. The fully grown caterpillar is basically black, but looks yellowish brown because of the rows of orange-yellow spots that adorn it. The finely branched spines are about as long as the diameter of the body – 2 on the head, 4 on each thoracic segment, 6 on the others but none on the mid-dorsal line. Food plants Passion Flowers, especially *Passiflora foetida* and *P. laurifolia*.

The abundance of the butterfly in many places may be in part due to the great extent to which Passion Flowers are grown as garden plants.

PHILAETHRIA DIDO Clerck 1764   *Bamboo Page*   **Pl. 10**
This large green and black butterfly has been reported to occur both in Cuba and Hispaniola, but there are no confirmed records. It is so similar to *Siproeta stelenes* (p. 77) that confusion could easily result from observations made only on butterflies in flight. *P. dido* has longer and narrower forewings, a very characteristic long spear-shaped green streak in the cell of the forewing, *and no hindwing tail*. *Philaethria dido* is a common butterfly in Trinidad, where its black and white banded caterpillar feeds on *Passiflora laurifolia*. RANGE: C. America to Brazil. TL: 'America'.

This is a small family of rather small butterflies instantly recognisable by their relatively enormous palpi, which project straight forward from the front of the head like a snout, and may exceed the thorax in length. The very angular outer margin of the forewing is also characteristic, and suggests relationship with Nymphalidae such as *Polygonia*. The modified condition of the forelegs, especially in the males, further suggests relationship with that family, rather than the Riodinidae with which they have frequently been associated.

The three species of Libytheidae that occur in the West Indies are often treated as subspecies of the continental *L. carinenta* or *L. bachmanii*. They appear, however, to be sufficiently isolated and dissimilar as to merit treatment as distinct species, each very much restricted in range and showing none of the migratory tendencies of the mainland species. That such a small family as the Libytheidae, which musters only about a score of species, should have a world wide distribution with both strongly migratory and highly sedentary species is of considerable interest. It seems to suggest a very ancient lineage approaching extinction.

Nothing is known of the early stages of any of the West Indian species. From what is known of other species it is to be expected that their caterpillars are slender, cylindrical, green and clothed with only the shortest of hair, and that their heads will be narrower than the somewhat expanded thoracic segments, round and smooth. The body may have longitudinal stripes and the food plant will almost certainly be *Celtis*.

LIBYTHEANA MOTYA Boisduval and Leconte 1833
Cuban Snout Butterfly   Pl. 10
Description. Fw ♂ and ♀ 21–23 mm. Upperside white; outer two-thirds of forewing black and enclosing *one large and two smaller white spots*, outer margin broadly black, basal half of cell suffused fulvous; hindwing costal area irregularly black, outer margin broadly but diffusely black or dark grey. On the underside the forewing base is more broadly fulvous, its apex and all the hindwing finely speckled clouded silvery grey or, especially in the female, rather uniform slaty grey.
Distribution. Confined to Cuba. Widespread throughout the island. RANGE: Cuba. TL (not stated): Cuba.
Early stages. Not known.

LIBYTHEANA TERENA Godart 1819
Haitian Snout Butterfly   Pl. 10
Description. Fw ♂ and ♀ 21–25 mm. Upperside warm fulvous; forewing apical half and outer margin black, the *apical area enclosing a small white spot towards wing tip* and two larger pale ochreous spots postdiscally which are sometimes conjoined, especially in the female; hindwing with dark marginal shading and an irregular black patch between costa and cell. Underside pattern as above but

forewing apical markings paler and marginal black replaced by finely mottled silvery grey; hindwing wholly finely mottled silvery grey with basal discal and postdiscal darker cloudy bands.

Distribution. Dominican Republic: La Vega, Villa Rivas, Chacquey, etc., February and June. Haiti: Sources Puantes, etc., apparently fairly widespread but scarce. Porto Rico: no exact data, very scarce. Jamaica: a solitary male taken by Philip Gosse at Alligator Pond in June 1846 is the only certain record. RANGE: Hispaniola to Porto Rico. TL: 'Antilles'.

Early stages. Not known.

LIBYTHEANA FULVESCENS Lathy 1904
Dominican Snout Butterfly

Pl. 10

Description. Fw ♂ 24 mm. Upperside black with *fulvous markings*, the spots in the outer half of forewing small and isolated, the broad basal fulvous of *L. terena* broken into large just separated patches, intermediate in effect between *L. terena* and *L. bachmanii* of the southern U.S.A. On the underside the resemblance is rather closer to *L. terena*, the apical forewing spot being almost white, and the spots nearer the centre of the wing not as dark fulvous as the basal area; silvery areas as in *L. terena*. Female not known.

Distribution. Dominica only. Very rare. Nothing is known of its habits, habitat or early stages. RANGE and TL: Dominica.

This very large family of small butterflies is essentially tropical in distribution, though a very few species do occur in north temperate regions. Their metropolis is South America, which makes it especially remarkable that only one species has penetrated the Caribbean subregion and that one has apparently arrived from North rather than South America.

Many Metal Marks could readily be mistaken for Hairstreaks, of an unusual kind perhaps, for they have similar habits and are often dazzlingly beautiful. They are indeed more closely allied to the Lycaenidae than to any other family, the only readily recognisable morphological character that distinguishes them being the possession of a precostal vein on the hindwing. Lycaenidae lack this vein. The foreleg in the male is much reduced, the tarsus unsegmented and brushlike as in the Nymphalidae; in the female segmented and with articulated claws; palpi very small: antennae (in the sole W. Indian species) unusually long. Caterpillar hump-backed and slug-like as in the Lycaenidae.

APODEMIA CARTERI Holland 1902
Carter's Metal Mark   **Pl. 10**

Description. Fw ♂ and ♀ 15 mm. Upperside ground colour warm light chestnut brown. Forewing with 2 rather wide (1 mm) dark grey concentric transverse bands near base, a third at cell-end, a much bent dark postdiscal line edged subapically by an irregular row of 4 white spots, and a broad submarginal dusky band; hindwing similar but brighter, dark markings reduced; *both wings with anal ocellar spot*, largest on hindwing. Underside uniformly grey, markings as on upperside, but the forewing anal spot the larger.

Distribution. Occurs in two subspecies, both very rare. *A. carteri carteri* described above is known only from Nassau, Bahamas, where it is very local. *A. carteri ramsdeni* Skinner 1912 (TL: La Iberia, Cuba) appears to be even rarer. Only known from near Baracoa in September, it differs in having a narrow white postdiscal fascia on the forewing extending along the dark line below the white postdiscal spots, a group of three marginal black dots on the hindwing and, on the underside of the hindwing, some 19 to 20 isolated black basal and subbasal spots. RANGE: Cuba and the Bahamas. TL: Nassau, Bahamas.

Early stages. Not known.

Of all the families of butterflies this is probably the most numerous, with the possible exception of the Skippers. With one or two exceptions, *Eumaeus* for example, they are all small or very small. The family is world wide in distribution, from Greenland to Patagonia, and throughout the tropics. The shimmering blue colours that so many of them display are structural in nature, not pigmental. The morphological characters that distinguish them from the Riodinidae, their nearest relations, are slight but constant; the one most easily appreciated is a negative one, namely the absence of the precostal vein on the hindwing which is always present in the Riodinidae. In the forewing one or two of the small radial veins that run towards the apex are lacking, so that, using the numerical system for identifying the veins, there are only ten or eleven veins, numbers 7 and 8 being those most usually affected. The forelegs of the male lack tarsal claws and are reduced, those of the female are normal. The head and palpi are small, antennae very slender with a short and delicate club (except in *Eumaeus*) and arising so close to the rim of the eye that its edge is emarginate so as to accommodate them. The hindwing very often has a filamentous tail at vein 2, sometimes a short one at vein 3 and, in the Hairstreaks, the anal angle is generally lobed.

Of the three main subdivisions (subfamilies) of Lycaenidae, Hairstreaks, Blues and Coppers, that occur in America, only the first two occur in the West Indies. The first (Theclinae) are easily recognised by their very triangular, and almost always tailed, hindwings. They are swift and elusive on the wing, tending to fly high and to settle out of reach, and derive their popular name from the delicate hair-line patterns with which their undersides are decorated. In America this subfamily is essentially tropical in distribution, the great bulk of the species being found in Central and South America; so numerous are they indeed, and so similar morphologically, that a convenient and satisfactory classification of the species into genera has not yet been devised. The much less numerous West Indian representatives of the second subfamily, the Blues (Polyommatinae), have rounded hindwings and only one of them, *Pseudochrysops bornoi*, which seems to be a New World off-shoot of a fairly extensive group of Old World genera, has a tail. The whole subfamily is indeed essentially an element of the fauna of the Old World temperate zone.

The Hairstreaks and the Blues share a common love for sweet-scented flowers. The former tend to concentrate on the flowers of trees and shrubs, the latter on those of herbaceous plants, a relationship that also extends to their choice of larval food plants. But the stumpy, hunched-up, slug-like caterpillars feed on the flowers and fruits rather than the foliage. Because of this habit some species have even become pests, especially of peas and beans. On the other side of the balance sheet, however, there are two species of Hairstreak, *Strymon bazochii* (p. 101) and *Tmolus echiolus*, that have been introduced into Hawaii to control the spread of *Lantana*.

On the backs of many Lycaenid caterpillars, between the terminal segments, there are specialised glands that secrete a sweet honey-like fluid. Those cater-

Plate 11   LYCAENIDAE

1. **Eumaeus atala**   *Atala Hairstreak*   p. 98
   E. a. atala. Hindwing rounded; body orange or red.
   1a ♂ Bayate, Santiago de Cuba. 1b ♀ Gibara, Cuba.

2. **Pseudolycaena marsyas**   *Giant Hairstreak*   98
   ♂ *P. m. cybele*, St Vincent. March. Underside grey-blue with bold
   white-edged black markings.

3. **Thereus bourkei**   *Bourke's Hairstreak*   99
   ♂ Port Antonio, Jamaica. October. Discal line on hindwing
   underside diagonal; orange spots in spaces 1b, 1c and 2.

4. **Allosmaitia coelebs**   *St Peter's Hairstreak*   99
   Hindwing underside without orange spot in space 1b and 1c, but
   sometimes in space 3 as well as 2.
   4a ♂ *A. c. coelebs*, Cuba. 4b ♀ *A. c. fidena*, Haiti.

5. **Allosmaitia piplea**   *Godman's Hairstreak*   99
   Hindwing underside with oval or conical scarlet spot in space 2.
   5a ♂, 5b ♀, St Vincent.

6. **Cyanophrys crethona**   *Jamaican Green Hairstreak*   100
   No discal line on forewing underside. 6a ♂, 6b ♀, Jamaica.

7. **Chlorostrymon simaethis**   *St Christopher's Hairstreak*   100
   C. s. simaethis. Forewing underside with unbroken white-edged
   discal line. 7a ♂ Haiti. 7b ♀ Balthazar, Grenada.

8. **Chlorostrymon maesites**   *Clench's Hairstreak*   100
   Forewing underside discal line broken, not white-edged .8a ♂, 8b
   ♀, *C. m. clenchi*, Dominica.

9. **Nesiostrymon celida**   *Lucas's Hairstreak*   101
   Underside blue-grey with pattern of fine blue-black lines. 9a ♂,
   9b ♀, *N. c. celida*, Cuba.

10. **Strymon toussainti**   *Toussaint's Hairstreak*   102
    Hindwing underside with blue marginal area in space 1c. 10a ♂,
    10b ♀, Haiti.

11. **Strymon martialis**   *Cuban Grey Hairstreak*   102
    Both wings on underside with bold white black-edged discal line;
    hindwing with large postdiscal orange and yellow area. 11a ♂,
    11b ♀, Matanzas, Cuba.

12. **Strymon bazochii**   *Gundlach's Hairstreak*   101
    S. b. gundlachianus. Hindwing underside with very confused
    pattern of markings and no eye-spots.
    12a ♂ Blue Mts, Jamaica. 12b ♀ Haiti.

12

1. **Strymon rufofusca**   *Red Crescent Hairstreak*   p. 103
   Underside discal lines broken and red.
   1a ♂ Balthazar, Grenada. 1b ♀ St Vincent.

2. **Strymon acis**   *Drury's Hairstreak*   103
   Underside markings bold, white spot in cell.
   2a ♂ *S. a. gossei,* Cayman Brac. May. 2b ♀ *S. a. acis,* Antigua.

3. **Strymon bubastus** · *Bubastus Hairstreak*   104
   S. b. ponce. 3a ♂ St Johns, Antigua. July. 3b ♀ Dominica.
   Tailless; forewing discal band angled at vein 3.

4. **Strymon columella**   *Hewitson's Hairstreak*   104
   S. c. cybira. 4a ♂, 4b ♀, Grand Cayman. May, July.
   Tailed; discal band on forewing underside evenly curved.

5. **Strymon limenia**   *Disguised Hairstreak*   106
   5a ♂, 5b ♀, Holguin, Cuba. Anal lobe on hindwing upperside red.

6. **Electrostrymon angerona**   *Bronze Hairstreak*   106
   6a ♂, 6b ♀, St Vincent. Hw upperside with orange lunule in space 2.

7. **Electrostrymon angelia**   *Fulvous Hairstreak*   107
   E. a. angelia. 7a ♂, 7b ♀, Cuba. No orange lunule in space 2.

8. **Electrostrymon dominicana**   *Dominican Hairstreak*   107
   8a ♂, 8b ♀, Dominica. December. Red line from costa to vein 4.

9. **Electrostrymon pan**   *Pan's Hairstreak*   107
   9a ♂, 9b ♀, Jamaica. Black eye-spot on hindwing underside.

10. **Leptotes cassius**   *Cassius Blue*   108
    10a ♂ *L. c. theonus,* St Christobal, Cuba. 10b ♀ *L. c. chadwicki,* Dominica.
    Hindwing underside with two blue ocelli at anal angle.

11. **Hemiargus ammon**   *Lucas's Blue*   109
    11a ♂, 11b ♀, *H. a. erembis,* Grand Cayman. May.
    Hindwing upperside with two conspicuous black marginal ocelli.

12. **Hemiargus hanno**   *Hanno Blue*   109
    12a ♂, 12b ♀, *H. h. filenus,* Grand Cayman. July.
    Hindwing upperside with only one black marginal ocellus.

13. **Hemiargus thomasi**   *Thomas's Blue*   110
    Hindwing underside with a series of four dark basal spots (*H.
    ammon* has only three). 13a ♂, 13b ♀, *H. t. noeli,* Haiti.

14. **Leptotes perkinsae**   *Miss Perkins's Blue*   109
    ♂ Claremont, Jamaica. March. A single anal ocellus, in space 2.

15. **Hemiargus dominica**   *Jamaican Blue*   111
    ♂ Claremont, Jamaica. May. No black basal spots or hw.

16. **Pseudochrysops bornoi**   *Haitian Tailed Blue*   111
    ♂ Pont Beudet, Haiti. March. Hw with tail at vein 2.

17. **Brephidium exilis**   *Pygmy Blue*   114
    17a ♂, 17b ♀, *B. e. thompsoni,* Grand Cayman. June. Hindwing
    underside with row of six marginal ocelli.

18. **Phyciodes phaon**   *Cayman Crescent Spot*   79
    ♂ Grand Cayman, West End. August. Fw discal band yellow. .

pillars that produce this 'honey' are tended by ants which 'milk' them and avidly lap up the secretion. Extreme developments of this apparently mutually beneficial association have led to situations in which the ants 'stable' the caterpillars in 'barns' at the foot of their food plants, or carry them off bodily to their nests.

EUMAEUS ATALA Poey 1832   *Atala Hairstreak*   **Pl. 11**
Description. Fw ♂ 20–22 mm, ♀ 21–24 mm. A large *black round-winged tailless Hairstreak with* metallic blue-green suffusion and marginal spots, and a *red abdomen*. The metallic blue on the upperside extends to near the margin of the forewing and fills the cell of the hindwing in the male, but is less extensive in the female. Beneath, the forewing is essentially dull black, but the hindwing is decorated with three concentric rows of blue-green or blue spots. Quite unmistakable.
Distribution. Only the typical subspecies, *E. atala atala*, occurs in the Antilles, in Cuba, the Isle of Pines and on Great Abaco Island in the Bahamas. Specimens from the last locality should be carefully compared with the Florida subspecies, *E. atala florida* Roeber 1926, which has more extensive blue-green on the upperside and larger spots of that colour on the underside of the hindwing. The Central American *Eumaeus minijas* Huebner is smaller, has black fringes and a black body with only the tip red beneath. A lowland butterfly, local but sometimes abundant. RANGE: Florida, Cuba and Bahamas. TL: Cuba.
Early stages. The full-grown caterpillar is brilliant red, the body segments rather humped-up and each with a transverse row of four tubercles bearing tufts of short hair. In shape it is much less slug-like than usual for a Lycaenid caterpillar. It feeds openly on the leaves of the Cycad, *Zamia integrifolia*, 'Coontie' and is known as the Coontie Worm in Florida. In Cuba the food plant is known as 'Yuquilla'. The red coloration suggests that the caterpillar is distasteful.

PSEUDOLYCAENA MARSYAS Linnaeus 1758
Giant Hairstreak   **Pl. 11**
Description. Fw ♂ 22–30 mm, ♀ smaller. The largest known West Indian Hairstreak and very distinct. Forewing falcate. Upperside shining sky-blue tending to green basally, the broad black margins inwardly diffuse and little broader in the female than in the male. Hindwing with two long tails. *Underside* ground colour light grey with a purplish cast, both wings *with scattered blue-edged black spots*; hindwing much bluer towards the tails and with a broken black line that parallels the outer margin, a large black marginal spot between the tails and another on the anal lobe.
Distribution. In the West Indies *P. marsyas* is known to occur only on St Vincent, as a distinct subspecies, *P. marsyas cybele* Godman and Salvin 1896. It stands apart from *P. marsyas marsyas* of South America and *P. m. damo* Druce 1875 not only in its geographical isolation but also in the greater extent of the black markings on both upper- and undersides. It is sometimes treated as a distinct species. RANGE: C. and S. America; St Vincent. TL: 'Tropics'.
Early stages. Not known.

THEREUS BOURKEI Kaye 1924 *Bourke's Hairstreak* **Pl. 11**
Description. Fw ♂ 15–18 mm, ♀ larger. Hindwing with a stubby tail 1 mm
long at vein 3, and a filamentous tail 5 mm long at vein 2. Male upperside
blackish brown with strong blue reflections over all but the apical third of the
forewing and the whole of the hindwing except the abdominal and costal areas;
a prominent black sex-brand in the forewing cell. Female upperside blue-grey
over the basal halves of both wings. Underside grey, darker in male than female,
the postdiscal lines outwardly edged with light grey; the area beyond basically
lighter in ground colour and enclosing a broad diffuse dark submarginal band; a
marginal black spot crowned with pale orange between the tails, and a further
somewhat diffuse *spot at the anal angle of the hindwing* which *is vivid orange-red*
on both surfaces.
Distribution. Bourke's Hairstreak is restricted to Jamaica, where it occurs as a
lowland insect, though thought originally to have come from Trinidad. There
are no close West Indian relatives of this rare and very lovely Hairstreak, but it
has a few distant relatives on the mainland. RANGE and TL: Jamaica.
Early stages. Not known.

ALLOSMAITIA COELEBS Herrich-Schaeffer 1862
St Peter's Hairstreak **Pl. 11**
Description. Fw ♂ and ♀ 14–18 mm. Upperside blackish brown; forewing
without sex-mark; basal third of forewing and most of the hindwing (cell and
spaces 1c to 4) flashing blue in the male, duller blue in the female; hindwing
with or without a tail at vein 3. Underside ground colour brown; on the forewing the broken postdiscal line extends from costa to about vein 2; on the hindwing it extends right across the wing and is outwardly white-edged; beyond it is
a broader broken less well defined blackish submarginal line sometimes with
faint traces of white along its inner edge; anal spot large and black and crowned
with yellow and flanked with blue scales; a yellowish marginal spot in space 2
encloses a tiny black speck; *no orange spot in space 1b or 1c.*
Distribution. *A. coelebs coelebs* is widespread in Cuba and not rare. There is a
single record from Jamaica, perhaps a wind-blown stray. It is replaced in
Hispaniola and Porto Rico by subspecies *fidena* Hewitson 1867 in which there
is no hindwing tail at vein 3, the underside is grey rather than brown, and the
marginal spot in space 2 is much redder – sometimes treated as a distinct species.
RANGE: Greater Antilles only. TL: Cuba.
Early stages. The caterpillar, in Cuba, lives in the buds of *Tetrapteris* (Bejuco
de San Pedro), a liana. Head ochreous yellow with black lateral stripe; body
greenish orange, first segment with a black rhomboid shield and divided, like
the longitudinal body line, by a white line; most segments with two or more stiff
hairs on their anterior edges and four tubercles.

ALLOSMAITIA PIPLEA Godman and Salvin 1896
Godman's Hairstreak **Pl. 11**
syn. *subobscura* Lathy 1904
Description. Fw ♂ and ♀ 14–16 mm. Upperside black. Male without sex-mark.
Forewing from inner margin to base of cell, hindwing from vein 5 and cell to
grey abdominal area rather deep metallic blue in male, pale grey-blue in female.
Underside brown with faint grey tint; a postdiscal interrupted line of distally
white-edged dark spots crosses both wings, and there are brown submarginal

shades; hindwing with filamentous tail at vein 2, anal lobe black; a very *pro-minent round or oval isolated scarlet spot in space 2* looks as if it has been painted on, and is diagnostic.

Distribution. Known only from St Vincent, Grenada and Dominica, December, January and February. RANGE: Lesser Antilles only. TL: St Vincent.

Early stages. Not known.

CYANOPHRYS CRETHONA Hewitson 1873
Jamaican Green Hairstreak **Pl. 11**

Description. Fw ♂ and ♀ 15–17 mm. The largest West Indian Hairstreak with a green underside. Hindwing with filamentous tails at vein 3 (1–3 mm) and vein 2 (4 mm). Upperside rather dull metallic greenish blue with narrow black borders (wider in the female) and, in the male, a minute rather diffuse scent patch in the end of the forewing cell. Underside bright green, the *forewing* dull dark grey beneath the cell and *without a postdiscal line*; hindwing with reddish brown marginal band speckled with grey, from vein 6, where it is narrowest, to anal angle, which it fills; postdiscal line reduced to a delicate wavy 'W' in black outwardly edged white between the cell and the inner margin.

Distribution. A lowland species, scarce and local. Has been taken at white *Lantana* flowers or settled on the foliage of trees, especially lime. RANGE: Jamaica only. TL: Jamaica.

Early stages. Not known.

CHLOROSTRYMON SIMAETHIS Drury 1773
St Christopher's Hairstreak **Pl. 11**

Description. Fw ♂ 12–14 mm, ♀ smaller. Upperside brown, underside green, only one tail. There is a *purplish sheen on the upperside* of the male when fresh or when the light strikes it at the right angle. On the green underside the narrow chocolate-coloured *uninterrupted postdiscal line* is boldly and broadly *edged with silvery white*; on the forewing there is a greyish brown submarginal patch against the rather pale yellowish brown inner margin; hindwing margin broadly grey and separated from the undulating postdiscal band by a band of green. No other West Indian Green Hairstreak has such a striking white postdiscal line. See *C. maesites* (below) and *C. crethona* (above).

Distribution. *C. simaethis simaethis* ranges from Cuba to St Vincent and Grenada in the Lesser Antilles with very little variation, and has been reported from Andros Island in the Bahamas. In Jamaica, however, it is replaced by a distinct subspecies, *C. s. iago* Comstock and Huntington, which differs as follows: it is larger, the males measuring 15–16 mm, and on the underside of the hindwing the postdiscal line is shifted somewhat basad, leaving a wider zone of green between it and the marginal grey-brown area, especially towards the costa. Haitian specimens have a rather similar wide green area, and a much straighter postdiscal line. RANGE: Texas to Argentina. TL: St Kitts.

Early stages. The caterpillar has been found feeding on *Eupatorium villosum*, but seems never to have been described.

CHLOROSTRYMON MAESITES Herrich-Schaeffer 1864
Clench's Hairstreak **Pl. 11**

Description. Fw ♂ and ♀ about 10 mm only. Tiny. *Upperside vivid deep metallic purplish blue* in male, dull grey-blue in female. Hindwing with a stubby tail at vein 3 and a long filamentous one at vein 2. Underside green, but posterior half of forewing grey-brown, changing to yellowish along the inner margin, and with a delicate black broken postdiscal line; hindwing postdiscal line lacking in space 3, and from vein 3 to inner margin edged white, the area below vein 5 varicoloured in cinnamon, blue, grey and red-brown scaling.

Distribution. *C. maesites maesites*, as described above, occurs in Cuba, Jamaica, the Bahamas, Porto Rico and St Vincent, but is not known from Hispaniola. In the Lesser Antilles it is replaced on Dominica by *C. maesites clenchi* Comstock and Huntington which lacks a tail at vein 3; it is also duller above in both sexes, and the male has a noticeable black apical border (which *C. m. maesites* lacks), which becomes so extensive in the female that only a small area at the wing base remains blue. RANGE: Florida to Dominica. TL: Cuba.

Early stages. Not known.

Note. Of the two other West Indian Hairstreaks that have green undersides one, *C. simaethis*, has a broadly white-edged postdiscal line on the underside of the forewing, the other, *C. crethona*, has none. The Venezuelan *C. telea* is very similar to *C. maesites* and could be conspecific.

NESIOSTRYMON CELIDA Lucas 1857
Lucas's Hairstreak   **Pl. 11**

Description. Fw ♂ and ♀ 9–11 mm. Upperside bright metallic blue, the apical half of forewing black, the blue less vivid in the female than the male. *Underside light grey, almost whitish*, decorated on the forewing *with* three broken rows of *delicate black crescentic lines*, subbasal, postdiscal and submarginal, all outwardly edged white; on the hindwing these three rows are continued, somewhat confusedly, the submarginal spots each enclosing a dark marginal spot; upper tail 2 mm long, lower tail 4 mm, a small orange patch between them and another at the anal angle. The underside pattern is much more suggestive of a Blue than a Hairstreak.

Distribution. In Jamaica *N. celida* is rare and local, chiefly met with in open upland country. Elsewhere it seems to be equally rare though widespread. The typical subspecies, *N. celida celida* has a black-centred orange and yellow tailspot on the hindwing underside and is confined to Cuba. In the Jamaican subspecies, *N. c. shoumatoffi* Comstock and Huntington, this spot is smaller and wholly black. *N. c. aibonito* Comstock and Huntington, which inhabits Hispaniola and Porto Rico is very like *N. c. celida* but has a more restricted black forewing apex, and a tail spot that is orange, black-pupilled and ringed with white, thus combining the features of the other two subspecies. RANGE: Greater Antilles only. TL: Cuba.

Early stages. Not known.

STRYMON BAZOCHII Godart 1822
Gundlach's Hairstreak   **Pl. 11**

Description. Fw ♂ and ♀ 11–12 mm. Upperside dark brown; forewing with sex mark occupying distal half of cell in male; hindwing solidly blue-scaled from vein 1b to vein 7 in male, less extensively in female; hindwing in both sexes with a series of dark submarginal spots in spaces 1c to 3 or 4, the largest always in space 2. Underside dark brown; forewing with some grey irroration in the apex and a delicate submarginal line that extends to anal angle; hindwing a little darker, irrorated with grey and marked by a greyish line that extends from the wing base to the middle of the outer margin, whence another similar line extends to the middle of the inner margin; a third much shorter line extends from mid-costa to meet the first line at right angles in the cell. The *mottled underside pattern is unlike any other West Indian Hairstreak* and best appreciated by reference to the figure. The sharply angled apex of the hindwing is also highly characteristic.

Distribution. *S. bazochii* occurs in the Antilles only on Cuba, Hispaniola and Jamaica where it is not uncommon at lower altitudes. It differs from continental *bazochii* in being less strongly marked on the underside, and has been named subspecies *gundlachianus* Bates 1935 (TL: Cuba). RANGE: southern U.S.A. to Brazil; Hawaii and Fiji (introduced). TL: Brazil.

Early stages. The early stages of the Antillean subspecies are unknown. In Hawaii, where the butterfly was introduced from Mexico in 1902 to control *Lantana*, the caterpillar is dull leaf-green and covered with short white and longer dark bristles, and has a pale yellowish head. It feeds in the flower heads of basil, *Hyptis pectinata*, and *Lantana*.

STRYMON MARTIALIS Herrich-Schaeffer 1864
Cuban Grey Hairstreak   **Pl. 11**

Description. Fw ♂ and ♀ 14–15 mm. Upperside almost black, with a large area of silvery grey-blue on the inner margin of the forewing and another covering about two-thirds of the hindwing; hindwing with two small black marginal spots near the anal angle and a red anal lobe. A small black area, hardly a sex-brand, at the end of the forewing cell in the male is replaced by a similar but paler area in the female. Underside ground colour soft mouse grey; forewing with a faint submarginal line and a *postdiscal line*, the latter outwardly *edged with white*; *hindwing with a similar* white-edged black postdiscal *line from costa to abdominal margin*, and black spots at anal angle and at the base of the first tail between which and the second stubby tail there is a grey shade; anal spot narrowly, the other very broadly, crowned with orange, and the latter surmounted by a wedge of black that extends almost to the apex.

Distribution. Bahamas, Cuba, Isle of Pines, Cayman Islands and Jamaica. Taken mostly in the summer months in sunny fields and open spaces in lowland country. Nearest, amongst West Indian Hairstreaks, to *Strymon acis*, but readily distinguished by its blue upperside and the lack of the two white basal spots. RANGE: Florida to Jamaica. TL: Cuba.

Early stages. The caterpillar, in Florida, feeds on *Trema micrantha*, known as Guacimilla or Calo de Cabra. It is dull green, devoid of pattern, but covered densely with very short bristly white hair.

STRYMON TOUSSAINTI Comstock and Huntington 1943
Toussaint's Hairstreak   **Pl. 11**

Description. Fw ♂ 11–12.5 mm, ♀ 10–11 mm. Like *S. columella* but upperside somewhat darker; male with faint sex-brand at cell-end and a few scattered blue scales, female with much more blue scaling. Underside ground colour much lighter, dusted with grey scales; postdiscal line on both wings composed of round black spots in a very disjointed row, and both wings with marginal and submarginal rows of pale lunules, those on hindwing extending only from apex to vein 3; hindwing with prominent black basal spot in cell, in space 7 and centrally in space 1b; anal lobe black; a marginal black spot surmounted by orange in space 2; *a heavily blue-scaled black marginal spot in space* 1c.

Distribution. *Strymon toussainti* has been taken in July and from December to April at Fond Parisien and Port au Prince in Haiti and at Montserrat in the Dominican Republic. It flies with *S. columella* from which it is easily distinguished by the much paler marginal areas and very irregular postdiscal lines on both wings. *S. christophei*, which also flies in Hispaniola is much lighter beneath than either *S. columella* or *S. toussainti*. RANGE: Hispaniola. TL: Haiti.

Early stages. Not known.

STRYMON RUFOFUSCA   Hewitson 1877
Red Crescent Hairstreak   **Pl. 12**

Description. Fw ♂ and ♀ 12–13 mm. Upperside uniformly brown in both sexes. Male without sex brand in forewing cell. Hindwing with filamentous tail at vein 2, a black marginal spot surmounted by a red crescent in space 2, a small black marginal dot in space 1c, and anal lobe touched with red; head white between the antennae, collar orange. Underside light brown, the hindwing marginal spots of the upperside repeated below, *both wings crossed by a postdiscal chain of crescent-shaped red spots* outwardly edged black then white, the spot in space 7 of hindwing the largest.

Distribution. So far reported from the Lesser Antilles only, St Lucia, St Vincent and Grenada. RANGE: Mexico to Paraguay. TL: not stated.

Early stages. Not known.

STRYMON ACIS   Drury 1773   *Drury's Hairstreak*   **Pl. 12**

Description. Fw ♂ and ♀ 12–15 mm. Upperside brown, a small red-orange submarginal spot above the shorter tail and another at the anal angle. Head orange between the bases of the antennae. Underside grey, boldly patterned; forewing submarginal line evanescent, but the very narrow *black postdiscal line is outwardly flanked and overshadowed by a broad shining white band*, which is continued on the hindwing from near the costa to the large decorative submarginal area, where it turns abruptly to the inner margin. The extent of the orange, white and black patches along the margins varies with the subspecies, but the bold *white spot in the hindwing cell* and the other one above it near the costa remain very characteristic.

Distribution. *Strymon acis* appears to be commonest, at least in Jamaica, in the early spring in lowland and coastal areas, where it is attracted to a low-growing shrub, *Croton discolor*, which, it is thought, may be the food plant of its unknown caterpillar. The butterfly varies considerably from island to island. The Florida population, *S. a. bartrami* Comstock and Huntingdon 1943, is the one most heavily marked with white. The Cuban subspecies *casasi* Comstock and Huntingdon 1943 is very similar. In the Bahamas subspecies *armouri* Clench 1943 occurs on some of the eastern islands: its white bands and decorated submarginal area are quite narrow. *S. a. gossei* Comstock and Huntingdon from Jamaica and the Cayman Islands, and *S. a. mars* Fabricius from the Virgin Islands, St Kitts and Porto Rico, resemble *S. a. armouri* in the narrowness of the white bands, but the submarginal zone is broader; the orange area here is larger in *mars* than in *gossei*. Typical *Strymon acis* from Antigua and Dominica inclines to be the largest race. The Hispaniolan *S. a. petioni* Comstock and Huntington is very

close to *S. a. mars* but grey on the underside rather than brown. RANGE: from Florida throughout the Antilles to Dominica. TL: Antigua.
Early stages. Not known.

STRYMON BUBASTUS Cramer 1775
Bubastus Hairstreak   **Pl. 12**

Description. Fw ♂ 11–14 mm, ♀ rather smaller. Upperside black-brown; underside grey-brown; *tailless*. Male with a black sex-brand about 2 mm square at cell-end. On *forewing* underside the *postdiscal line*, composed of rounded black spots outwardly edged with white, is short, arises at right angles to the costa not far from the apex and runs towards the middle of the outer margin (where it is *sharply angled in space* 3) against which there is a row of faint double spots in each interspace; between these spots and the postdiscal line there is yet another row of single light spots, which are perhaps best appreciated by noting the two lines of faint white crescents that define them. The hindwing postdiscal line is similar but very disjointed, the spots irregular in size, the costal spot the largest; basad of the postdiscal line is a pair of black spots wholly ringed with white, one in the cell, a larger one on the costa; beyond the postdiscal line are two rows of light coloured crescent-shaped marks open towards the margin; the black ocellar marginal spot in space 2 is capped with orange that fades to yellow.

Distribution. Typical *Strymon bubastus bubastus* is confined to the mainland of S. America and does not occur in the West Indies. It is replaced there by *S. b. ponce* Comstock and Huntington (TL: Porto Rico), which is rather greyer on the underside, has a brighter and larger orange-yellow capping to the marginal spot in space 2, which is itself a good deal larger and closer to the margin, although the basal and discal spots on the whole are a good deal smaller and less conspicuous than in typical *bubastus*. The butterfly occurs in Porto Rico and throughout the Lesser Antilles, and is often common. On St Vincent and Dominica it was mistakenly reported as *Strymon eurytulus* Hewitson, a southern S. American species. It can easily be mistaken for *Strymon columella* or *S. limenia*, but both these, unlike *S. bubastus*, have a hindwing tail. Separation is less easy if this tail is missing. *S. columella,* which only overlaps *S. bubastus* in Porto Rico is easily separated by the fact that the postdiscal line on the forewing is evenly curved, not sharply elbowed in space 3; in *S. limenia*, which nowhere overlaps *S. bubastus*, this line is more prominent and almost straight. Again, on the underside of the hindwing the postdiscal line, which meets the inner margin at about its mid-point, in both *S. bubastus* and *S. columella*, ends in two or three spots and a short inconspicuous white line: in *limenia* these are replaced by a pair of prominent white-edged black lines that lie at right angles to one another.
RANGE: Porto Rico to S. Brazil. TL: Surinam.
Early stages. Not known.

STRYMON COLUMELLA Fabricius 1793
Hewitson's Hairstreak   **Pl. 12**
syn. *antigua* Comstock and Huntington 1943

Description. Fw ♂ 12–14 mm, ♀ 11–14 mm. This species looks exactly like a *Strymon bubastus*, but with a tail. One of the most noticeable differences between the two species, apart from the matter of tails, is that in *S. columella* the *black spots basad of the postdiscal spots on the hindwing sometimes have red scales on their* *inner edges.* The female, unlike that of *bubastus*, almost always has a large and well marked silver-grey area occupying most of the upperside of the hindwing, and the marginal spots are larger and more conspicuous.

Distribution. *S. columella* is a widespread and common species especially favouring open ground at low altitudes. Three subspecies occur in the West Indies. *S. c. columella* of the Virgin Isles and Antigua has bold but not elaborate markings on the underside and the postdiscal line of spots on both wings is straighter than in the other subspecies. In Cuba, the Bahamas and the Cayman Islands, Jamaica and Hispaniola there is a variable population that is best called *S. c. cybira* Hewitson 1874; it has a very strongly marked underside pattern. On Porto Rico there is a third subspecies, *arecibo* Comstock and Huntington 1943, very lightly marked. RANGE: southern U.S.A. to Brazil. TL: St Croix, Virgin Isles.

Early stages. The caterpillar of the Californian subspecies of *S. columella*, *S. c. istapa* Reakirt, has been reared on the common *Malva*, although the eggs were laid on *Sida hederacea*, a plant of a genus that also occurs in the West Indies. When full grown it is dark green, with a darker line along the back, and is covered with translucent white points each bearing a chestnut coloured translucent hair. Head very small and, like the legs, mostly hidden from view. The segments, from head to 3rd abdominal, increasingly humped, then decreasing to tail. The thoracic shield dirty white. In the Cayman Islands *S. columella* is especially associated with *Suriana*, a plant of the beaches known as Bay Cedar or Juniper, which could be the larval food plant.

Note. Similar species are *S. bubastus* (p. 104), *S. limenia* (p. 106), *S. toussainti* (p. 102) and *S. christophei* (below).

STRYMON CHRISTOPHEI Comstock and Huntington 1943
Haitian Hairstreak

Description. Fw ♂ and ♀ 12–13 mm. Another member of the *S. columella* group and indistinguishable from that species on the upperside except by the presence of scattered blue scaling, especially in the female. Underside light grey without dark grey-brown underscaling; postdiscal lines broken and only scantily white-edged outwardly; submarginal and marginal rows of dark spots strongly developed, the latter separated from the margin only by a thin grey line; in addition to the anal spot and the marginal spot in space 2 there is a conspicuous dark spot in space 7 near the middle of the costa; *no basal spot*.

Fig. 12. *Strymon christophei.* ♂ Port au Prince, Haiti, January. × 1½.

Distribution. *S. christophei* is known only from Haiti and the Dominican Republic, where it flies with *S. columella* and *S. toussainti* and occasionally with *S. limenia*. It differs from all these by its lighter underside ground colour, the bold series of equally dark spots forming the postdiscal, marginal and submarginal lines, and the absence of a basal spot. RANGE: Hispaniola only. TL: Haiti.

Early stages. Not known.

STRYMON LIMENIA Hewitson 1868
Disguised Hairstreak   **Pl. 12**

Description. Fw ♂ and ♀ 11–14 mm. A little larger than *S. columella*; the upperside similar but browner, the male sex-mark at cell-end less definite. Underside ground colour dark brown; forewing postdiscal line straight and composed of small round intensely black spots; hindwing postdiscal line formed of elongate spots which, in space 1C (below vein 2), are acutely angled to the abdominal margin; *space 7 with two large black subcostal spots, the outer one the larger*; a similar but smaller spot in cell; all spots ringed white or pale yellow; anal spot black surmounted by yellow; marginal blue scales in space 1C, and a large orange submarginal patch in space 2. The single tail, at vein 2, is about 3 mm long. In the female the forewings are more rounded than in the male, and the marginal spots on either side of the tail are inwardly edged with blue and sometimes also with orange.

Distribution. Widespread and apparently common in Cuba and Hispaniola, less common in Jamaica and Porto Rico. St Thomas. Often found flying with *S. columella* and other species of the group. Best distinguished by the dark underside and the characteristically angled postdiscal line on the hindwing near the anal angle. RANGE: Confined to the West Indies. TL: Jamaica.

Early stages. Not known.

ELECTROSTRYMON ANGERONA Godman and Salvin 1896
Bronze Hairstreak   **Pl. 12**

Description. Fw ♂ 12–13 mm, ♀ 11–13 mm. Upperside dark brown, male with faint bronze tinge, *both sexes with an orange lunule above the marginal black spot in space 2 on hindwing*. Underside a little lighter; forewing costal edge orange; postdiscal line black, well defined, outwardly white-edged; submarginal line very faint; hindwing postdiscal line unbroken and edged white, the red-orange patch in space 2 overflowing broadly into space 3 and three or four times as big as the black marginal spot that it surmounts.

Distribution. *E. angerona* does not seem to be particularly rare, and occurs throughout the Lesser Antilles, taking the place of *E. angelia* with which it is easily confused. It differs in the brighter red and the greater extent of the submarginal patch in space 2 on the underside of the hindwing, in having, like *E. dominicana*, much fainter submarginal lines, and unbroken postdiscal lines. It also differs from *E. dominicana*, with which it flies on Dominica, in lacking the red line that extends from mid-costa to vein 4 on the underside of the hindwing. RANGE: Lesser Antilles. TL: St Vincent.

Early stages. Not known.

ELECTROSTRYMON ANGELIA Hewitson 1874

Fulvous Hairstreak **Pl. 12**

Description. Fw ♂ 11–13 mm, ♀ 8–11 mm. Upperside dark brown, underside brownish grey. On the upperside in the male especially there is a large fulvous area on the forewing, and a small one on the hindwing, in most subspecies; but these may be almost absent at times in the female; *no orange lunule in space 2.* On the underside the postdiscal line is bolder on the forewing than the submarginal line and both are rather straight; on the hindwing it is broken, edged outwardly white and reasonably straight from costa to near the anal angle, then sharply angled to the inner margin; near vein 2 it also tends to join the submarginal line; a black anal patch and black marginal spot in space 2, the latter surmounted by red or yellow.

Distribution. *E. angelia* is a lowland butterfly, like most of the Hairstreaks of this group, most often seen in spring and summer. It has developed a number of island races. Cuba and the Isle of Pines are inhabited by the typical subspecies characterised by a largely reddish brown upperside with broad dark brown borders, postdiscal lines almost continuous and outwardly flanked by white on the hindwing, the marginal spot in space 2 surmounted by yellow that sometimes spreads into space 3. *E. a. dowi* Clench from the Bahamas is similar above, greyer beneath; the hindwing postdiscal line broadly broken and prominently white-edged, the marginal spot in space 2 smaller than the yellow mark above it. In the Jamaican *E. a. pantoni* Comstock and Huntington the reddish brown of the upperside is reduced, the postdiscal lines are as in *E. a. dowi* but the marginal ocellus is capped with red instead of yellow. *E. a. boyeri* Comstock and Huntington of Hispaniola, Porto Rico and the Virgin Islands reverts rather to typical *angelia*, the hindwing postdiscal line very broken, but the ocellar spot in space 2 is very large with a smaller sharply defined orange capping. RANGE: Bahamas to Virgin Isles. TL: Cuba.

Early stages. Not known.

ELECTROSTRYMON DOMINICANA Lathy 1904

Dominican Hairstreak **Pl. 12**

Description. Fw ♂ 11–14 mm, ♀ 15 mm. Upperside very like that of *E. angerona,* but forewing with a dark shade below the costa, and hindwing without an orange lunule. Underside warm brown; forewing postdiscal line normal, submarginal line shadowy and faint; *hindwing postdiscal line red from costa to vein 4,* then black, interrupted, white-edged; submarginal line lunulate and followed by a short series of faintly darker marginal spots.

Distribution. Apparently confined to the island of Dominica and rather scarce. Flies with *E. angerona* and easily confused with it. The red postdiscal line on the hindwing is unique amongst West Indian Hairstreaks. RANGE and TL: Dominica.

Early stages. Not known.

ELECTROSTRYMON PAN Drury 1773

Pan's Hairstreak **Pl. 12**

Description. Fw ♂ and ♀ 12–16 mm. Sexes alike. No other known West Indian Hairstreak is *entirely 'black' above* and below, or has such *a large black eye-spot on the underside of the hindwing* just above the tail. On the underside the position of the postdiscal line is indicated by a faint shade on the forewing and by a few white specks on the hindwing. Between the submarginal line and the margin on the hindwing underside there is a series of barely discernible rounded dark spots; the inconspicuous black anal spot and the much larger spot above the single tail are both edged with orange-yellow.

Distribution. Pan's Hairstreak is only known from Jamaica, where it occurs in rather moist upland bushy country, chiefly in the spring and summer months. Settles high up, but not very fast on the wing. RANGE and TL: Jamaica.

Early stages. Not known.

Note. Of the four species of *Electrostrymon* found in the West Indies *E. pan* is the most easily recognised. It is almost sooty black above, and also is much darker than the others beneath. The latter also have much more white associated with the postdiscal line, and much smaller tail spots that are neither so circular nor outlined in yellow-orange.

LEPTOTES CASSIUS Cramer 1775   *Cassius Blue*   **Pl. 12**

Description. Fw ♂ 11–15 mm, ♀ 9–13 mm. Male upperside violet blue; hindwing sometimes with some short white streaks, eye-spots lacking, but sometimes showing through from below. Female largely white above with pure blue reflections over most of the forewing, broad blackish costal and outer marginal borders on the forewing and the outer border on the hindwing almost entirely replaced by marginal ocelli. Underside whitish, strongly marked with spots of brownish, especially along the outer margins of both wings, along the costa of the forewing and the base of the hindwing; *blue-scaled ocelli in spaces* 1C *and* 2.

Distribution. A common butterfly of the lowlands and moderate altitudes, especially attracted to flowers of *Bauhinia divaricata*. The mainland males are lighter blue on the upperside than those from the islands and have smaller eye-spots on the underside of the hindwing. In the Antilles three subspecies are recognised. The Virgin Islands are inhabited by *L. cassius catalina* Fabricius, which has much more blue on the upperside of the females and the underside rather more heavily marked with brown. The Greater Antilles and Bahamas are the home of *L. c. theonus* Lucas, a rather more lightly coloured race that also occurs on the Cayman Isles. The darkest race, *L. c. chadwicki* Comstock and Huntington, flies on Guadeloupe, Dominica and St Lucia. RANGE: Florida to Argentina. TL: Surinam.

Early stages. The fully grown slug-like caterpillar is green with russet overtones, has a slightly roughened appearance, two rows of white specks along the back and a clear green lateral stripe. It would seem that the russet colour may sometimes be replaced by pink, or that the colours vary in different parts of the insect's range. The lateral stripe may also be pink at times. Food plants consist exclusively of the flowers of a variety of plants, e.g. *Galactia pilosa*, *Plumbago*, *Indigofera*, *Desmodium*, *Crotalaria incana* and Lima beans.

Note. There are two species of *Leptotes* liable to be confused with *L. cassius*: *L. perkinsae* (p. 109) and *L. marina* (mainland only). The underside of *L. marina* tends to be more densely covered with rows of brownish spots, and less white, especially on the forewing. It is mentioned because it is alleged to have been taken on Porto Rico. *L. perkinsae* is at once separable from *L. cassius* because it has only one marginal eye-spot on the underside of the hindwing as against the two always present in *L. cassius*.

LEPTOTES PERKINSAE Kaye 1931

Miss Perkins's Blue **Pl. 12**

Description. Fw ♂ and ♀ 11–12 mm. Very similar to *Leptotes cassius*, but the upperside in the male darker blue. Underside much less patterned with brown and therefore displaying much more extensive white areas; *hindwing with only one marginal eye-spot*, i.e. the one in space 2, none at anal angle – *L. cassius* has two.

Distribution. A rare species, confined to Jamaica, where it flies with *L. cassius* with which it is easily confused. Widespread, with a preference for scrublands. RANGE: Jamaica. TL: Trelawney.

Early stages. Not known.

Note. The two West Indian species of *Leptotes* are readily separated from all the other W. Indian Blues by the very confused pattern of their underside markings.

HEMIARGUS HANNO Stoll 1790 *Hanno Blue* **Pl. 12**

Description. Fw ♂ and ♀ 9–10.5 mm. Upperside shining violaceous blue in male, black margins at most 1 mm wide; female brownish black above, shot with shining blue at the wing bases; both sexes with *single black marginal spot in space 2* of hindwing. Underside in both sexes light grey with a macular pattern of squarish darker white-edged markings; forewing with dark bar at cell-end, the postdiscal line succeeded by two submarginal rows of darker spots many of which are sagittate, and wing base free of markings; on the hindwing this general pattern is repeated, with a rather crowded effect, and there are in addition the following quite black spots, viz. two small ones close to the wing base, two larger ones against the costa, and a fifth very much larger spot (the eye-spot) at the margin in space 2; the last, like the two dusky anal spots, bears a few metallic scales.

Distribution. *H. hanno* occurs commonly all year round throughout the Antilles, in three subspecies. The distinguishing characters of these are by no means sharply defined and depend largely upon the relative sizes of the anal eye-spot and the extent of the white areas beyond the postdiscal band. In the Bahamas, Cuba and the Isle of Pines subspecies *filenus* Poey occurs; it has relatively large and bold underside markings. At the other end, and approaching the pale and somewhat insipid continental *H. hanno hanno*, *H. hanno watsoni* Comstock and Huntington 1943 flies, from Porto Rico (TL) southwards throughout the Lesser Antilles. The intermediate islands, Jamaica and Hispaniola are occupied by subspecies *H. h. ceraunus* Fabricius 1793 (TL: Jamaica). RANGE: southern U.S.A. to Argentina. TL: Surinam.

Early stages. In Jamaica the caterpillar has been reared on the leaves of Mimosa and on the buds and young fruits of *Crotalaria*. Other plants, on which eggs have been laid, in Florida, are *Chamaecrista brachiata*, *C. aspera* and *Abrus precatorius*. The caterpillar when full grown is yellowish green with dorsal and lateral stripes that may be darker green, pink or pale yellow. In Porto Rico it has been found feeding on *Macroptilium lathyroides* (poison pea).

HEMIARGUS AMMON Lucas 1857 *Lucas's Blue* **Pl. 12**

Description. Fw ♂ and ♀ 10–12 mm. Both sexes blue above, the female brighter but paler than the male and with wide black borders; veins delicately lined with darker scales; fringes faintly chequered; *two anal ocelli one of which is always capped prominently with red*, especially in the female. Underside pattern as normal for the genus *Hemiargus*; forewing with postdiscal line in the apical area broad, well-defined and flanked on both sides with white; white *postdiscal band of hindwing abruptly widened towards the margin in spaces 4 and 5* (diagnostic character), narrow and wedge-shaped in space 3; no black spot at the base of space 2, i.e. the basal row of black spots consists only of three, not four.

Distribution. Typical *H. ammon ammon* is a common Cuban insect and also flies on the Isle of Pines. In the Bahamas it is only certainly known from Nassau on Providence Island. The Cayman Islands population, *H. ammon erembis* Nabokov 1948, is distinguished by its large size and darker and bolder underside markings. It is abundant in open coastal areas on Grand Cayman, Little Cayman and Cayman Brac. RANGE: Bahamas to Cayman Isles. TL: Cuba.

Early stages. In Cuba the caterpillar has been found on Brasilete (*Caesalpinia*), but it has not been described.

Note. Similar species. The two ocelli on the underside of the hindwing at the anal angle at once distinguish *H. ammon* from *H. hanno*. Separation from *H. thomasi*, which also has two hindwing ocelli, is less easy: males of *H. thomasi* lack the pinkish yellow lunule (prominent in the female) that surmounts the marginal spot in space 2 on the upperside of the hindwing; on the underside the white postdiscal band on the hindwing is nearly uniform in width in *H. thomasi* (the spot in space 3 square rather than wedge-shaped) whereas the central portion is nearly twice as wide as the end portions in *ammon*; and there are 4 black spots in the basal row.

HEMIARGUS THOMASI Clench 1941
Thomas's Blue

Pl. 12

Description. Fw ♂ and ♀ 10–12 mm. Male upperside rather powdery blue; of the two small black hindwing marginal spots in spaces 1c and 2 the anterior one is capped with pink in the summer brood but not in the winter brood. Female upperside brown with a variable extent of blue suffusion that always leaves at least a wide dark margin; both bold black marginal spots capped with orange or pink and, between them and the wing apex, one or two series of white marks. Underside ground colour grey-brown marked as in *H. ammon* but with the following differences: on the forewing the postdiscal markings, especially towards the apex, are much less regular, not falling into regular concentric bands; on the *hindwing* the *white postdiscal band* is *narrower but more even in width*, and the *basal spots* are *four in number* of which the upper two are much the largest; the orange capping not larger than the black marginal spot it surmounts in space 2.

Distribution. *H. thomasi* occurs in five fairly well-marked races distinguished chiefly by variations in the orange caps of the marginal spots and in the development of the postdiscal bands on the underside. *H. thomasi bethunebakeri* Comstock and Huntington 1943, of Florida, occurs rarely as a stray in the Bahamas; it tends to have relatively broad postdiscal white bands on both wings. True Bahaman *thomasi* comes from Cat Island and has narrow postdiscal bands, the female extensively blue on the upperside. Another Bahaman subspecies, *H. t. bahamensis* Clench inhabits the more remote Crooked Island. Hispaniolan *H. t. noeli* Comstock and Huntington 1943 is quite distinct: underside strongly contrasting and white spots crisply outlined, postdiscal white band narrow and of irregular width, female upperside usually with a well developed double row of spots along the margin of the hindwing. In *H. t. woodruffi* Comstock and

Huntington 1943 (TL: Anegada) the upperside is rather dark blue in the males, and in the females the blue flush is restricted by a square black apical patch; on the hindwing the two dark marginal spots are relatively large in both sexes, and in the females there are two rows of whitish spots between them and the apical angle; underside ground colour darker brown than in *H. t. thomasi*, the forewing postdiscal band sharply angled at vein 5 and the white areas beyond small, hindwing band narrow, the spot in space 3 rectangular, not wedge-shaped, discal line wide and offset inwardly at vein 3: Porto Rico to St Kitts. RANGE: Florida to St Kitts, excluding Cuba and Jamaica. TL: Bahamas.

Early stages. Not known.

Note. The little group of small Blues comprising *Hemiargus ammon*, *H. thomasi* and *H. dominica* presents several puzzles not helped by uncertainties about the precise application of some of the names given to them by earlier authors. However, the treatment accorded them here tallies well with what is known of original sources and with the present known geographical distributions of the members of the group, which clearly all are derived from a common stock. Only in the Bahamas do any two members of the group occur, namely *H. ammon ammon* and *H. thomasi*, but so widely separated as not to overlap. Otherwise they are completely allopatric. The butterflies are probably not so rare as, in some places, they seem to be, being difficult to separate in the field from *Leptotes cassius* and *Hemiargus hanno* which largely overlap them.

HEMIARGUS DOMINICA Moeschler 1886
Jamaican Blue   **Pl. 12**

Description. Fw ♂ and ♀ 11 mm. Upperside blue, paler and with considerable white on the hindwing in the female. Male with a single orange-capped marginal spot on the hindwing, female with two such spots, but only the anterior one capped with orange, the other broadly ringed with white. Underside white, a short double postdiscal band on the forewing and the usual submarginal markings; hindwing with smudgy brownish markings in the basal half of the wing leaving a broad clear white band before the marginal markings; *no black basal spots*.

Distribution. Local and rather rare, but could easily be mistaken in the field for *Leptotes cassius* or *Leptotes perkinsae*. Its lack of black basal spots distinguishes it at once from *H. ammon* which, however, does not occur on Jamaica. It is interesting that in its underside pattern this rather rare little butterfly appears to have moved quite definitely towards the two species of *Leptotes* with which it flies, and away from the standard pattern of the genus. This suggests a mimetic evolutionary trend of survival benefit to the species. RANGE and TL: Jamaica.

Early stages. Not known.

PSEUDOCHRYSOPS BORNOI Comstock and Huntington
Haitian Tailed Blue   **Pl. 12**

Description. Fw ♂ 11 mm, ♀ 12 mm. Unique among West Indian Blues in possessing *a short filamentous tail at vein 2 of the hindwing*. Upperside greybrown shot with lavender in the male, with deeper purple-blue in the female, both sexes with a dark bar at the end of the forewing cell; hindwing with a full series of black marginal spots, the largest immediately above the tail. Underside pattern as in *Hemiargus* but with the following differences: the submarginal area of the hindwing is yellowish and carries a full series of dark spots each

Plate 13   PIERIDAE   *Scale:* × ⅔

1. **Ascia josephina**   *Giant White*   p. 115
   1a ♂, 1b ♀, *A.j. josephina*, Haiti. Very large and with a large black spot at forewing cell-end.

2. **Ascia menciae**   *Ramsden's Giant White*   116
   ♂ Holguin, Cuba. Forewing not falcate and with no black spot at cell-end.

3. **Ascia monuste**   *Great Southern White*   116
   Upperside with dark wedge-shaped marginal markings.
   3a ♂ *A. m. evonima*, Santiago, Cuba. June.
   3b ♀ *A. m. evonima*, Jamaica.

4. **Appias drusilla**   *Florida White*   117
   Upperside border of forewing in ♂ a fine black line, in ♀ wider but not formed of wedges.
   4a ♀ *A. d. boydi*, Haiti. March.
   4b ♂ *A. d. poeyi*, Tanamo, Cuba. March.
   4c ♀ *A. d. poeyi* ♀-f. *peregrina*, Rio Cana, Cuba. March.

5. **Melete salacia**   *Island Melete*   119
   Apex of forewing upperside black, wholly or mainly including a white spot. February.
   5a ♂ *M. s. cubana*, Santiago, Cuba. February.
   5b ♀ *M. s. cubana*, Holguin, Cuba.

6. **Zerene cesonia**   *Dog Face Butterfly*   131
   Popular name derived from profile of large yellow area on forewing.
   6a ♂ *Z. c. cesonia*, Cuba.
   6b ♀ *Z. c. cynops*, Haiti.

7. **Dismorphia spio**   *Haitian Mimic*   137
   ♂ Haiti. Forewing discal bar only tinged yellow near costa.

8. **Dismorphia cubana**   *Cuban Mimic*   137
   ♂ Sierra Maestra, Loma del Gato, 1000 m, Cuba. July. Forewing discal bar wholly clear yellow.

9. **Kricogonia lyside**   *Guayacán Sulphur*   131
   Forewing upperside with orange basal patch; ♂ hindwing often with grey bar.
   9a ♂ Nassau, Bahamas. July.
   9b ♀-f. *unicolor*.
   9c ♂ Port au Prince, Haiti.

1a

1b

3a

2

3b

4a

4b

4c

5a

6a

5b

7

6b

8

9a

9b

9c

14

1a
1b
2a
2b
3a
3b
4a
4b

5a
5b
5c
5d
6a
6b
7a
7b
8a
8b
9
10
11
12
13a
13b

1. **Eurema nise**   *Jamaican Sulphur*   p. 120
No spot at cell-end on forewing upperside; apical spots on
hindwing apex in female round.
1a ♂, 1b ♀, Polly Ground Track, Jamaica. February.

2. **Eurema larae**   *Sauco Sulphur*   121
Apical rusty spot on hindwing underside hugs the margin, not
round.
2a ♂ Cuba. 2b ♀ Hills south of Moca, District of Rio Yuma,
Dominican Republic.

3. **Eurema leuce**   *Hall's Sulphur*   121
Both wings clear lemon yellow.
3a ♂, 3b ♀, *E. l. antillarum*, St Kitts.

4. **Eurema venusta**   *Little Yellow*   122
Hindwing paler yellow than forewing.
4a ♂ 4b ♀, St Lucia.

5. **Eurema daira**   *Barrred Sulphur*   122
Dark bar along inner margin of forewing in male always grey;
♀ ground colour white or almost white.
5a ♂ wet season form, Bonao, Dominican Republic. November.
5b ♀ wet season form, Cuba.
5c ♂, 5d ♀ dry season form, Kingston, Jamaica.

6. **Eurema elathea**   *False Barred Sulphur*   123
Forewing dark bar black; female ground colour, at least on forewing, evenly pale yellow.
6a ♂ St Kitts. December. 6b ♀ 'Antilles'.

7. **Eurema lisa**   *Little Sulphur*   123
Outline of inner edge of dark borders is specific.
7a ♂ Jamaica. 7b ♀ Antigua. February.

8. **Eurema lucina**   *White Barred Sulphur*   124
Forewing with large square black apical patch. 8a ♂, 8b ♀, Cuba.

9. **Eurema priddyi**   *Priddy's Sulphur*   124
Forewing black border cut off squarely at vein 2. ♂ Haiti.

10. **Eurema albula**   *White Sulphur*   124
Almost unmarked, except for the dark forewing margin.
♂ St Vincent.

11. **Eurema amelia**   *Poey's Sulphur*   124
Forewing with wide triangular black apex tapering to anal angle.
♂ Cuba.

12. **Eurema portoricensis**   *Porto Rican Sulphur*   125
Black borders of both wings narrow but continuous. ♂ Porto Rico.

13. **Nathalis iole**   *Dainty Sulphur*   130
Forewing apex very broadly black, inner margin broadly dusky.
13a ♂, 13b ♀, Matanzas, Cuba. June.

B.W.I.   H pupilled with metallic green scales, the spot in space 2 by far the largest, black, and surrounded by a ring of metallic scales; three prominent white-ringed black costal spots (*Hemiargus* has only two).

Distribution. Haiti. Rare and local in a few localities in March and May. Reported from Porto Rico once, possibly a vagrant. The possession of a short filamentous tail is by no means uncommon in related Old World genera of Blues though admittedly a much more characteristic feature of the Hairstreak division of the Lycaenidae. RANGE: Hispaniola. TL: Haiti.

Early stages. Not known.

BREPHIDIUM EXILIS Boisduval 1852 *Pygmy Blue* **Pl. 12**
Description. Fw ♂ and ♀ 8–9 mm. Size alone is almost sufficient to identify this tiny butterfly. Upperside brown, with a variable amount of blue basal flush in both sexes; fringes white, or mostly white. Underside ground colour grey, the outer half of both wings, but especially the forewing, chocolate coloured; hindwing with a characteristic *continuous row of silver-studded black marginal spots*.

Distribution. Typical *Brephidium exilis* is confined to the mainland. It is replaced in the West Indies by two subspecies, *B. e. isophthalmia* Herrich-Schaeffer 1862 (TL: Cuba) of Cuba, the Bahamas, the Isle of Pines, Jamaica and Hispaniola, and *B. e. thompsoni* Carpenter and Lewis 1943, which is confined to the Cayman Islands. Both these differ from the mainland race principally on the underside, the colour contrast (basally grey, distally brown) being weaker than in the continental subspecies. In *B. e. thompsoni* the two parallel series of short white submarginal lines are brighter, sharper and closer together than in *B. e. isophthalmia*. *B. exilis barbouri* Clench 1943, which flies on Great Inagua, is only doubtfully separable, as a third subspecies. Very local but sometimes abundant in its very restricted habitats. RANGE: southern U.S.A. to northern S. America. TL: California.

Early stages. Caterpillars have been reared in California on various species of *Atriplex* and are very variable in colour. In Jamaica the butterfly is associated with the low-growing coastal plants, *Sesuvium portulacastrum* and *Batis maritima*.

BREPHIDIUM PSEUDOFEA Morrison 1873
Eastern Pygmy Blue
Description. Fw ♂ and ♀ 8–9 mm. Very similar to *B. exilis*, but *separable by the following characters:* fringes wholly brown; on the forewing underside the two parallel submarginal rows of white specks are much less conspicuous, sometimes largely lacking, in *B. pseudofea* as compared with *B. exilis*; across the base of the hindwing underside there is an easily recognised row of three brownish spots ringed with white which, in *B. exilis*, appear as brownish spots on a white field, or even as almost black.

Distribution. Bahamas, probably as a stray from Florida. RANGE: Gulf States of U.S.A.; Bahamas. TL: Florida.

Early stages. Not known.

The members of this cosmopolitan family are well named 'The Whites', for the best known species are nearly all white. Other common colours are yellow and orange, with black usually forming a border to the wings. Patterns are always simple on the upperside, very often leaf-like on the underside, especially in the dry or winter season forms. Sexual dimorphism is the rule, and often very marked. Females also are themselves often dimorphic, both 'yellow' and 'white' forms occurring within a species.

The Pieridae resemble the Papilionidae and Hesperiidae, and differ from all the other families of butterflies in having all six legs fully developed and functional. They differ from the Papilionidae in having two anal veins in the hindwing. Three major subfamilies occur in the West Indies: (i) the Dismorphiinae, containing only two species, both with long and very narrow forewings, disproportionately ample hindwings, and markings resembling the Heliconiinae; (ii) the Pierinae, comprising the true Whites of the genera *Pieris*, *Ascia*, *Appias* and *Melete* all of which have a fully developed precostal vein on the hindwing; and (iii) the Coliadinae with only a vestigial precostal vein or none, and including the genera *Phoebis*, *Anteos*, *Kricogonia*, *Zerene*, *Eurema* and *Nathalis*. The basic morphological characters that separate all these genera are not always easy to appreciate but the generic similarities that unite the species within each genus, such as size, colours and markings provide good guides for their recognition.

The favoured food plants of Pierid caterpillars are cresses (Cruciferae) and peas, beans, clovers and *Cassia*. The caterpillars are nearly all green, sometimes yellow-tinted, covered at most with very short fine hair, smooth and with longitudinal stripes, features that render them surprisingly difficult to see as they rest on the leaves of their food plants. Eggs are rather tall, slender, strongly ribbed and reticulate. The chrysalis rests upright, fastened by the cremastral hooks to a silken tail pad and secured by a silken girdle as well. Most pupae have a central projection, a sort of beak or nose, arising from the top of the head, and often the wing covers also project like a kind of keel.

The family includes a number of strongly migratory species, such as *Ascia monuste*, *Phoebis sennae*, *Anteos maerula* and several species of *Eurema*, particularly *Eurema lisa*.

ASCIA JOSEPHINA Godart 1819   *Giant White*   **Pl. 13**
Description. Fw ♂ 40–42 mm, ♀ 40–46 mm. Falcate. Male upperside silky white, the veins broadly bordered by chalky white streaks of white scent scales best seen against the light, a *large black circular spot at cell-end*. Female upperside faintly yellowish, additionally with a diffuse dark spot below vein 2, a double spot above vein 3, and cloudy marginal markings. Underside in both sexes with all hindwing and apex of forewing buff, the forewing marked as on the upperside of the female but without the spot in space 1b (below vein 2), the hindwing with a darker shade at the cell-end.
Distribution. *A. josephina josephina*, which occurs in Haiti and the Dominican Republic only, does not seem to be at all common there. In Jamaica it is replaced

by *A. josephina paramaryllis* Comstock 1942 (TL: Jamaica) which is slightly smaller, has a forewing that is not falcate but rounded and a much smaller spot at the end of the cell; female upperside yellower and devoid of discal markings; underside of hindwings and of forewing apex yellow, not buff, forewing without discal markings. It flies in the Blue Mountains at 5–800 ft in December to March and is scarce. *A. josephina krugii* Dewitz 1877 is smaller still, forewing about 35 mm, and resembles the Jamaican subspecies except that faint discal markings are sometimes present on the forewing; known only from south western Porto Rico, its type locality. Prefers the flowers of trees, especially *Bauhinia*. RANGE: confined to West Indies. TL: Hispaniola.
Early stages. Not known.

ASCIA MENCIAE Ramsden 1915   *Ramsden's Giant White* **Pl. 13**
Description. Fw ♂ and ♀ 29–32 mm. A good deal smaller than *Ascia josephina* which it much resembles. Forewing apex square, not falcate, and outer margin straight. The *cell-end spot*, so conspicuous on the forewing of *A. josephina*, *completely lacking*, but bands of modified scales present along the forewing veins.
Distribution. Cuba, near Guantanamo, April to September, commonest in late summer. St Lucia, Castries, January. The mainland race was described by Dixey in 1915 as *A. janeta*. RANGE: Cuba; Santa Lucia; Venezuela. TL: Cuba.
Early stages. Not known.

ASCIA MONUSTE Linnaeus 1764
Great Southern White   **Pl. 13**
Description. Fw ♂ and ♀ 28–32 mm. Male upperside white, *the outer margins with distinctive black wedge-shaped markings centred on the veins.* Female upperside white, very pale yellowish or even pale grey, the marginal markings often larger than in the males. Underside white, or with ground colour of hindwing and apex of forewing pale yellow, with or without streaky grey-brown markings on and between the veins and in the cell, and cloudy markings towards the base of spaces 2 and 4. In life the tip of the antenna is turquoise blue.
Distribution. *A. monuste monuste*, described above, only reaches the West Indies in the Lesser Antilles, especially in the Grenadines, Grenada and Barbados. There are, however, two truly indigenous Caribbean subspecies. From the Bahamas through Cuba, Hispaniola and Jamaica to Porto Rico the northern subspecies, *A. m. evonima* Boisduval 1836 (TL: Cuba) prevails. It is as large as *A. m. monuste* or even at times larger. On the forewing upperside the marginal wedges are smaller especially towards the apex, particularly in the males, in which the underside is only very rarely pure white, generally pale yellow, especially in specimens with striate grey-brown markings. The females tend to be more heavily striate on the underside; and in the grey migratory form, f. *phileta* Fabricius, which sometimes spreads to the Antilles from the southern United States, both surfaces may be almost uniformly grey and the striate markings hardly visible. The area between the Virgin Islands and St Vincent is occupied by the much smaller subspecies *A. m. virginia* Godart 1819, forewing 22–28 mm (TL: not given, taken as St Vincent). It differs markedly in having the marginal black wedges greatly reduced in size or even absent, and the apex of the forewing and the whole of the hindwing on the underside bright ochreous with no trace of striate markings. RANGE: southern U.S.A. to Argentina. TL: 'Exteris terris', *recte* Surinam.

Fig. 13. *Ascia monuste.* **a**, ♂, **b**, ♀ *A.m.phileta*, migratory form, Nassau, Bahamas, April; **c**, ♂ *A.m.virginia*, Montserrat, February, **d**, ♀ St Lucia. × ⅔.

Early stages. Caterpillar light yellow, with a dark greenish to blackish wide lateral stripe and numerous very small black dots many of which are grouped in subsidiary longitudinal or transverse bands. Food plants Cruciferae, especially *Brassica* and *Cleome*, also *Tropaeolum*.

APPIAS DRUSILLA Cramer 1777 *Florida White* **Pl. 13**

Appias drusilla ranges from Florida to southern Brazil (TL: Surinam) and occurs in the West Indies in the following five subspecies:

1 **A. drusilla poeyi** Butler 1872. Fw ♂ 26–31 mm, ♀ 24–30 mm. *Male* upperside silky white, pearly towards wing base, forewing *costa finely black-edged*; underside shiny pale pinkish yellow, the forewing usually with a small yellow basal area. *Female* dimorphic, but with intermediates, either (*a*) like the male but yellowish, especially on the hindwing, the forewing with a narrow black border, f. *peregrina* Röber, apparently a dry season form; or (*b*) typically larger with wide *uneven border on forewing upperside* and with three quarters of the cell black or dark grey, the hindwing upperside yellowish and with grey wedges at the ends of the veins – the wet season form; both female forms have the base of the forewing yellow on the underside.

Distribution. Bahamas (doubtfully resident). Cuba: Santiago, Oriente, Habana (TL), Holguin, Tanamo, etc., in February and March, and no doubt in other months. Cayman Isles, May and June.

2 **A. drusilla castalia** Fabricius 1793 (syn. *jacksoni* Kaye 1920) (TL: Jamaica). Slightly smaller than *A. d. poeyi* as a rule, the male like the female of that subspecies, female with forewing upperside yellower, markings smaller in both seasonal forms. Occurs only in Jamaica, where it is fairly common in the Blue Mountains in February and August.

3 **A. drusilla boydi** Comstock 1943 (TL: Hispaniola). Indistinguishable from *A. d. poeyi* except in the female of the wet season form, which has the whole of the cell on the forewing upperside black. Flies in Haiti, the Dominican Republic, Porto Rico, the Virgin Isles, St Thomas and St Lucia.

4 **A. drusilla comstocki** Dillon 1947 (TL: La Haut, Dominica). Both sexes like *A. d. castalia* but pale greenish white especially in the female. Male underside glossy dull cream on hindwing and at forewing apex. Female upperside black border 2.5 mm wide at apex, thence 1 mm but irregular to anal angle, underside creamy areas paler but more glossy. Dominica in November to February.

5 **A. drusilla monomorpha** Hall 1936 (TL: Grenada). Both sexes wholly white without any black scaling at apex or base of forewing, and without yellow at base of forewing beneath. Grenada.

Early stages. The caterpillar is dark green on the back, greyish green along the sides, the back with numerous short hairs and rather granular in appearance. Food plants Capers.

APPIAS PUNCTIFERA d'Almeida 1939 *D'Almeida's White*
Description. Fw ♂ and ♀ 26–29 mm. White like *A. drusilla* but *forewing with a short black bar at cell-end* which is larger on under than upperside. Underside glistening white, not creamy. Female hindwing upperside creamy white with or without fuscous border; on the underside of the hindwing the yellow basal area is larger than in the male and fills at least half the cell. Not seen.
Distribution. Porto Rico and Virgin Islands, March, April, June and July.
RANGE: Porto Rico and Virgin Islands. TL: Porto Rico.
Early stages. Not known.

PONTIA PROTODICE Boisduval and Leconte 1829
Chequered White
Description. Fw ♂ and ♀ 23–25 mm. Upperside white; *forewing with quadrilateral black mark at cell-end enclosing white veins*; postdiscal spot in space 3

Fig. 14. *Pontia protodice*. ♂ Nevada, N. America.

larger than the subapical spots. On the underside of the forewing there is an additional rather large black spot below vein 2, and the veins towards the apex are lined grey; on the hindwing all veins are lined with grey-green stripes which vary in intensity according to the brood. Female more heavily marked than the male and, on the underside with a series of dark grey wedges on the veins with their bases resting on the margin.

Distribution. Occurred in 1933 and 1934 near Havana in Cuba, probably as a sporadic incursion from Florida, and not truly a resident. Not known elsewhere in the islands. RANGE: U.S.A. TL: New York.

Early stages. The caterpillar is striped alternately with yellow and purplish green and feeds on a wide variety of cruciferous plants.

PIERIS RAPAE Linnaeus 1758   *European Small White*

Description. Fw ♂ and ♀ 23–27 mm. Smaller than any other 'White' occurring in the West Indies. Forewing upperside in *male without*, in *female with grey spot in space* 1b as well as in space 3; on underside apex of forewing and all hindwing yellowish with grey dusting.

Fig. 15. *Pieris rapae.* ♂ Ithaca, New York, August.

Distribution. Bermuda, no doubt introduced, common. Also taken once in a greengrocer's shop in Kingston, Jamaica, probably imported with vegetables from Florida. RANGE: Europe, N. Africa and temperate Asia; N. America; Australia and New Zealand. TL: Sweden.

Early stages. The inconspicuous green caterpillar feeds on various Cruciferae such as cresses, also on mignonette and nasturtium, and is sometimes a pest on cabbages. In southern localities several broods every year.

MELETE SALACIA Godart 1819   *Island Melete*   **Pl. 13**

Description. Fw ♂ 24–28 mm, ♀ 25–27 mm. Upperside white in male, slightly yellowish in female; underside of hindwing ochreous, especially in female. May be confused with *Appias drusilla* (p. 117), but readily distinguished by the *black line on the underside of the hindwing* that runs from near apex straight to anal angle, though sometimes reduced to a mark on the costa in the dry season form. The forewing black triangular apical patch encloses (female) or is divided by (male) a pale spot or series of spots.

Distribution. Typical *M. s. salacia* is confined to Dominican Republic and Haiti, where it flies at least in April and November. In the Cuban subspecies, *M. s. cubana* Fruhstorfer 1908, the dark markings on the underside are less

intensely black – distributed throughout the island, January to June and no doubt in other months as well. RANGE: Cuba and Hispaniola. TL: Hispaniola.
Early stages. The caterpillar has been found feeding on *Petitia* (Roble-guayo) and on *Phoradendron Randiae* (a mistletoe) but has not been described.

EUREMA EUTERPIFORMIS Munroe 1947   *False Lisa Sulphur*

Description. Fw ♂ 17–18 mm. In general appearance very similar to *Eurema lisa*, but *both wings brilliant clear yellow*, not greenish yellow, and the broad black border of the forewing, instead of tapering towards the anal angle, ends broadly on the inner margin. The *small black spot at the end of the forewing cell*, characteristic of *E. lisa*, *is lacking*. The female is not known.

Distribution. Haiti: Kenscoff, 4800 ft, October; Ennery, 2500 ft, August; Furcy, 5000 ft, September. Dominican Republic: La Vega, June. Local. RANGE: Hispaniola only. TL: Haiti.

Early stages. Not known.

Fig. 16. *Eurema euterpiformis*. ♂ Furcy, Haiti, 5,000 ft., September. × 1½.

EUREMA NISE Cramer 1775   *Jamaican Sulphur*   **Pl. 14**

Description. Fw ♂ and ♀ 14–15 mm. Male upperside clear rather deep yellow, female slightly paler; forewing border 2–3 mm wide at apex, tapering towards, but in winter form rarely reaching, anal angle; *no spot at cell-end*; hindwing border reduced to minute spots at the ends of the veins, the submarginal area sometimes flushed orange. The underside markings follow the usual pattern in the genus, but the forewing apex is always clear yellow and on the hindwing the *rusty marginal patch in space 6*, characteristic of the female, *is round and barely touches the margin*.

Distribution. Confined to Jamaica, in the typical subspecies, *E. nise nise*, and very local in Portland, St Thomas, Manchester and Westmoreland. Reported only in January and February, i.e. the winter brood, but a summer brood must also occur. A shy species frequenting woodland margins and disappearing into shrubs when alarmed. Long thought to be extinct in Jamaica, or to have been wrongly reported from the island in the first place. From a distributional point of view it is strange that *E. nise* has not been recorded from any other of the islands, especially Cuba. RANGE: southern U.S.A. to Argentina. TL: Jamaica.

Early stages. In the Brazilian subspecies the egg is tall, thin, pointed and very pale yellow. Caterpillar in final instar green, with short white pubescence and a whitish lateral line, the back turning ashy green towards pupation time. Food plant *Mimosa pudica*.

EUREMA CHAMBERLAINI Butler 1897   *Chamberlain's Sulphur*
Description. Fw ♂ and ♀ 14–15 mm. Differs from *E. nise nise* superficially only in that the colour of the upperside is rather more orange, but *at the base of the forewing on the underside*, and hidden beneath the costa of the hindwing, there is *a triangular area of brilliant white modified scales*, which is lacking in *E. nise*. Female similar but paler, the pink marginal patch on hindwing underside round as in *E. nise*.
Distribution. The original male taken by Neville Chamberlain is believed to have come from Andros Island. The typical subspecies also occurs on New Providence, Watling and Crooked Islands. *E. c. mariguanae* Bates 1934 (TL: Mariguana Island) male is brilliant orange and has a black spot at cell-end on forewing; female yellow, the apex of forewing and outer margin of hindwing orange. *E. c. inaguae* Munroe 1950 (TL: Inagua Island) is similar but lacks the cell spot. All dated specimens noted have been taken in the winter months. *E. c. banksi* Clench 1942 (TL: Cat Island) is paler in both sexes than any other named subspecies and has broader darker margins; a lemon-yellow stripe adjacent to and parallel to the dark outer margin of the forewing of the male upperside is unique. Other islands also have distinctive populations. RANGE: Bahamas. TL: Andros Island.
Early stages. Not known.

EUREMA LARAE Herrich-Schaeffer 1862   *Sauco Sulphur*   **Pl. 14**
Description. Fw ♂ and ♀ 15–17 mm. Suggests a small *E. leuce antillarum*. Male forewing border relatively broader at apex, less clear-cut on inner edge, the costa very narrowly red (yellow with some black scales in *E. leuce*) between wing base and apical patch; hindwing with *a red dot at the extremity of each vein*; female forewing apical patch much larger, 4–5 mm at widest; hindwing with clear deep orange oval apical patch and orange dots at ends of veins 4 and 5 at least. Underside deeper yellow on hindwings; in male the costal red line extends round apex to vein 2, the apex diffusely reddish; female similar but forewing apex broadly smooth rust-red, not mottled, and *hindwing apical patch browner than on upperside*; both sexes with shadowy discal markings on hindwing.
Distribution. A rare and local species known only from the neighbourhood of the city of Trinidad, Holguin, and near Bayamo, in August, in Cuba; from the district of Rio Yuma in the Dominican Republic; and Andros Island in the Bahamas. RANGE: Bahamas, Cuba and Hispaniola. TL: Cuba.
Early stages. Gundlach considered that the food plant might be Sauco amarillo (*Tecoma stans*, Bignoniaceae) to the flower of which the butterfly was much attracted, unlike other species, most of which frequent mud puddles, but the caterpillar is not known.

EUREMA LEUCE Boisduval 1836   *Hall's Sulphur*   **Pl. 14**
Description. Fw ♂ and ♀ 18–20 mm. So like *Eurema dina* in markings that it has been considered for many years to be its southern subspecies, but strikingly different in colour, being *clear lemon-yellow*. There are also important anatomical differences. Of the three West Indian subspecies *E. leuce antillarum* Hall 1936 (TL: St Kitts) is the best known. It has a very narrow black border on the forewing but no marginal markings on the hindwing. It occurs also on Dominica, St Lucia, St Martin and Guadeloupe. *E. l. sanjuanensis* Watson 1938 (TL: Porto Rico) has an even narrower forewing border; only one specimen seems to be

known, taken at San Juan in July. The most interesting race, *E. l. memulus* Butler 1871 (TL: Haiti), flies on Haiti, where it overlaps the very similar *E. dina mayobanex* (p. 126) thus confirming the distinctness of these two species. It is more orange than other races of *E. leuce*, has wider black borders, traces of marginal orange on the hindwings and, in the female, a large orange apical patch on the upperside of the hindwing; rare but widely distributed at 500–2500 ft.

Distribution. Flies freely and actively in bright sun and is much attracted to the flowers of the 'liane corail' (*Antigonon leptotus*). RANGE: Hispaniola to Argentina. TL: Missions de l'Uruguay, Brazil.

Early stages. Although a common butterfly throughout most of its range the early stages and food plants are not known.

EUREMA VENUSTA *Little Yellow*   Pl. 14

Eurema venusta ranges from Windward Isles and C. America to Para and Ecuador. It occurs in the West Indies in the following subspecies:

Eurema venusta emanona Dillon 1947

Description. Fw ♂ and ♀ 16–18 mm. Readily distinguished from all other West Indian species of *Eurema* because, in the male particularly, the *forewings are butter yellow, the hindwings very pale yellow* or almost white, and the dark borders are narrow. This difference is also present in the female but to a very much lesser degree. On the underside of the hindwing in the female there is usually a rusty red patch near the apex, not in space 6 as is usually the case, but in space 7. Males with yellowish hindwings are commonest in Dominica, Martinique and St Lucia; in St Vincent and Grenada white hindwings predominate, but this difference may in fact be more seasonal than geographical. The width of the black border certainly varies seasonally, being widest in the wet season.

Distribution. From Guadeloupe to Grenada, common. Not recorded from Barbados. Has a slow but deceptive zig-zag flight close to the ground in open sunny places; attracted especially to *Mimosa*. TL: Dominica.

Early stages. Have not been described, but the caterpillar is known to feed on *Mimosa*.

EUREMA DAIRA Godart 1819   *Barred Sulphur*   Pl. 14

Eurema daira ranges from south-east U.S.A. to Brazil. It occurs in the West Indies in the following subspecies:

Eurema daira palmira Poey 1819

Description. Fw ♂ and ♀ 15–18 mm. Occurs in two distinct seasonal forms. Wet season form *palmira*: in the male the anterior edge of the curved *grey bar extending along the inner margin of the forewing* is bounded above by the lower margin of the cell and by vein 2, and below is separated from the actual margin by a continuous orange stripe that reaches to the very base of the wing; the hindwing is broadly black-bordered. The female associated with this form is white and lacks the black bar on the forewing. In the dry season f. *ebriola* Poey the male has a much reduced bar that does not touch vein 2 or the cell but is still grey, the forewing costal area is brighter and the hindwing border reduced to a small apical patch and dots or lines at the ends of the veins. The female of this form has yellowish forewings especially towards the apex and creamy hindwings with markings as in the male. The undersides in both sexes are white in the wet season forms, reddish sandy in the dry season. TL: Cuba.

Distribution. Cuba, Jamaica, Hispaniola and Porto Rico to Grenada and

Barbados, usually common, often abundant, the wet season form *palmira* from spring to autumn, the dry form *ebriola* in the other months, but some overlap not uncommon. The N. American subspecies *E. daira daira* Godart, in which the hindwings are yellow like the forewings, seems occasionally to occur in Cuba and the Bahamas as a casual vagrant from Florida where it is common.

Early stages. Caterpillar light green, including the head, the surface covered with minute white dots, lateral line straw-coloured, underside paler greenish white. Food plants *Desmodium, Meibomia*, etc.

EUREMA ELATHEA Cramer 1775
False Barred Sulphur   **Pl. 14**

Description. Fw ♂ and ♀ 14–18 mm, very variable. In both sexes confusingly like *E. daira*. The male can always be distinguished by the fact that the *bar on inner margin of forewing is black, not grey:* it is also straighter and narrower, never touches vein 2, and dips to touch the inner margin 3 or 4 mm from the wing base thus cutting short the orange marginal stripe. There is no certain way of distinguishing the females, but two features may help: in the forewing, in the wet season form, the disc is more often clear white in *E. daira*, more widely yellow-flushed in *elathea*; and on the hindwing in the dry season form the shadowy discal band seems generally to be more widely broken on vein 4 in *E. daira* than in *E. elathea*. The wet season form is typical *elathea* and heavily marked. In the dry season form *elathides* Staudinger the bar in the male is greatly reduced in extent and both sexes have sandy undersides.

Distribution. Bahamas (Great Inagua Island), Cuba, Cayman Islands, Jamaica, Haiti and Dominican Republic, Porto Rico, St Kitts, St Lucia. Less common than *E. daira*. RANGE: Nicaragua to Paraguay. TL: 'N. and C. America'.

Early stages. The caterpillar is clear green with dense whitish pubescence, a dark shadow along the back and greenish grey underside. Food plant *Zornia* (Brazil) and *Stylosanthes* (Jamaica).

EUREMA LISA Boisduval and Leconte 1829   *Little Sulphur* **Pl. 14**

Description. Fw ♂ and ♀ 17–18 mm. Male sulphur yellow, with *complete black borders* to both wings, very broad at forewing apex, *rather jagged on inner edge*, a fine black line nearly always present along cell-end. Female much paler, sometimes white (f. *centralis* Herrich-Schaeffer), the forewing border ending at vein 2; hindwing border broad at apex, thence usually fragmented. Underside uniformly yellow, the black dot at the cell-end on each wing is characteristic as is also the *round* red apical spot, which only just touches the margin on the hindwing, always present in the female but sometimes lacking in the male.

Distribution. In Bermuda and the Bahamas the species occurs only in the continental subspecies *E. lisa lisa*. On many occasions swarms have been reported to alight on Bermuda. It may be that Bahaman records are due to similar events to some extent. In the rest of the West Indies, from Cuba and the Cayman Islands to Barbados, *E. lisa euterpe* Ménétriés occurs. This differs constantly in its smaller size, has less heavy black borders, and the forewing costa towards the base, at least in the males, is less heavily dusted with grey scales. RANGE: eastern U.S.A. to Costa Rica, and throughout the West Indies. TL: United States.

Early stages. The grass-green downy caterpillar feeds on a wide variety of leguminous plants such as clovers, peas and beans, *Trifolium*, *Cassia*, *Mimosa*, etc. Several annual broods.

EUREMA LUCINA Poey 1853 *White Barred Sulphur* **Pl. 14**
Description. Fw ♂ and ♀ 14–17 mm. Upperside ground colour *white*; forewing upperside *with broad black apical area ending abruptly on vein 2 and deeply stepped along vein 4*; hindwing with smaller black apical patch which may end at vein 5 or extend most of the way towards anal angle. Forewing cell in male wholly, in female only partially, filled milky grey, male with, female without broad grey streak along inner margin. On the underside the apical area of forewing is green, sprinkled with black and there is a black bar at cell-end, the hindwing has faint traces of discal markings; in the female these markings are intensified and the underside of the hindwing is pale buff to yellowish, densely sprinkled with dark scales. Form *fornsi* Klots is an extreme dry season form in which the black apical patch on the hindwing is reduced to two short lines along the veins and the whole underside except the disc of the forewing is intensely sandy greenish.
Distribution. Widespread, chiefly in rather open country. RANGE and TL: Cuba.
Early stages. Not known.

EUREMA PRIDDYI Lathy 1898 *Priddy's Sulphur* **Pl. 14**
Description. Fw ♂ and ♀ 12–14 mm. The smallest *Eurema* in the West Indies. Like *E. lucina* but yellow, the *black forewing border ending squarely on or just below vein 2*; cell and inner margin devoid of grey suffusion; hindwing border usually reduced to black lines along the veins, though it may develop at the apex. On the underside the forewing disc is pale yellow, hindwing white or sandy, speckled, markings as in *E. lucina*.
Distribution. Apparently a rare and local species, only recorded from Port au Prince, Haiti, in March. RANGE and TL: Haiti.
Early stages. Not known.

EUREMA ALBULA Cramer 1775 *White Sulphur* **Pl. 14**
Description. Fw ♂ and ♀ 15–18 mm. Both sexes *pure white above and below*. Forewing black border ends rather bluntly at or shortly before anal angle; hindwing occasionally with traces of a narrow border. Underside usually without markings, though faint traces of discal markings may sometimes be present. Markings tend to be heaviest in the rainy season.
Distribution. In the West Indies only known from Antigua and St Vincent. Flies deceptively slow and close to the ground in moist shady places. RANGE: Mexico to Argentina. TL: Surinam.
Early stages. Full grown caterpillar (Brazil) green on back, ashen near the whitish lateral line, clear yellowish green beneath, pubescent and transversely ridged. Food plant *Cassia*.

EUREMA AMELIA Poey 1851 *Poey's Sulphur* **Pl. 14**
Description. Fw ♂ and ♀ 14–15 mm. White, suggestive of a small *E. albula*, but on the forewing there is a *small spot or bar at cell-end and the dark border* (3 mm wide at apex) *extends uninterrupted to the anal angle* and is continued on the hindwing also from apex to anal angle, about 1 mm wide. On the underside the

forewing costa and apex and the whole of the hindwing are yellow, and both wings have a pair of black specks at the end of the cell.
Distribution. Said to have been abundant in its type locality. Now apparently rare. RANGE: Cuba. TL: Cuba, Cienega de Zapata.
Early stages. Not known.

EUREMA PORTORICENSIS Dewitz 1877
Porto Rican Sulphur **Pl. 14**
Description. Fw ♂ and ♀ 12–18 mm. Male butter yellow, with *continuous black border to both wings*, 2 mm wide on forewing apex, tapering thence to anal angle, narrower on hindwing; on hindwing underside a mottled brown triangular apical patch extends along the margin from vein 6 to vein 8 and has a chain of smaller spots running from its apex straight to the middle of the inner margin, as in *E. messalina* and *E. pyro*. Female similar, but upperside black border shorter on forewing and absent from hindwing.
Distribution. Widespread in, and confined to, Porto Rico, especially at higher levels, but not common. December to March, May to August. RANGE and TL: Porto Rico.
Early stages. Not known.

EUREMA PYRO Godart 1819 *Fiery Sulphur* **Pl. 15**
Description. Fw ♂ and ♀ 13–17 mm. *Deep orange, with moderate black border to both wings in male, to forewing only in female.* Underside pale yellow, male without, female with, mottled apical areas, especially large on hindwing on which a transverse shadowy band runs from the apex of the mottled patch to the middle of the inner margin; other faint markings the same in both sexes. In form *hyona* Ménétriés 1832 the basal two-thirds of the upperside of the hindwing is irregularly clear yellow.
Distribution. Known only from Haiti and the Dominican Republic: Port au Prince, La Vega at 700 to 900 metres, Puerto Plata, Mt Isabella, April, June, October to December. RANGE: Hispaniola only. TL (not stated): Haiti.
Early stages: Not known.

EUREMA MESSALINA Fabricius 1787 *Shy Sulphur* **Pl. 15**
Description. Fw ♂ and ♀ 12–18 mm, very variable in size. White. Forewing apex rounded, the black border wide from costa to space 5, thence half as wide, but not tapered, to anal angle; *hindwing border continuous from apex to anal angle and about 1 mm wide*. In the female the forewing border is sharply angled in space 4 then tapers quickly to vein 2; hindwing border reduced to small marginal patch in space 6. Underside yellow, except forewing disc which is white, sprinkled with black scales; in the female the apex of both wings has a large angular marginal red and lilac mottled area with a black patch at its inner apex; in the male these markings are sometimes equally well developed but more usually they are somewhat reduced.
Distribution. Cuba, throughout; Cayman Isles; Jamaica, widespread and common. A slow-flying bush-loving insect not attracted to mud puddles. In the Bahamas the underside markings are often much reduced or even barely indicated, subspecies *E. messalina blakei* Maynard 1891, particularly in the north-western and central islands. RANGE: Bahamas to Jamaica. TL: Jamaica.

Early stages. The caterpillar is very like that of *Eurema daira* and feeds on *Desmodium*.

EUREMA DINA Poey 1833   *Bush Sulphur*   **Pl. 15**
Description. Fw ♂ and ♀ 15–22 mm. Deep yellow or orange-yellow, or at least tinted with orange, the black border narrow and varying from island to island, less definite in the female than the male, only present on the hindwing in the Porto Rican subspecies. Underside in the male without markings except for *two cell-end dots on hindwing* and, rarely, traces of discal markings; the *female has* in addition *a rusty red apical patch on each wing, that on the hindwing triangular* in shape with one side based on the margin between veins 5 and 6.
Distribution. *E. dina* is a fast flying, zig-zagging butterfly that favours dense bushland and has developed a number of very distinct subspecies. *E. dina helios* Bates 1934 (TL: Bahamas) is uniformly orange with very narrow borders and appears to be common, as is *E. dina dina* of Cuba, in which the bright orange flush is confined to the outer area of the hindwings and the border is about 2 mm wide. *E. dina parvumbra* Kaye 1936 (TL: Jamaica) is the largest race, deep yellow with very little marginal orange flush and border about 1 mm wide in the male; the female however has a larger apical black patch which is stepped on its inner edge. The very rare Haitian *E. dina mayobanex* Bates 1939 (TL: Haiti) is distinguished by being dark orange in colour and having a black border on the hindwing, which none of the other races has. RANGE: Mexico to Panama; Bahamas to Hispaniola. TL: Cuba.
Early stages. Not known.

EUREMA ADAMSI Lathy 1898   *Adams' Sulphur*   **Pl. 15**
Description. Fw ♂ and ♀ 17–20 mm. Forewing pointed. Male white, female creamy white. *Male with wide black borders to both wings* in wet season form, much reduced in dry season form especially on hindwing. *Female borders reduced to a broad triangle at apex of forewing.* In both sexes the underside is light yellow in the wet season, deep ochreous in the dry season with the apex and costa of the forewing and the whole of the hindwing heavily sprinkled with minute reddish striae. The pointed forewing and richly mottled underside readily distinguish *E. adamsi* from other white West Indian species of *Eurema*.
Distribution. Known only from Jamaica where it is widespread in the uplands, e.g. Blue Mountains, Port Royal Mountains, Manchester and Mile Gully Mountains, Spur Hill, at elevations above 2500 ft. Flies fast and difficult to catch amongst the dense bushes it frequents in country where movement is not easy. RANGE and TL: Jamaica.
Early stages. Not known.

EUREMA GRATIOSA Doubleday 1847
Venezuelan Sulphur   **Pl. 15**
Description. Fw ♂ and ♀ 19–21 mm. Male *forewing yellow, hindwing white*, both wings with *wide black borders* with jagged inner edges; hindwing with large orange-yellow apical patch. Both sexes with hindwing angled at vein 3. Female forewing paler, the black border much reduced and not reaching anal angle, hindwing border reduced to patches at the ends of the veins. Underside yellow in both sexes; forewing with red flecks along the costa; hindwing with a linear

mark at mid-costa and red discal markings, only prominent in the dry season, running form near apex straight towards inner margin.
Distribution. Found on St Lucia in 1966 and 1967. Not reported from any other island. Possibly a casual or chance introduction from Venezuela, Trinidad or Tobago. RANGE: Panama to Venezuela. TL: Venezuela.
Early stages. Not known. Food plant said to be *Cassia*.

EUREMA BOISDUVALIANA Felder 1865
Boisduval's Sulphur

Description. Fw ♂ 18–23 mm, ♀ 20–24 mm. Male upperside with *both wings sulphur yellow and very wide black borders*, the hindwing also with an ochreous suffusion at apical angle against the black border. The female upperside is paler, the forewing black border apically very wide but not reaching the anal angle, the hindwing border reduced to a series of short black streaks along veins (4), 5, 6 and 7. On the underside both sexes are alike, the extent of the limited rust-red markings varying with the season.
Distribution. Boisduval's Sulphur has been taken in Cuba at Santa Clara in Central Soledad. It is closely related to *E. gratiosa* (p. 126) but differs in having the ground colour of the hindwing entirely yellow like the forewing, not white as in *E. gratiosa*; and the black borders of the male even wider, especially on the hindwing in space 4. It is also usually rather larger. Its occurrence in Cuba could well be due only to a chance invasion which did not lead to its establishment in that island. RANGE: Mexico to Costa Rica. TL: Mexico.
Early stages. Not known.

Fig. 17. *Eurema boisduvaliana*. ♂ San Pedro Sula, Honduras.

EUREMA PROTERPIA Fabricius 1775   *Jamaican Orange*   **Pl. 15**
Description. Fw ♂ and ♀ 21–24 mm, but very variable, dwarfs and giants not uncommon. Vívid deep orange. Male unique in its *broad black forewing costal border*, veins black and margins dusky; female duller orange with broad apical black border which extends to anal angle but only halfway along costa. In the dry season form, f. *gundlachia* Poey, only the extremities of the veins are black, the hindwing is produced to a point or a short tail, and the underside develops a cryptic leaf pattern. Female *E. proterpia* may perhaps be confused with female *E. nicippe*, but the angular hindwing of the former and the pale area at the anal angle of the forewing of the latter readily distinguish them.
Distribution. Widespread in Cuba, less so in Hispaniola, and in Jamaica now restricted to very few localities. An upland species, males strongly attracted to muddy puddles, females to flowers. RANGE: Texas to Peru. TL: Jamaica.

Plate 15   **PIERIDAE**

1. **Eurema pyro**   *Fiery Sulphur*   p. 125
   Deep orange red, black borders continuous on both wings in ♂,
   confined to forewing in ♀.
   1a ♂ Mt Isabella, Dominican Republic. May.
   1b ♀ Port au Prince, Haiti.

2. **Eurema messalina**   *Shy Sulphur*   125
   Pattern of markings almost as in *E. pyro*, but ground colour white.
   2a ♂ *E. m. blakei*, Nassau, Bahamas. October.
   2b ♀ *E. m. messalina*, Holguin, Cuba.

3. **Eurema dina**   *Bush Sulphur*   126
   Hindwing underside with two minute dots at cell-end.
   3a ♂ Nassau, Bahamas. July.
   3b ♀ Holguin, Cuba.

4. **Eurema adamsi**   *Adams' Sulphur*   126
   Upperside black borders exceptionally wide on both wings in ♂;
   reduced to apical triangle on forewing in ♀.
   4a ♂, 4b ♀, Newcastle, Jamaica. September.

5. **Eurema gratiosa**   *Venezuelan Sulphur*   126
   Very like *E. adamsi,* but ground colour yellow.
   5a ♂ Caracas.
   5b ♀ Merida, Venezuela.

6. **Eurema proterpia**   *Jamaican Orange*   127
   Forewing costa with wide black border in ♂.
   6a ♂ wet season form, Cuba.
   6b ♀ wet season form, Haiti.
   6c dry season form *gundlachia*, Haiti.

7. **Eurema nicippe**   *Black-bordered Orange*   130
   Hindwing black border with prominent tooth in space 4.
   7a ♂ Santiago, Cuba. February.
   7b ♀ Cuba.

8. **Eurema nicippiformis**   *Haitian Black-bordered Orange*   131
   Hindwing black border not toothed in space 4.
   8a ♂ Port au Prince, Haiti.
   8b ♀ Haiti.

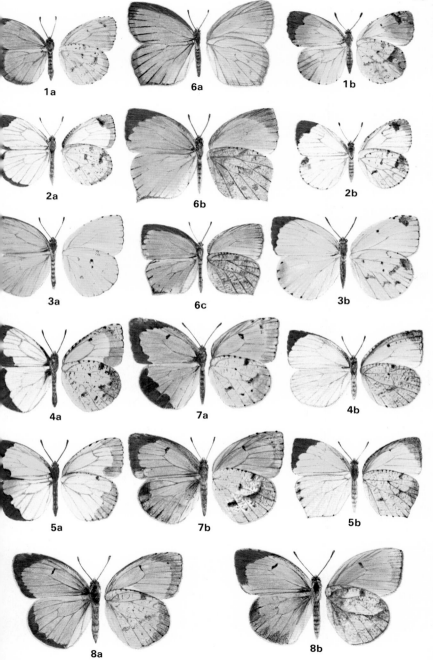

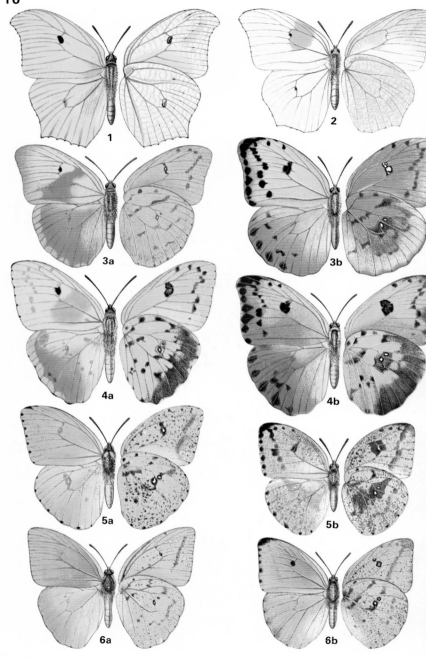

1. **Anteos maerula**   *Giant Brimstone*   p. 132
   Forewing upperside with black spot at cell-end; female similar
   but paler.
   ♂ Holguin, Cuba.

2. **Anteos clorinde**   *Ghost Brimstone*   132
   Forewing with yellow or orange patch across cell-end; ♀ similar
   but cell-end patch rather diffuse.
   ♂ Mexico.

3. **Phoebis avellaneda**   *Red-splashed Sulphur*   132
   Underside of hindwing uniformly coloured, often slightly paler
   towards outer margin.
   3a ♂, 3b ♀, Cuba.

4. **Phoebis philea**   *Orange-barred Sulphur*   133
   Underside of hindwing with wide dusky border along outer
   margin, except in ♂ of subspecies *thalestris*.
   4a ♂, 4b ♀, Cuba.

5. **Phoebis argante**   *Apricot Sulphur*   133
   Postdiscal line on underside of forewing interrupted at vein 4.
   5a ♂ Dominican Republic.
   5b ♀ Haiti.

6. **Phoebis agarithe**   *Large Orange Sulphur*   134
   Postdiscal line on underside of forewing not interrupted at vein 4.
   6a ♂, 6b ♀, Bahamas.

B.W.I.   I

Early stages. Eggs have been seen to be laid on 'Amor seco' (*Desmodium*), but there are no published descriptions of the caterpillar.

EUREMA NICIPPE Cramer 1782   *Black-bordered Orange*   **Pl. 15**
Description. Fw ♂ and ♀ 22–26 mm. The deep orange upperside and the shape of the wide black borders render this species unmistakable. The strong inwardly pointing *tooth on the hindwing border in space* 4 is particularly characteristic. The only similar species is *E. nicippiformis* (see below).
Distribution. Apparently widespread and common in the Bahamas, Cuba and the Cayman Islands, becoming rarer in Jamaica and Hispaniola, and in Porto Rico possibly only occurring as a casual. In flight it belies the vernacular name, Sleepy Orange, by which it is known in N. America. In the dry season (winter) brood the underside markings tend to be more intense than in the other broods. RANGE: eastern U.S.A. to Costa Rica; Bahamas to Porto Rico. TL: Virginia.
Early stages. The caterpillar is greyish green, covered in short white downy hair, with a white orange-spotted band along each side and white spiracles. In Cuba it feeds on various kinds of *Cassia*.

EUREMA NICIPPIFORMIS Munroe 1947
Haitian Black-bordered Orange   **Pl. 15**
Description. Fw ♂ and ♀ 22–26 mm. Very similar in all respects to *E. nicippe*. Male distinguished at once by the black border of the *hindwing lacking* the prominent *tooth in space* 4 that characterises *E. nicippe*. Female differs in having the veins on the upperside of the forewing scaled yellow, not orange, and in the border almost or quite lacking the projections along veins 2 and 3. There are also anatomical differences.
Distribution. Confined to Hispaniola, where *E. nicippe* also occurs, and apparently widespread but not common. RANGE: Hispaniola. TL: Haiti.
Early stages. Not known.

NATHALIS IOLE Boisduval 1836   *Dainty Sulphur*   **Pl. 14**
Description. Fw ♂ 11–14 mm, ♀ 11–15 mm. Both sexes pale yellow, suggesting a very small *Eurema daira* or *E. elathea* or female *E. lisa*. Distinguishing characters are, apart from size, its relatively longer and narrower forewing, the *broadening of the dark inner marginal bar as it nears the outer margin*, the absence of a dark apical patch on the hindwing and the presence there of a dark costal streak. On the underside of the forewing orange costal streak is much wider in the female than in the male, and the grey-brown ground colour of the hindwing in the female contrasts strongly with the yellow of the male. In the female the upperside is sometimes dusky orange, especially in Cuba, ♀-f. *felicia* Poey, or on the hindwing only; albinic males, known from Jamaica, are f. *albida* Avinoff.
Distribution. Bahamas: New Providence, Great Bahama, Bimini Isles. Cuba: St Christobal, Santiago, Oriente, Soledad, Matanzas (July and August). Jamaica, widespread at elevations above 2000 ft but very local, May to August. Hispaniola, at lower levels. Seasonal variation negligible, underside less dusky in wet season. RANGE: central and southern U.S.A. to Colombo. TL: Mexico.
Early stages. The caterpillar (in U.S.A.) is dark green, pubescent, with a broad purple dorsal stripe, double lateral yellow and black stripes, and a pair of reddish tubercles just behind the head. Food plants Marigold, Chickweed, etc.

KRICOGONIA LYSIDE Godart 1819 *Guayacán Sulphur* **Pl. 13**

Description. Fw ♂ and ♀ 20–28 mm, very variable in size. Male upperside very distinctively marked with bright *orange basal patch on forewing* and short straight black bar on hindwing near apex, though the latter may be reduced to a few small spots or even quite absent at times. In the female the basal patch is always paler, sometimes absent, and there is never a bar on the hindwing; in ♀-f. *unicolor* Godman and Salvin the whole upperside is uniformly yellow. The pale yellow underside has a faintly pearly sheen, the forewing disc white except in ♀-f. *unicolor*; and in many specimens of either sex a narrow shadowy streak runs from the base of the hindwing through the cell towards the outer margin due to a fold in the surface of the wing which distorts the arrangement of the scales, like the mid-rib of a leaf.

Distribution. Bahamas, April, May and June – small, hindwing bar very small or absent. Hispaniola, common sometimes in swarms. Jamaica, Kingston, Bath, Blue Mts, etc., not common. Porto Rico, rare. Cuban records probably refer to *K. cabrerai* (see below) or vagrants from N. America. RANGE: southern U.S.A. to Venezuela; W. Indies. TL (not stated): Haiti.

Early stages. Fully grown caterpillar dull green, with grey or silvery line along the back broadly bordered with chocolate brown, lateral lines also silvery, the sides between the lines variegated golden yellow and brown; head green. Food plant *Guaiacum officinale*. Feeds by night and hides by day in crevices of bark.

Note. This species has often been misidentified as *Papilio castalia* Fabricius, a name which properly belongs to the Jamaican subspecies of *Appias drusilla* (p. 117).

KRICOGONIA CABRERAI Ramsden 1920
Cuban Guayacán Sulphur

Description. Both sexes very similar to *K. lyside* but usually larger, and with the hindwing 'mid-rib' streak, best seen by holding the specimen against the light, more conspicuous and extending almost to outer margin; *forewing yellow basal patch reduced to a short narrow basal streak* against the costa; male hindwing apical black bar very large, about 8 × 3 mm. Underside of hindwing and forewing apex marbled pale greenish yellow with faint pink flush.

Distribution. Confined to Cuba. TL: Guantanamo.

Early stages. Not known.

ZERENE CESONIA Stoll 1790 *Dog Face Butterfly* **Pl. 13**
syn. *Meganostoma cesonia*

Description. Fw ♂ 29–33 mm, ♀ 25–34 mm. The sexes very similar but the '*dog face*' *outline* rather less sharply defined in the female than in the male. Underside yellow, but with the black pattern of the upperside clearly showing through. In the dry (winter) season form, which is rare in Cuba, the hindwing beneath and the apex of the forewing are flushed with rosy pink, f. *rosea* Roeber 1909.

Distribution. *Z. cesonia cesonia*, the N. American mainland subspecies, occurs freely in open country in western Cuba, e.g. Matanzas, St Cristobal, Holguin, etc. In Hispaniola it is replaced by *Z. cesonia cynops* Butler 1873, which is rather more orange-yellow above and below, and has the black dusting at the base of the forewing much reduced in extent and confined to the anterior part of the cell, or, in the female, sometimes absent. RANGE: southern U.S.A. to Argentina. TL: Georgia.

Early stages. Caterpillar grey-green above, olive-green below, with numerous small black tubercles, marked with transverse and longitudinal yellow and black lines which vary greatly in intensity. Food plant (in U.S.A.) False Indigo (*Amorpha fruticosa*) and Clovers (*Trifolium*); multibrooded.

ANTEOS MAERULA Fabricius 1775   *Giant Brimstone*   **Pl. 16**

Description. Fw ♂ and ♀ 35–48 mm. Male clear lemon-yellow, the upperside unmarked except for a *black spot at cell-end on forewing* and a similar but much less conspicuous brown spot on hindwing; female the same but much paler. A rare form of the female is yellow like the male, ♀-f. *flava* Roeber 1910. The faint underside markings simulate a leaf, and the outline of the wings readily distinguishes *A. maerula* from the similar but mostly smaller species of the genus *Phoebis*.

Distribution. Cuba, especially in eastern provinces; Haiti and San Domingo; Porto Rico (rare); Jamaica. Dated specimens suggest two broods, one about November, the other in July and August. RANGE: southern U.S.A. to Peru. TL: 'America'.

Early stages. Caterpillar olive-green with two very irregular subdorsal rows of yellowish blotches on either side, a line of minute black tubercles (one to each segment) and a broad paler yellowish buff lateral spiracular stripe. Food plant, in Cuba, a species of *Cassia* known locally as Frijol de Gallina.

ANTEOS CLORINDE Godart 1823   *Ghost Brimstone*   **Pl. 16**

Description. Fw ♂ and ♀ 45–50 mm. White, with a roughly *rectangular yellow to orange patch*, clear-cut in male, rather diffuse in female, *across end of cell of forewing* to costa. The outer half, more or less, of both wings in the male 'mealy' in appearance; the black, red-ringed cell-end spots larger in the female than the male. Underside pale greenish, leaf-patterned.

Distribution. First taken in Cuba some forty years ago in the neighbourhood of Soledad, where it occurred in the Central American form known as subspecies *nivifera* Fruhstorfer, said to differ in having the yellow forewing patch more orange than in the typical South American subspecies – a distinction of somewhat doubtful validity. Has been taken once in Jamaica. Not known elsewhere in the islands. RANGE: southern U.S.A. to Argentina. TL: Brazil.

Early stages. Fully grown caterpillar yellowish green, covered with numerous very small green tubercles, back light pea-green with transverse line of black hairs, an interrupted thin yellow lateral line above the spiracles and a wide whitish green line below, an irregular row of black or iridescent tubercles above the spiracles. Food plant *Cassia spectabilis*.

PHOEBIS AVELLANEDA Herrich-Schaeffer 1864
Red-splashed Sulphur   **Pl. 16**
syn. *solstitia* Butler 1869

Description. Fw ♂ and ♀ 40–45 mm. A very distinct species, the male only likely to be confused with the male of *P. philea* but at once distinguished by the blood red colour of the irregular discal splash on the upperside of the forewing. The females are hardly distinguishable on the upperside, but abundantly different in the pattern of the markings of the *underside of the hindwing, which, as in the male, is uniformly sandy red.*

Distribution. Occurs in Cuba, especially in the eastern provinces, and in Hispaniola. Not known elsewhere. TL: Cuba.

Early stages. Not known.

PHOEBIS PHILEA Johansson 1763   *Orange-barred Sulphur*   **Pl. 16**
Description. Fw ♂ and ♀ 38–45 mm. One of the most brilliant of all West Indian butterflies, the vivid yellow of the male's upperside enhanced by the brilliant orange of the forewing disc and of the outer two-thirds of hindwing. The red, black-spotted and orange-tinted female is almost equally brilliant. The underside ground colour is deep yellow in both sexes, the markings larger, bolder and much darker in the female, *the hindwing border broadly dusky.*
Distribution. *P. philea* is represented in Cuba by *P. p. huebneri* Fruhstorfer 1907 and in Hispaniola by *P. p. thalestris* Illiger 1802. Both these subspecies differ from *P. p. philea* of the mainland in having a prominent black spot at the end of the cell on the forewing, and a large discal orange patch that extends fully to reach the inner margin. They differ from one another in the intensity of the underside markings, especially of the females, very dark and strongly contrasting in *P. p. huebneri*, purplish brown against a suffused sandy background in *P. p. thalestris*. The butterfly occurs throughout Cuba and Hispaniola and is a strong and elusive flier much attracted to flowers and to damp roadside puddles and wet riverside sands. Records from Porto Rico need confirmation. RANGE: southern U.S.A. to S. Brazil. TL: 'in Indiis'.
Early stages. Fully-fed caterpillar green, darker above than below, the head first three and last segments and the backs of the other segments orange, covered with small black spots bearing short shiny black spines, the sides of segments 4 to 11 blue-black. Food plants *Cassia fistula*, *C. fruticosa* and *C. occidentalis*, *Poinciana pulcherrima*, etc.

PHOEBIS ARGANTE Fabricius 1775   *Apricot Sulphur*   **Pl. 16**
Description. Fw ♂ and ♀ 32–37 mm. Male upperside rich deep ochreous yellow unmarked except for marginal black dots; female upperside paler, irrorated with red scales; a dark spot at cell-end, and irregular dark marginal and postdiscal spots. Very similar to the next species, *P. agarithe*, with which it is frequently confused. The markings on the underside of the forewings provide a simple distinguishing character: in both species a rather shadowy *dark line* runs *from the apex* diagonally towards the inner margin; in *P. argante* this line is *broadly interrupted at vein 4*, in *P. agarithe* it is straight and unbroken. The general tone of the underside is also darker in *P. argante* than in *P. agarithe* and the dark brown speckling usually heavier, sometimes coalescent.
Distribution. Three subspecies occur in the islands. In the Cuban *P. a. fornax* Butler 1871 the female is quite dark yellow and both wings are heavily suffused with red on the upperside. In *P. a. rorata* Butler 1869 (Sept.) from Haiti, the Dominican Republic and E. Jamaica the ground colour, especially below, is rather paler ochreous in both sexes, and the female is much paler on the upperside and only faintly dusted with red scales. The Porto Rican *P. a. martini* Comstock 1944 is smaller, darker and paler above, the underside more lemon than orange with widely scattered red scaling. Form *minuscula* Butler 1869 (Oct.) is a dwarf with the forewing only about 24 mm long. The butterfly is a

roadside and garden species with a rapid and erratic flight much attracted to flowers and to damp sandy riverside patches and shallow puddles. RANGE: Mexico to Paraguay. TL: Brazil.

Early stages. The full grown caterpillar is green or yellow-green with numerous very small creamy granulations. The back covered with barely visible short reddish hairs with here and there some larger brown cones; lateral stripe white or yellow, belly greenish white. Food plants *Inga laurina*, 'Pois doux' (in Trinidad); various Leguminosae and Capparidaceae.

PHOEBIS AGARITHE Boisduval 1836

Large Orange Sulphur   **Pl. 16**

Phoebis agarithe ranges from southern U.S.A. to Peru (TL: Mexico). It occurs in the West Indies in the following subspecies:

Phoebis agarithe antilla Brown 1929

Description. Fw ♂ 29–39 mm, ♀ 27–37 mm. Upperside deep ochreous in both sexes, the female sometimes paler. Very similar to *P. argante* (p. 133). Additional distinguishing characters are: Male hindwing upperside in *P. agarithe* always a little yellower than the forewing; female upperside *forewing postdiscal band always straight and uninterrupted*, not dusted with red scales; underside ground colour not ochreous but sulphur-yellow to whitish (in female).

Distribution. Bahamas, Cuba, Hispaniola, Porto Rico and West Jamaica. In the Lesser Antilles, St Kitts to Grenada, the species is smaller, male forewing 27–32 mm, female 27–30 mm, the upperside marginal markings better developed and the cell-end spot on the underside of both wings more prominent and usually silver-pupilled, subspecies *pupillata* Dillon 1947. The white form of the female, f. *albarithe* Brown, seems to be confined to the mainland races. Flight and habitats the same as for *P. argante*. TL: Haiti.

Early stages. Full grown caterpillar smooth leaf-green, densely covered with very short pile, a yellow lateral line, black-edged below, low down on the side and not sharply defined. Food plant, in Jamaica, *Inga vera*.

PHOEBIS SENNAE Linnaeus 1758   *Cloudless Sulphur*   **Pl. 17**

syn. *eubule* Linnaeus 1767

Description. Fw ♂ 32–35 mm, ♀ 30–35 mm. Female usually rather smaller than the male. The clear unmarked yellow *upperside of the male is relieved in certain lights by a pale silky wavy-edged marginal border that runs inwards between the veins*. The pattern of markings in the female is very constant, with no post-discal markings on the forewing below vein 3, but the ground colour varies very considerably, from yellow like the male to orange-yellow, cream or pinkish, or almost pure white (♀-f. *sennalba* Brown 1929). Underside markings are the same in both sexes, but very much more strongly developed in the female, *the two pearly spots at the end of the cell equal in size or almost so*.

Distribution. A sun-loving open country species much attracted to the nectar of flowers and to moist puddles. Abundant throughout the islands and throughout the year from sea level to at least 5000 ft. RANGE: southern U.S.A. to Argentina. TL: Jamaica.

Early stages. The full grown caterpillar is pale yellowish green, much speckled with black dots, and with a yellow lateral line on each side and bluish transverse lines. Food plant *Cassia*, of several species, senna, clover, etc.

Note. Similar species. *Aphrissa neleis* (p. 135) and *A. statira* (p. 136).

PHOEBIS EDITHA Butler 1870   *Scarce Sulphur*
Description. Fw ♂ 36 mm, ♀ 34 mm. Male like *Phoebis sennae* but larger, the forewing squarer, upperside *marginal silken area very faint*. *Female upperside rose-red*, forewing disc with some yellow scaling and postdiscal markings extending at least into space 2. *Underside* ground colour yellow in male, red-brown in female and wholly (except inner margin of forewing in male) *densely sprinkled with red-brown scales* producing a sandy effect.
Distribution. Known only from Haiti and apparently rare. The female has been variously regarded as an extreme dry season form of *P. sennae* or *P. philea*. On anatomical grounds a distinct species. RANGE and TL: Haiti.
Early stages. Not known.

PHOEBIS TRITE Linnaeus 1758   *Straight-line Sulphur*   **Pl. 17**
Phoebis trite ranges from Mexico to Argentina (TL: the Tropics). It occurs in the West Indies in the following subspecies:
Phoebis trite watsoni Brown 1929
Description. Fw ♂ 28–36 mm, ♀ 28–30 mm. Bright sulphur-yellow, the fore-wing narrowly edged black in the female only; female very liable to rubbing that produces a scaleless translucent effect. Underside clear pale green in the male, pinkish buff in female, both sexes distinguished at once from all other species of *Phoebis* by the *dusky grey-brown straight line that crosses both wings diagonally* from the apex of the forewing to near the middle of inner margin of hindwing.
Distribution. Hispaniola, Porto Rico, in February and March and again in June and July; Dominica (December and January), St Kitts (December), St Lucia, Guadeloupe (September), Montserrat. Not easy to catch as it chiefly favours tree tops. TL: San Domingo.
Early stages. Not known.

APHRISSA ORBIS Poey 1832   *Orbed Sulphur*   **Pl. 17**
Description. Fw ♂ 29–35 mm, ♀ 29–33 mm. A very distinct species closely related to *A. godartiana* (p. 136). In the male the marginal band of modified scales is very wide, occupying the whole wing between the cell and the outer margin. The *orb-like orange basal area* renders the species quite unmistakable. *Female upperside deep ochreous*, very constant, underside ground colour less strikingly different. Underside markings in both sexes unusually sharply defined for a species of *Aphrissa*.
Distribution. The above description applies to the widespread Cuban sub-species, *A. orbis orbis*. Hispaniola is populated by *A. orbis browni* Munroe 1947 (TL: Pivert, Haiti), which is larger in both sexes and has a wider band of modified scales on the forewing in the male. RANGE: Confined to Cuba and Hispaniola. TL: Cuba.
Early stages. Caterpillar green, head paler than body, segments paler in front but tending to orange behind, with transverse lines; the first and last segments different from the others; a white lateral line above the spiracles bordered above with dark olive and below with green; tubercles yellowish. Food plant Guaca-maya colorada (*Poinciana pulcherrima*).

APHRISSA NELEIS Boisduval 1836   *Pink-spot Sulphur*   **Pl. 17**
Description. Fw ♂ and ♀ 33–37 mm. Male upperside bright sulphur-yellow, the wide *mealy outer area of modified scales only slightly paler*. Female slightly

more ochreous, the forewing with a bold black spot at the cell-end, marginal spots brown, square, widely separated and not continued on to the costa. Male underside dull pale ochreous, unmarked; female underside with faint lilac markings, forewing cell-spot as on upperside, hindwing with *two white spots at cell-end, the spot in space 5 much the smaller*; both sexes with a minute patch of pink scales at the extreme base of hindwing close against the thorax.

Distribution. Known only from the Bahamas (Nassau, July) and Cuba (e.g. Habana, Holguin) and apparently rare. RANGE: Bahamas and Cuba. TL: Cuba.

Early stages. Not known.

Note. Often confused with *Aphrissa statira* or *Phoebis sennae* from both of which it is morphologically quite distinct. It can always be distinguished from both of these species at once by the pink spot at the base of the hindwing below, referred to above, which both the other species lack.

APHRISSA GODARTIANA Swainson 1821
Swainson's Sulphur **Pl. 17**

Description. Fw ♂ 32–38 mm, ♀ 30–35 mm. Like *A. orbis* but the base of the forewing is sulphur, not orange, and the *area of modified scales is pure white* and extends well into the end of the cell; hindwing pale sulphur-yellow from base to edge of the area of modified scales. The *female* upperside may be pale sulphur-yellow (subspecies *hartonia*) or slightly pinkish yellow (subspecies *godartiana*), but the *startling bold black spot at the cell-end of forewing* renders this sex unmistakable. Underside with a faint pearly sheen, especially in the female, markings lilac, sparse in female, almost or quite absent in the male, except at cell-ends.

Distribution. *A. g. hartonia* is restricted to the Cockpit country of Jamaica, is very fast on the wing and frequents the blossom of tall trees. *A. g. godartiana* of Haiti and the Dominican Republic is faintly buff coloured on the underside in the male. Records from Porto Rico need confirmation. RANGE: Hispaniola and Jamaica; Porto Rico (?). TL (not stated): Haiti.

Early stages. Not known.

APHRISSA STATIRA Cramer 1777 *Migrant Sulphur* **Pl. 17**

Description. Fw ♂ 30–32 mm, ♀ 26–33 mm. Male upperside sulphur-yellow, except the mealy marginal area of modified scales, which is much paler, almost white, broad and sometimes extending into the apex of the cell on the forewing; underside pure yellow, except the whitish area against the inner margin. Female upperside rather light sulphur-yellow, cell-end spot black and prominent, marginal markings black, linear, joined together and extending round the apex some distance along the costa; underside markings rusty red, *at most one cell-end spot on hindwing, usually none*. See also *Phoebis sennae* (p. 134) in which the band of modified scales in the male is narrow and inconspicuous, the two cell-spots on the underside of the hindwing in the female prominent, silvery and of equal size; and *Aphrissa neleis* (p. 135).

Distribution. Two subspecies have been recognised so far in the West Indies. *A. statira cubana* d'Almeida 1939 (TL: Cuba), described above, is widespread in Cuba and the Cayman Islands. In Hispaniola the larger *A. statira hispaniolae* Munroe 1947 (TL: Sanchez, Dominican Republic) replaces it and is distinguished also by having the forewing underside uniformly brighter yellow. Specimens taken in Porto Rico in July to September seem to be migrant *A. s.*

cubana. Others that occur from time to time in the Lesser Antilles are probably migrant *A. s. statira* from farther south, for each year this typical subspecies migrates through Trinidad in large numbers. RANGE: Southern U.S.A. to Argentina. TL: S. America.

Early stages. The head of the fully grown caterpillar is pale orange, the body similar but with a faint greenish tinge; each of the first eleven segments has a blue-black band low down on the side, the last segment is more rust coloured; legs coloured like the body; spiracles white. Food plant Guacama cimarrona (a species of *Cassia*); also said to feed on Quenepa (*Melicocia bijuga*).

DISMORPHIA SPIO Godart 1819   *Haitian Mimic*   **Pl. 13**
Description. Fw ♂ and ♀ 30–36 mm. The coloration and markings of the upperside of both sexes of this species, and even the shape of the wings, are very unusual for a 'White', and strongly suggest a species of *Heliconius* or an Ithomiine from the mainland of Central or South America. It is in fact a mimic, like nearly all the species of *Dismorphia*, but its model, if it still exists, has not been recognised. Like all mimetic species it is very variable: the *forewing markings* may be wholly bright fulvous (f. *virago* Avinov 1925), *partly orange and partly yellow* (typical f. *spio*), or the markings of both wings may be wholly yellow. The male always has the costal half of the hindwing white. On the underside the disc of the forewing in the male is white, in the female marked as on the upperside, the rest of the wings cryptically patterned and spattered with white flecks.

Distribution. Confined to Hispaniola and Porto Rico in heavy forest at 2000 ft or more; not common. January, April, June, August. RANGE: Hispaniola and Porto Rico. TL: Antilles.

Early stages. Not known.

DISMORPHIA CUBANA Herrich-Schaeffer 1862
Cuban Mimic   **Pl. 13**
Description. Fw ♂ and ♀ 28–35 mm. In the male the subapical spots and *solid discal band on the forewing* are *yellow*, the other markings and the costal area of the hindwing fulvous. In the female all the markings are yellow. The dazzle pattern of the underside is much enhanced by the spatter of very fine grey specks and striae.

Distribution. Cuba only, where it is confined to the highest mountains, at about 3000 ft, in July. The marked sexual dimorphism of this mimetic species suggests that the model for the male may be either *Eueides m. cleobaea* (p. 86) or some other species no longer present in Cuba. The resemblance of the female to *Heliconius charitonius* (p. 85) is sufficiently striking not to need emphasis, size not being a factor of importance in mimicry. RANGE and TL: Cuba.

Early stages. Not known.

The Swallowtails are a worldwide family of large butterflies particularly numerous in the tropics. They include, for example, the dazzlingly beautiful Bird-winged butterflies (*Ornithoptera*) of the East Indies. The fact that in nearly all of them the hindwing has a conspicuous tail gives them their popular name. There is one simple character that distinguishes them from all other butterflies: the hindwing has only a single anal vein, i.e. between the inner margin and vein 2 (the vein that arises from the lower margin of the cell, fig. 2) there is only one vein that runs from the base of the wing to the anal angle. All the legs are fully developed and clawed and the forelegs bear a small leaf-like expansion (epiphysis) on the tibia, the function of which is not understood. Another character not found in any other family of butterflies is the osmeterium, a kind of protrusible 'stink gland' which normally lies hidden under the skin just behind the head of the caterpillar. The large day-flying Uraniid moths, some of which are very brilliant, are often mistaken for Swallowtails, but can always be distinguished by their thread-like antennae.

Although all the Swallowtails were originally placed in the single genus *Papilio*, and still are in a popular sense, they really are made up of three large groups each of subfamily rank and each comprising several genera. The first of these divisions contains the Aristolochia Swallowtails, so-called because their caterpillars all feed on *Aristolochia*. These species are 'distasteful' and avoided by predators. A common feature is the long fold along the inner margin of the hindwing that contains a dense mass of woolly scent scales. Their caterpillars have fleshy thorn-like lateral outgrowths on many of their body segments. The genera *Parides* and *Battus* belong to this division. The second division contains the Fluted or True Swallowtails. In these the inner margin of the hindwing is fluted (best seen on the underside) and has no scent scales. The caterpillars are hump-backed, without fleshy outgrowths, the hump being formed by the enlargement of the first three segments immediately behind the head, and the third of these segments often has a 'threatening' eye-spot on either side. All the West Indian species of this division belong to the genus *Papilio*. The third division is that of the Kite Swallowtails. These have rather long narrow hindwings which end in a long tail so that, when in flight, the butterflies have the outline of a kite. The caterpillars are hump-backed but without eye-spots and usually patterned in fine lines and dots. Only one genus, *Eurytides*, occurs in the West Indies. The pupae of all Swallowtails tend to be rough and angular, particularly those of the Aristolochia division. All rest in an upright position secured by the cremastral hooks at the tail and a silken girdle round the waist.

PARIDES GUNDLACHIANUS   Felder and Felder   1864
Gundlach's Swallowtail   **Pl. 18**
syn. *columbus* Herrich-Schaeffer (invalid homonym)

Description. Fw ♂ 36–45 mm, female usually larger. Upperside ground colour in both sexes black; *forewing with brilliant blue curved transverse band*; *hindwing with series of bright red patches* near outer margin, rich deep red in winter specimens, duller and almost orange in summer. Underside similar but hindwing with a line of conspicuous white crescents along outer margin. Male distinguished by having the inner margin of hindwing folded over to enclose a mass of modified cream-coloured scent scales. Female red hindwing patches usually larger than those of the male. Tail about 8 mm long.

Distribution. Only in Cuba, and principally in the eastern provinces. January and February and again in June and July, probably in other months as well; apparently in two broods. RANGE and TL: Cuba.

Early stages. The caterpillar's head is black, the body ashen with a violet tint, a more or less continuous fine black line runs along the back and another on each side, a creamy white band immediately behind the head, segments 2 to 4 and 10 to 12 with thorn-like fleshy appendages, spiracles black. Food plant *Aristolochia*.

BATTUS ZETIDES Munroe 1971 *Zetides Swallowtail* Pl. 18
syn. *zetes* Westwood 1847 (invalid homonym)

Description. Fw ♂ 39 mm, ♀ 41 mm. Upperside rich very dark brown in both sexes, *both wings crossed* near the outer margin *by a series of deep ochre-yellow spots* which are larger and farther from the margin on the hindwing than on the forewing. Underside reminiscent of *B. devilliersi* (p. 142), but on the forewing the submarginal spots are orange or pale yellow and not arrow-shaped, and the hindwing is characterised by a series of six long silvery white pointed streaks arranged in a semicircle on the disc.

Distribution. Known only from Haiti, La Vega, and apparently very rare. Should also occur in the Dominican Republic. RANGE: Hispaniola. TL: Haiti.

Early stages. Not known.

BATTUS POLYDAMAS Linnaeus 1758
Polydamas Swallowtail Pl. 18

Description. Fw ♂ 40–50 mm, ♀ usually larger. Upperside in both sexes black, with a faint silky greenish tinge, especially on the hindwing; *forewing with a series of rather small triangular yellow spots close to the outer margin*; hindwing yellow spots rectangular, further from the margin and only separated by the veins; no tail, but outer margin scalloped. Underside smoky brownish grey; basal half of forewing darker, the marginal yellow spots larger but less numerous; hindwing devoid of yellow submarginal spots, but with a marginal series of double-crescentic narrow red marks followed by pale yellow crescents between the ends of the veins.

Distribution. *B. polydamas* is a common butterfly, especially of gardens, open spaces and waste lands. Throughout its continental range it varies little, but in the Antilles on the other hand nearly every island of any size has its own island race, a remarkable development unequalled by any other local species, unless it be *Dryas iulia* (p. 86), and suggesting that the butterfly wanders little from island to island, and that the island populations must have been isolated for considerable periods of time. Typical *B. polydamas* (described above) is confined to the American mainland, and does not now occur on any of the islands, though it seems to have been present earlier on the island of Barbados. RANGE: southern U.S.A. to Argentina. TL: 'America'.

The following Caribbean subspecies have been described:

1 **B. p. cubensis** du Frane 1946 (TL: Cuba). On the underside of the hindwing the wide dark marginal area is darker and more clearly separated from the paler discal area than in *B. p. polydamas*. Common throughout Cuba wherever *Aristolochia* grows. Also in the Cayman Islands, but not so common.

2 **B. p. jamaicensis** Rothschild and Jordan 1906 (TL: Jamaica). Upperside submarginal spots much paler than in *B. p. cubensis*, creamy with a greenish tint. Underside more brilliant, both the pale and the red markings brighter. The commonest Jamaican Swallowtail, often to be seen in numbers at blossom, May to October and no doubt at other times.

3 **B. p. polycrates** Hopffer 1866 (TL: 'Para', *recte* Haiti). Upperside pale markings of hindwing smaller than in most other subspecies, little larger than those of forewing, not yellowish. Red markings of hindwing underside narrow and regular, three prominent silvery white triangular marks marginally in spaces 4 to 6. Haiti and Dominican Republic (La Vega and San Pedro Macoris in June). Porto Rico.

4 **B. p. lucayus** Rothschild and Jordan 1906 (TL: Nassau, Bahamas). On the upperside the yellow-green spots of the hindwing are much larger than those of the forewing, and relatively much larger than those of *B. p. polycrates*, especially in the female. The hindwing underside is pale, only very faintly darker towards the submarginal markings, white bar from inner margin near anal angle well developed and usually reaching vein 3, silver wedge-shaped spots absent or almost so, red markings narrow and dull. Bahamas: New Providence, Grand Bahama, Long Island, Eleuthera Island. March, April, May, July to October.

5 **B. p. thyamus** Rothschild and Jordan 1906 (TL: St Thomas). Similar to *B. p. lucayus* in the size of the pale markings of the upperside, but the hindwing with a well-marked small pale spot about mid-costa separated from the main band and liable to be covered by the overlap of the inner margin of the forewing. Underside rather dark chocolate, darkening towards margin, three silver wedges present but small, red markings large but not very bright. Virgin Isles: St Thomas, St Croix, St John, Tortola, etc.

6 **B. p. antiguus** Rothschild and Jordan 1906 (TL: Antigua). The three pale spots nearest the apex of the forewing all very small on upperside and reduced to dots on underside. Red submarginal markings on hindwing underside exceptionally large, the three silvery wedge-shaped marks well developed. Antigua. Known only from the figure by Moses Harris in Dru Drury's *Illustrations of Exotic Insects* published in 1770. Certainly extinct.

7 **B. p. christopheranus** Hall 1936 (TL: St Kitts). On the upperside the spots of the postdiscal band much yellower on the forewing than on the hindwing, and on the hindwing the band tapering noticeably towards the anal angle. Underside ground colour almost black; underside hindwing red markings large bold and irregular, contrasting strongly with the black ground colour, silver wedges present in spaces 6, 5 and (4), but smaller than in *B. p. polycrates*. St Kitts, at about 800 ft; doubtfully on Nevis.

8 **B. p. neodamas** Lucas 1852 (TL: 'Antilles' – Guadeloupe). Forewing band reduced to five small spots, those above vein 4 being lost; hindwing band

typically very narrow. On the underside the spots of the forewing postdiscal band almost white, reduced to five, small and narrow; hindwing very dark, red markings rather small, white marginal markings very delicate and inconspicuous, no transverse bar from inner margin. A very distinct subspecies, the darkest of all and representing the extreme in reduction of pale markings. Known only from Guadeloupe.

9 **B. p. dominicus** Rothschild and Jordan 1906 (TL: Dominica). On the forewing upperside the three pale apical spots present but very small, hindwing band wide. On the underside the forewing spots are creamy, and the hindwing transverse bar from the inner margin is represented by one small spot or is absent. Intermediate in markings between *B. p. neodamas* and *B. p. xenodamas*. Dominica only.

10 **B. p. xenodamas** Huebner 1825 (TL: Martinique). Upperside markings well developed, including the forewing apical spots. Best distinguished by the grey-green stripe on the hindwing underside along the base of the costa, and the patch of similar colour usually present below this stripe. Martinique, Fort de France. January, May, November, and no doubt in other months as well.

11 **B. p. lucianus** Rothschild and Jordan 1906 (TL: St Lucia). Upperside pale bands wide, on forewing almost cream, on hindwing bluish, when fresh, much as in *B. p. xenodamas*. Hindwing underside with faint pale costal stripe in most specimens, but without a pale patch below it, silver wedges present in spaces 4 to 6. St Lucia, March, April, November and no doubt in other months.

12 **B. p. vincentius** Rothschild and Jordan 1906 (TL: St Vincent). Upperside markings yellowish and decidedly small on the forewing, greenish yellow and of moderate size on hindwing, forewing band nearer to outer margin than in other subspecies on upper and underside. Underside black, hindwing marginal markings bold, red spots and white crescents large, silver wedges often present in all spaces from apex to anal angle, grey costal streak pronounced. St Vincent, Kingstown, March to May.

13 **B. p. grenadensis** Hall 1930 (TL: Grenada, St Georges). Upperside pale spots as in *B. p. polydamas* of the mainland on forewing, very square-cut distally on hindwing. Underside ground colour uniformly black (shaded black and chocolate in mainland subspecies), hindwing red and white marginal markings large and prominent though less so than in *B. p. vincentius*. Grenada and Grenadines, February, March, etc.

Early stages. The caterpillar is dusky olive to black, a yellowish band behind the head is continued along the sides of the first few segments; first segment with a pair of rather long fleshy black and red lateral outgrowths (tentacles), four rows of shorter tentacles (papillae) along the back, and another two rows along the sides except on segments 6 to 9; head black. Gregarious when young. Food plants various kinds of *Aristolochia*.

BATTUS DEVILLIERSI Godart 1824
Devillier's Swallowtail
Pl. 18
Description. Fw ♂ 40–48 mm, ♀ to 52 mm. Upperside both sexes dark velvety green, the veins noticeably paler, each wing with a series of paler grey-green marginal spots which are much longer on the hindwing than on the forewing.

Underside strikingly different: forewing black, often with a greenish flush; hindwing chocolate; hind margins of *both wings with double series of white markings,* simple on forewing, rather complex on hindwing where there is also a submarginal series of red-brown spots; tail about 9 mm long; inner margin of hindwing folded over but without enclosed scent scales.

Distribution. Cuba: Guantanamo, Habana, Sta Clara, Matanzas, Baracoa, Gibara, Holguin, etc. March to May and again in August and September, apparently in two broods. Bahamas: Andros Island, June. RANGE: Cuba to Bahamas. TL: Cuba.

Early stages. The caterpillar is known to feed on *Aristolochia* but has not been described.

PAPILIO THOAS Linnaeus 1771 *Thoas Swallowtail* **Pl. 18**

Description. Fw ♂ 52–56 mm, ♀ 55–60 mm. Upperside ground colour black; forewing with broad yellow band, cut by dark veins, from apex to inner margin, the outer edges of spots in spaces 2 to 5 rounded, spot in space 6 much the largest; a submarginal series of four to six smaller yellow spots and one or two small yellow spots against the costa just before the cell-end; on the hindwing the yellow band is continued and reaches the inner margin, the submarginal lunules are longer than wide, and the black-edged tail is marked with a yellow streak. On the underside the forewing is patterned as on the upperside but the black areas are almost entirely replaced by yellow; hindwing similar but with a discal row of blue black-edged lunules, the *bases of spaces 3 and 4 brick-red* and the *veins closing the cell-end yellow.*

Distribution. The above description applies to *Papilio thoas oviedo* Gundlach 1886, the subspecies that is confined to Cuba, where it is widespread, e.g. Sta Clara, San Blas, Guantanamo, Santiago, Baracoa, etc., in lowlands and foothills. It frequents the flowers of *Bauhinia, Poinsettia, Bougainvillea* in December to February and again in July and August.

Jamaica is populated by *Papilio thoas melonius* Rothschild and Jordan 1906. Both sexes differ from *P. t. oviedo* in that the yellow bands on the upperside and underside are clear pale yellow, the hindwing underside has three (instead of only two) brick-red spots at the end of the cell, and the blue crescents of the discal band are narrower. Widespread but generally rare, Portland, St Thomas, St Andrew, Manchester, Trelawney, Hanover, Westmoreland and St James. Continental races of *Papilio thoas* are readily distinguished from both these subspecies by the much less colourful and more restrained pattern of the discal markings on the underside of the hindwing. It is curious that this widespread species should have reached none of the West Indies other than Cuba and Jamaica. RANGE: Texas to Argentina. TL: Surinam.

Early stages. The fully grown caterpillar is mottled brown, with a white lateral streak on the thoracic segments, a white saddle-mark above the prolegs and the last segments also mostly white; prolegs brown, no white marks above the third and fourth pairs. Food plants *Citrus.* An admirable description of the caterpillar of the Amazonian subspecies was published by Miles Moss. It reads as follows: 'the young white and yellow-brown larva clearly foreshadows the adult, except that it has more yellow in its composition, and up to the final instar is very oily-looking. Both then, and even after, it bears a striking resemblance to a piece of freshly deposited bird's dung. When full-grown it is sometimes to be found on the branch, but is more usually to be seen resting fully exposed upon the upper

Plate 17   PIERIDAE   *Scale:* × $\frac{2}{3}$

1. **Phoebis sennae**   *Cloudless Sulphur*   p. 134
   Marginal border of modified scales on forewing upperside in the
   male very narrow; both sexes with two cell-end spots of almost
   equal size on hindwing underside.
   1a ♂, 1b ♀, Holguin, Cuba.

2. **Aphrissa orbis**   *Orbed Sulphur*   135
   The 'orb-like' basal patch on the forewing upperside in the male
   quite unmistakable; ♀ deep ochreous.
   2a ♂, 2b ♀, Cuba.

3. **Aphrissa neleis**   *Pink-spot Sulphur*   135
   Mealy border on forewing upperside of male little paler than the
   ground colour, cell-end spot on hindwing underside in space 4
   much the smaller of the two.
   3a ♂ Bahamas.
   3b ♀ Cuba.

4. **Aphrissa godartiana**   *Swainson's Sulphur*   136
   Mealy border on forewing margin white; female with very large
   spot at cell-end on forewing upperside.
   4a ♂, 4b ♀, Haiti.

5. **Aphrissa statira**   *Migrant Sulphur*   136
   Underside of hindwing with at most one spot at cell-end, usually
   none.
   5a ♂, 5b ♀, Holguin, Cuba.

6. **Phoebis trite**   *Straight-line Sulphur*   135
   Underside with a straight diagonal line across both wings.
   6a ♂, 6b ♀, St Lucia.

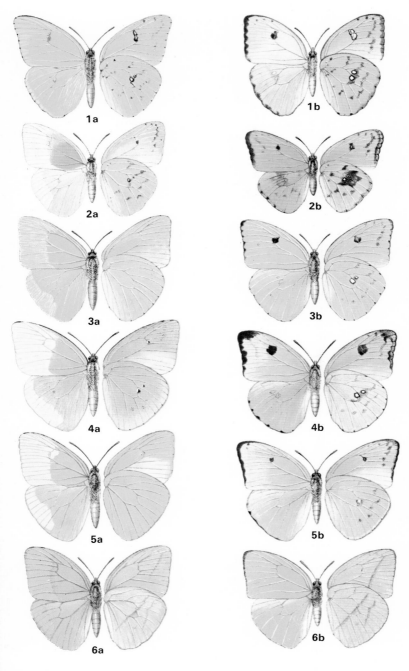

1a

1b

2a

2b

3a

3b

4a

4b

5a

5b

6a

6b

1. Parides gundlachianus   *Gundlach's Swallowtail*   p. 139
The woolly border along the inner margin of the hindwing is
confined to the male.
♂ Santiago, Cuba. January.

2. Battus zetides   *Zetes Swallowtail*   140
Postdiscal spots brownish ochreous.
♂ Haiti.

3. Battus polydamas   *Polydamas Swallowtail*   140
Postdiscal spots yellow on forewing, greenish on hindwing.
♂ Jamaica.

4. Battus devilliersi   *Devillier's Swallowtail*   142
Postdiscal spots on forewing small and almost white, on hindwing
grey-blue.
♂ Holguin, Cuba.

5. Papilio thoas   *Thoas Swallowtail*   143
On the underside of the hindwing the brick red marks just beyond
the end of the cell completely fill the bases of spaces 3 and 4.
♂ *P. t. oviedo*, Guantanamo, Cuba.

6. Papilio cresphontes   *Giant Swallowtail*   146
On the underside of the hindwing the bases of spaces 3 and 4
are not brick red.
♂ Florida.

7. Papilio aristodemus   *Dusky Swallowtail*   146
Forewing upperside with submarginal row of yellow crescents
beyond the main yellow transverse band; no yellow streak on tail.
♂ *P. a. temenes*, Cuba.

8. Papilio andraemon   *Bahaman Swallowtail*   147
Forewing upperside with no submarginal row of yellow crescents;
tail with yellow streak.
♂ Santiago, Cuba. June.

surface of a leaf. Viewed at a certain angle from the front, it bears a distinctly snake-like and forbidding appearance, the thoracic segments being humped up and exhibiting a dark eye-like mark on either side.'

PAPILIO CRESPHONTES Cramer 1775
Giant Swallowtail   **Pl. 18**

Description. Fw ♂ 52–63 mm, ♀ 55–72 mm. Upperside black, with a diagonal yellow band and numerous yellow spots. Distinguishable from the very similar *Papilio thoas* (p. 143) with difficulty, by the following characters: on the forewing upperside the yellow spot of the diagonal band in space 4 is longer than the spot below it in space 3; marginal yellow spot in space 4 very small or (more usually) absent; the hindwing underside with a curved black bar in the cell and the *veins closing the cell also black, brick-red patches in spaces 3 and 4 not reaching cell*. In general the male *P. cresphontes* is a darker insect with narrower upperside bands than *P. thoas* (except *P. thoas oviedo*). Females on the other hand are often paler, and always paler than the males. Martin Brown writes: 'the only positive way to recognise ♂ *cresphontes* (without dissection) is to run the tip of the finger nail over the back of the abdomen. This is smooth throughout in *thoas*, but a distinct notch is present near the tip in *cresphontes*.'

Distribution. Cuba: said to be widespread, but records are very suspect owing to confusion with *P. thoas*. The butterfly is a wanderer and has been taken once on S. Bimini Island in the Bahamas and seen on Bermuda. RANGE: Canada to Colombia. TL: New York, Carolina, etc.

Early stages. The caterpillar is dark mottled brown, with a broad stripe along the sides of the first three segments, a broad saddle-shaped mark over the back, and a patch on the last few segments all creamy. It feeds on the foliage of various Rutaceae, e.g. *Citrus, Zanthoxylum*, etc., and also on *Piper*.

PAPILIO ARISTODEMUS Esper 1794
Dusky Swallowtail   **Pl. 18**

Description. Fw ♂ 49–54 mm, ♀ 50–55 mm. Upperside *ground colour dark brown, not black,* pattern of yellow markings as in *P. thoas* and *P. cresphontes,* with the following differences: forewing discal yellow band straight-edged on outer side at least between inner margin and vein 6, the individual spots rounded on inner edge; on the hindwing the basal yellow band (forming a continuation of the forewing discal band) is broad but not sharply defined on either edge and almost fills the basal half of the cell; *tail black but without a yellow spot or streak.* Underside dull ochreous; hindwing with no bold brick-red markings at end of cell, but discal series of blue crescents usually bordered proximally with traces of dull brown.

Distribution. Typical *P. aristodemus*, as described above, occurs in Haiti and the Dominican Republic, at low levels, but is not common. In Cuba and the Cayman Islands it is replaced by the subspecies *P. aristodemus temenes* Godart 1819, in which the diagonal yellow band is noticeably broader, straight-edged on both sides, and only faintly cut by the veins, on the forewing, also wider and extending to or beyond the end of the cell on the hindwing; on the underside of the hindwing the blue crescents are bordered internally almost throughout by a prominent chocolate-brown band. Santiago de Cuba (June), Gibara, Matanzas, etc. Little Cayman (May) on woodland paths. RANGE: Cuba to Puerto Rico; Florida. TL: Haiti.

Early stages. Caterpillar (in Florida) brown, with very irregular white or cream-coloured blotches along the sides, and blue or metallic dots; prolegs white or whitish. Solitary on Torchwood (*Amyris elemifera*).

PAPILIO ANDRAEMON Huebner 1823
Bahaman Swallowtail   **Pl. 18**
Confined to the Greater Antilles (TL (not stated): Cuba) in three subspecies:

1 **P. andraemon andraemon** Huebner. Fw ♂ 45–46 mm, ♀ 46–50 mm. Upperside ground colour black; forewing postdiscal yellow band parallel to outer margin and of even width throughout, the intersecting veins not darkened; a narrow diffuse yellow bar across the end of the cell, and three yellow apical spots beyond tip of band; *no submarginal spots*; hindwing deeply scalloped, especially at vein 2, which is produced to form a short tail; yellow band continues to end in a point immediately above eye-spot; six yellow lunules all close to margin and variable blue scaling between lunules and discal band, especially in female, in which the marginal lunules are lightly dusted with brownish. Underside similar, but basal black areas suffused yellowish; forewing black border divided by a longitudinal yellow stripe; hindwing outer edge of yellow band formed by a series of blue black-edged lunules, the lunule in space 3 surmounted by a chocolate-brown mark. In form *hernandezi* de la Torre 1936, there is a small cinnamon spot in each of the orange submarginal lunules on the hindwing upperside.

Distribution. Throughout Cuba: Havana, Santiago, Matanzas, Baracoa, St Christobal, etc. Introduced into Jamaica and now a pest there.

2 **P. andraemon bonhotei** Sharpe 1900. Differs in both sexes from *P. a. andraemon* in that the bold yellow band on the upperside is narrower on both wings (about 5 mm as against 8 mm in space 3 of forewing), and there are faint traces of narrow yellow submarginal lunules on the forewing from apex to anal angle. Underside similar.

Distribution. Restricted to Bahamas: Nassau, Andros, Cat Cay, South Bimini, Eleuthera, etc. April to September, possibly all the year round. TL: Nassau, Bahamas.

3 **P. andraemon tailori** Rothschild and Jordan 1906. Closer to *P. a. bonhotei* than to *P. a. andraemon*, the bold yellow upperside band being narrow as in the former, the forewing with faint linear lunules in space 1b to space 3. On the underside of the hindwing the chocolate mark in space 3 is usually long and pointed and often faintly repeated in space 2 and space 4.

Distribution. Confined to the Cayman Islands, where it flies at least from April to August. Specimens taken on Cayman Brac in May and June are much smaller than those from Grand Cayman and have rather wider yellow bands. TL: Grand Cayman.

Early stages. Full grown caterpillar very dark olive-green to black; first thoracic segment, saddle mark above 1st and 2nd pairs of prolegs and last two segments white or white marked; numerous blue spots along the back; prolegs and underside of body lilac. Very similar to the caterpillar of *P. thoas* which, how ever, does not have white lateral marks above the 3rd and 4th pairs of prolegs. Food plant *Citrus, Ruta*, etc.

PAPILIO MACHAONIDES Esper 1796
Machaonides Swallowtail   Pl. 19

Description. Fw ♂ 50–55 mm, ♀ slightly larger. Upperside in both sexes very dark brown, almost black; forewing with rather *narrow diagonal yellow band* from about mid-costa to just before inner angle, a parallel much shorter band below apex, and a submarginal series of double swallow-shaped yellow lunules; hindwing with broad discal band from mid-costa tapering to a point on vein 3 where it joins the inner of two yellow lunules, submarginal lunules rather narrow. On the underside of the forewing the yellow markings of the upperside are repeated and greatly expanded; the hindwing is clear yellow from base to postdiscal band of powdery blue lunules.

Distribution. Haiti and the Dominican Republic: Mt Isabella, La Cumbre, near La Vega, etc., June and December at least. Widespread at elevations above 1000 ft, but uncommon. Porto Rico. RANGE: Hispaniola and Porto Rico. TL: Port au Prince.

Early stages. Not known.

PAPILIO POLYXENES Fabricius 1775
American Black Swallowtail   Pl. 19

Description. Fw ♂ and ♀ 42–45 mm. Upperside black, both wings with a complete row of small round or crescentic yellow spots along the margin; forewing also with a parallel postdiscal row of oval or wedge-shaped yellow spots; hindwing with wider discal yellow band dissected by black veins, and with a shadowy blue area beyond, especially in the female. Underside similar but marginal markings tending to be paler, *other yellow markings suffused deep ochreous especially on hindwing*.

Distribution. Cuba, especially near Habana, and only in the typical subspecies *P. polyxenes polyxenes*. Other subspecies inhabit the mainland of America, where the species is common. RANGE: N. America to Peru. TL: Cuba.

Early stages. The caterpillar when full grown is greenish, each segment encircled by a black band bearing yellow spots – very like the caterpillar of the common European Swallowtail, *Papilio machaon*, to which it is closely related. It feeds on various Umbelliferae, such as carrot and parsley. Many-brooded.

PAPILIO PALAMEDES Drury 1773
Palamedes Swallowtail   Pl. 19

Description. Fw ♂ and ♀ 52–54 mm. Upperside black. Forewing with a full row of wedge-shaped postdiscal and round submarginal spots, a further spot in base of space 8, and a line at cell-end also yellow; hindwing with continuous narrow *yellow discal band* and a series of lunular submarginal spots. Underside of forewing patterned as on the upperside; hindwing with narrow yellow stripe from costa near base to middle of space 1b; submarginal markings brownish; a discal band of larger spots, and a row of powdery blue spots between the two bands. In the female the markings tend to be smaller than those of the male.

Distribution. Cuba: reported once only at 'some distance from Habana'. Almost certainly a stray, as it is common in Florida. RANGE: southern U.S.A. to Mexico. TL: Carolina.

Early stages. In America the caterpillar feeds on Magnolia. It is hump-backed, pale speckly green, with 'eye-spots' on the third segment.

PAPILIO TROILUS Linnaeus 1758
Spice Bush Swallowtail   **Pl. 19**

Description. Fw ♂ and ♀ 43 mm. Upperside black, without yellow discal bands; forewing with complete row of bold *yellow bullet-shaped submarginal spots* and greenish shading from inner margin to space 4; hindwing with similar but much larger yellow submarginal spots, the area between them and the cell-end powdered green. Underside similar; forewing markings larger; *hindwing submarginal markings orange*; a discal row of smaller orange spots (replaced by a green wedge in space 3); powdery blue crescents between the two rows. Female upperside submarginal spots smaller and round on forewing; hindwing postdiscal area blue rather than green; underside as in male.

Distribution. There is a single 1945 record of the occurrence of the N. American subspecies, *P. troilus ilioneus* Smith, at Cojimar, Havana Province, Cuba in May – certainly a vagrant from the mainland. Not reported from any other West Indian island. RANGE: Canada and eastern U.S.A. to Florida. TL: 'Indiis'.

Early stages. The full grown caterpillar is rich green above, brown beneath, little ornamented except for the eye-spot on either side slightly behind the head. Food plants include Spicebush, Sassafras and Magnolia.

PAPILIO THERSITES Fabricius 1775
False Androgeus Swallowtail   **Pl. 19**

Description. Sexes dissimilar. Male forewing 60–62 mm. Deceptively like *P. androgeus*. Most readily distinguished by the *submarginal lunules on the upperside of the hindwing*, which in *P. thersites* are rather *broad and flat and all yellow*, whereas in *P. androgeus* only the lunule (somewhat misshapen) in space 7 is yellow. On the underside of the hindwing the postdiscal blue lunules are large and conspicuous, but in *P. androgeus* they are almost linear. Female forewing 60–62 mm, also very like female *P. androgeus*: upperside ground colour black, forewing with a broad curved yellowish band from costa just before cell-end tapering to anal angle; hindwing dark discal area lacking green scaling and bounded by a series of dull red lunules followed by blue and then rather flat yellow lunules; underside markings as on upperside but the hindwing red and blue lunules rather larger.

Distribution. Jamaica: in parishes of St Elizabeth, Portland, St Thomas, St Andre and Manchester. March to May, July and August, October to December. Local and rather rare but widespread, frequenting woodland glades and hill tops. RANGE: Jamaica only. TL: 'America', *recte* Jamaica.

Early stages. Caterpillar brownish black, marbled pinkish white, resembling bird droppings when at rest, hump-backed. Head shining black with an inverted Y-mark; a white lateral line on either side of first four segments, a white saddle-mark on segments 6 to 8 and further white areas on last segments, body colour otherwise blackish interspersed with faint bluish markings except beneath, where it is pale greenish or pinkish. Food plants foliage of lime, lemon, orange etc.

PAPILIO ANDROGEUS Cramer 1775

Androgeus Swallowtail **Pl. 19**

Description. Sexes very dissimilar. Male forewing 65–70 mm. Upperside yellow, with black borders; forewing black border extending broadly from wing base through cell to apex, interrupted around cell-end and narrower thence and along outer margin; hindwing border 10–15 mm wide, confined to outer margin, and enclosing a series of faint *narrow highly arched greenish yellow submarginal lunules* from space 2 to space 6. On the underside of the forewing the markings are as above but reduced in area and intensity; on the hindwing the border is reduced to 2 mm wide and next to it there are a series of bold yellow lunules followed by a series of narrow blue crescents and a row of conical orange markings. Female forewing 60 mm. Upperside black; forewing unmarked; hindwing with rather large diffuse discal green area, followed by two rows of green lunules, the inner flat, the outer crescentic. On the underside the forewing is black but with a short dusky curved greenish band from costa just beyond cell-end to about space 4, and some narrow lunules beyond; hindwing also black, but with three rows of lunules towards the margin, the first brick-red, the second blue and narrower, the third greenish yellow; hind margin so deeply scalloped as to be almost tailed at veins 3 and 5. *P. thersites* (see above) is confusingly similar.

Distribution. Cuba, Haiti and Dominican Republic. Reputed to occur in St Lucia. Typical *P. androgeus* is confined to America south of Panama. In the male it hardly differs from the West Indian subspecies *P. androgeus epidaurus* Godman and Salvin, which is described above, though females differ considerably. RANGE: Mexico to Argentina. TL: Surinam.

Early stages. The caterpillar of *P. androgeus* feeds on citrus and is known to fruit growers as the Orange Puppy. Head olive-brown, body dark olive with an orange line across front of first segment which is continued along the sides of the first four segments, expands and becomes greenish on the 6th segment, and on the 7th unites with the similar band on the other side, ending on the 9th segment; a further similar saddle-shaped patch on segments 10 to 12; most segments with blue spots on the back; body beneath and false legs white (lilac in *P. andraemon*).

Note. The rather similar American *Papilio astyalus* Godart 1819, better but wrongly known as *Papilio lycophron* Huebner, has been reported on one occasion from St Lucia. It is fairly obvious from the separate accounts published independently by Sharpe and Butler, both in 1901, that the insect concerned was *P. androgeus*, and probably a stray. *P. astyalus* has not been reported from any other West Indian island. It is widespread from Mexico to Paraguay and could conceivably occur as a rare vagrant.

PAPILIO HOMERUS Fabricius 1793 *Homerus Swallowtail* **Pl. 20**

Description. Fw ♂ and ♀ about 75 mm. Broad winged and the largest of all American Swallowtails. Upperside ground colour black, both wings with wide yellow discal bands; forewing with yellow bar in cell and a row of yellow apical spots; hindwing with a series of *powdery blue postdiscal markings* and a *submarginal row of brick-red linear marks*. Underside ground colour dark chocolate-brown; forewing markings as on upperside; hindwing discal band much narrower, yellowish brown and dusted with blue scales.

Distribution. Jamaica: Blue Mts and Cockpit country: Portland, Trelawney,

St Thomas and St Elizabeth. Affects woodland glades near mountain streams. February to April; September and October. RANGE and TL: Jamaica.

Early stages. Full grown caterpillar rich deep green on back and sides, dark brown beneath, an eye-spot on each side of the third segment and a transverse white band on the fourth segment, brown markings on 9th and 10th segments. Food plants *Hernancia catalpaefolia* and *Thespesea populnea*.

PAPILIO ARISTOR Godart 1819
Scarce Haitian Swallowtail
Pl. 20

Description. Fw ♂ 40 mm, ♀ 52 mm. Very similar to *Papilio caiguanabus*, from which it differs as follows: on the upperside the forewing has an additional row of *five discal spots surrounding the cell-end* and the submarginal spots are not so close to the margin; on the hindwing the postdiscal spots are smaller and well separated. On the underside the forewing has a diffuse yellow spot in the cell and on the hindwing the postdiscal spots are pale, not darker than those of the forewing. The only known female, which is somewhat worn, has the spots of both bands paler than in the male and those of the discal band in spaces 5 and 6 smaller, but these could well be only individual differences.

Distribution. Haiti, near Port au Prince. The female was taken at Haut Turgeau, Port au Prince, in July. RANGE and TL: Haiti.

Early stages. Not known.

PAPILIO OXYNIUS Huebner 1827
Cuban Black Swallowtail
Pl. 20

Description. Fw ♂ and ♀ 40–50 mm. Upperside black, both wings with prominent *yellow or white marginal spots* which are square on the forewing, lunulate on the hindwing; *forewing without other markings* except for occasional faint white spots at cell-end suggesting the remnants of a transverse band; hindwing with up to six narrow red submarginal lunules, or none. Underside similar, markings more definite; on the hindwing the red lunules are larger than on the upperside and there is an additional row of smaller paler discal spots.

Distribution. Cuba only. Widespread; May to September. TL: Cuba.

Early stages. The full grown caterpillar is about 5 cm long: head orange-yellow with a white dot on each lateral lobe; body dusky olive with a chain-like line of markings along the back and numerous lines and white spots along the sides some of which are marked with red dots; spiracles white. Food plant *Zanthoxylum* (Ayua). The caterpillars feed at night, resting gregariously by day on tree trunks.

PAPILIO PELAUS Fabricius 1775 *Prickly Ash Swallowtail* Pl. 20
Papilio pelaus, though confined to the Greater Antilles, has developed three quite distinct subspecies:

1 **P. pelaus pelaus** Fabricius. Fw ♂ and ♀ 48–50 mm. Upperside black; forewing with a rather *narrow diagonal white band from costa at cell-end to inner angle*; hindwing with bold white marginal lunules along the deeply scalloped outer margin, and four or five small red submarginal lunules that change to white towards the anal angle. Underside similar; forewing white band wider; hindwing with red spots in all spaces from inner margin to costa and with an additional series of faint white discal spots. Markings usually bolder in female.

Distribution. Jamaica: in parishes of Portland, St Thomas, St Andrew, St Ann, Clarendon, Manchester and Trelawney. Flies slowly and frequents shady paths. Recorded dates of appearance are March and May to September. Never common, more frequent above 3000 ft. TL: 'India', *recte*, Jamaica.

2 **P. pelaus atkinsi** Bates 1935. Both sexes distinguishable from *P. p. pelaus* by the fractionally narrower diagonal white forewing band, but more easily by the noticeably larger red submarginal spots on the upperside of the hindwing.
Distribution. Cuba, Guantanamo, in April. TL: Cuba, Guantanamo.

3 **P. pelaus imerius** Godart 1824. In both sexes the diagonal white forewing band is less than 2 mm wide, and the hindwing submarginal red spots fewer, smaller and inconspicuous.
Distribution. Hispaniola: La Vega, Mt Isabella, La Cumbre, etc., at 1200 ft in April and May. Porto Rico: widely distributed in April to August, December. TL: 'Ind. Or.,' *recte* Haiti.

Early stages. Full grown caterpillar purplish or greenish brown, intricately marked behind the head with darker brown, and with irregular creamy white lateral markings on segments 5–7, 10 and 11. Head pale yellow. Several segments bear a pair of short lateral tubercles. Gregarious, on Prickly Ash, *Zanthoxylum martinicense*.

PAPILIO CAIGUANABUS Poey 1851
Poey's Black Swallowtail
                                                     Pl. 20
Description. Fw ♂ 48–49 mm, ♀ 49–50 mm. Upperside black; forewing with a straight *row of equal-sized yellow spots close to the outer margin*; hindwing with a postdiscal row of larger deeper yellow spots, narrower yellow marginal crescents and a red anal ocellus. Underside markings as on upperside, but hindwing with two additional brick-red spots just beyond the cell-end and a series of narrow blue discal crescents. Female pattern of markings as in the male, but on the upperside the forewing marginal spots are paler and the hindwing postdiscal spots white; underside as in the male.
Distribution. Cuba: Oriente, Matanzas, etc., sea level to 1000 ft. Rare, most frequent in the east. RANGE: Cuba only. TL: Cuba.
Early stages. Full grown caterpillar black dorsally, dark brown along the sides, with bold white markings on first thoracic segment laterally rather than dorsally, third to fifth segments laterally (not united to form a saddle mark), and dorsolaterally on the last two or three segments not united over the back. Food plant *Securinega acidothannus* (Miss M. E. Fountaine, unpublished drawings and notes).

EURYTIDES CELADON Lucas 1852
Cuban Kite Swallowtail
                                                     Pl. 20
Description. Fw ♂ and ♀ 35–40 mm. Very similar to *E. marcellinus* of Jamaica. Most readily distinguished by the following characters: on the upperside the forewing discal grey band is wider, angled at the base of vein 3, but does not enter space 3, and there are *two short pale bars between the cell-end and the apical spots*; on the underside of the hindwing the two long parallel dark stripes are both brown.
Distribution. Cuba: Pinar del Rio, Camaguey, Oriente, etc. July, September

and October. Apparently widespread. RANGE: Cuba only. TL 'Amer. sept',
recte Cuba.
Early stages. Not known. For description of the caterpillar of the closely
allied American *E. marcellus* see *E. marcellinus* (below).

EURYTIDES ZONARIA Butler 1869
Haitian Kite Swallowtail

Pl. 20

Description. Fw ♂ and ♀ 35–40 mm. Very like the Jamaican *E. marcellinus*, but
may be distinguished by the following characters: on the upperside the *pale
discal band on the forewing* extends fully into the base of space 3, where it is
divided into two narrow bars that extend to the costa; and on the hindwing the
scarlet anal spot is larger and extends from the inner margin to vein 3; on the
underside of the hindwing the outer of the two long parallel stripes is not red
(or has only a few red scales) beyond the end of the cell.
Distribution. Hispaniola: Mt Isabella, La Vega, etc. Widespread and not
uncommon, apparently single brooded with a rather brief flight period. RANGE:
Hispaniola. TL: San Domingo.
Early stages. Not known.

EURYTIDES MARCELLINUS Doubleday 1845
Jamaican Kite Swallowtail

Pl. 20

Description. Fw ♂ and ♀ 30–35 mm. Upperside black, with bold pale green
stripes and submarginal spots; on the forewing the discal pale band broadens
from about mid-costa to middle of inner margin, its outer edge cutting across
the base of space 3; and there is *only one short pale bar between the cell-end and
the apex*; on the hindwing the pale discal band tapers to a point in space 4, and
two long narrow pale bands run from the wing base to the red anal spot. The
underside markings are as on the upperside but the ground colour is brown;
hindwing with a wide red stripe from near base towards tail paralleled by a
light brown stripe nearer the inner margin. Tail about 10 mm long.
Distribution. Jamaica: St Thomas, foothills of the Blue Mts, Constant Spring,
etc. May, June. Widespread but not common. Sporadic, often not seen for
long periods. RANGE and TL: Jamaica.
Early stages. Not known. The caterpillar of the closely related common
American *Eurytides marcellus* feeds on Pawpaw (*Asimia triloba*). It is stumpy,
pale greenish, each segment with a number of fine transverse black lines and, in
most cases, a single broader yellow line.

One can be forgiven for mistaking these stout-bodied short-winged butterflies for some kind of day-flying moth. The really vigorous kinds have a flight almost like that of the Humming Birds. They differ from all other butterflies in so many features that they are often referred to as a separate suborder, the Grypocera, equal in status to the whole of the rest of the butterflies, the Rhopalocera. Amongst other characters of the family are the short body and the very wide head with antennae set far apart. The club of the antennae provides further characters not found in other families, for it is often hooked, and even more often ends in a pointed apiculus which is bent at an angle beyond the end of the main club. The forewing has the full complement of twelve veins, those arising from the cell (discoidal cell) always simple and unbranched.

There should be little difficulty in recognising a Skipper for what it is. But when it comes to the matter of a classification of the family the situation is very different. It is easier to find characters that separate the species than those that unite them in genera or larger groups. This is due to the complex anatomy of the hard parts of the male genitalia, which provide excellent specific but less good generic characters. However, due to the labours of the late W. H. Evans, there does now exist a complete reclassification of the Hesperiidae based on uniform criteria, and this is adopted in this guide. Of the subfamilies into which Evans divided the Hesperiidae two are represented in the West Indies, namely the Pyrginae and the Hesperiinae. In the former, vein 5 of the forewing arises nearer to vein 6 than to vein 4, the males very often have a costal fold (containing androconia), the wings are usually held flat (as in moths) when the insect is at rest, and the caterpillars so far as known all feed on dicotyledons such as Leguminosae, Myrtaceae, Anonaceae, Piperaceae, etc. In the Hesperiinae on the other hand vein 5 of the forewing arises nearer to vein 4 than to vein 6, the males very often have conspicuous sex-brands of androconia on the forewing, but never a costal fold, the insects rest with their wings held erect, and the caterpillars feed exclusively on monocotyledons such as grasses, rushes, palms, bamboos, etc. The Pyrginae are usually subdivided again into two Sections, based largely on the length of the forewing cell in relation to the costa, long in Section I (*Phocides* to *Cabares*), short in Section II (*Cogia* to *Heliopetes*). The remaining genera (*Synapte* to the end) fall into the Hesperiinae. These subdivisions are largely corroborated by what little is known of the life histories of the Skippers.

Hesperiid caterpillars all have one curious and rather grotesque character in common, their large and conspicuous heads that seem to be but loosely attached to the body by what looks like a narrow neck (and is often so described) but is in fact the attenuated first segment of the thorax. Pyrgine caterpillars are mostly rather spindle-shaped, those of the Hesperiinae much more cylindrical. Nearly all live in shelters formed by drawing leaves together with silken threads, and most of them pupate within these same shelters. Their colours are seldom striking, as one would expect of a caterpillar that is almost always hidden from sight; yet the head is often vividly coloured and sometimes startlingly 'monkey-faced' and can be quite frightening when suddenly exposed at the entrance to its shelter.

PHOCIDES PIGMALION Cramer 1779
Mangrove Skipper

Pl. 21

Description. Fw ♂ 27–30 mm, ♀ 29–32 mm. Upperside deep lustrous blue-black, marked with *shining bright blue stripes*; forewing only with three transverse groups of transparent spots, which are wider in the female than in the male but seldom, even in that sex, more than 2 mm wide; male forewing with the costal fold extending almost to wing base. Underside markings as on upperside, but the forewing ground colour much duller and the hindwing blue stripes brighter.
Distribution. *P. pigmalion bicolora* Boddaert 1783, the subspecies described above, occurs in Haiti, the Dominican Republic and in Porto Rico. It differs from *P. pigmalion* of the mainland in having all the transparent bands of the forewing equally reduced in width. In the Bahamas, Cuba and the Cayman Islands it is replaced by *P. p. batabano* Lucas 1857 in which the forewing is uniformly purplish black in the male, purplish brown in the female, with no markings other than a little blue scaling at the wing base; the hindwing markings are also greatly reduced and in the female virtually absent. This subspecies is so different that one could be forgiven for treating it as a distinct species. RANGE: southern U.S.A. to Argentina. TL: Surinam.
Early stages. In the United States the fully grown caterpillar is bright frosted white, tapering to either end, and covered with minute frosted hairs each in a minute pit; head light brown, rough, spotted with orange. Food plant Red Mangrove (*Rhizophora mangle*).

PHOCIDES PERKINSAE Kaye 1931
Miss Perkins' Skipper

Pl. 21

Description. Fw ♂ 26 mm, ♂ 32 mm. Upperside ground colour rather light brown; forewing with three transverse bands of hyaline spots, as in *P. pigmalion*, but the discal row not extending below vein 2; hindwing margin somewhat scalloped, fringes almost white between the ends of the veins, *traces of two faint yellow stripes towards anal angle*; underside the same.
Distribution. *Phocides perkinsae* is confined to Jamaica, where it is both rare and local. It has been taken at the flowers of Cheese Wood and the flowering tree *Gliridia sepium*. It is only when feeding like this that it is not too difficult to catch. It is sometimes treated as a subspecies of *Phocides linciae* Herrich-Schaeffer, a species of similar coloration but with very much wider hyaline bands and known only from Guiana. RANGE and TL: Jamaica.
Early stages. Not known.

PROTEIDES MERCURIUS Fabricius 1787
Mercury Skipper

Pl. 21

Description. Fw ♂ and ♀ 27–32 mm. Upperside ground colour almost black; head, thorax and wing bases ochreous and hairy; hindwing margin gently scalloped and anal angle lobed; cilia white on hindwing throughout but only below vein 4 on forewing; forewing rather falcate and with a row of four detached hyaline discal spots, a linear spot in space 3 and one or two very small subapical costal spots. Underside wholly dark brown, *palpi white, forewing margin and a* *large central wedge-shaped area of the hindwing sprinkled more or less densely with white scales.* Hyaline spots larger in female than in male.

Distribution. Typical *P. mercurius* is a continental insect. In the West Indies it is replaced by a series of well-marked subspecies, on one of which, *P. mercurius sanchesi* Bell and Comstock 1948 from Haiti, the above description is based. *P. m. mercurius* is more boldly marked and much whiter on the underside. *P. m. sanantonio* Lucas 1856, the Cuban subspecies, is at once distinguished by the absence of hyaline spots, except the minute costal spots. *P. m. jamaicensis* Skinner 1920 is like the Haitian subspecies on the upperside but the underside is rather evenly greyish purple without a great deal of white scaling, the black basal, inner marginal and short postdiscal bars (the last from inner margin to vein 3) all standing out very boldly. In the remaining subspecies the general tone of the underside is reddish brown unrelieved by white scaling: *P. m. pedro* Dewitz 1877 from Porto Rico is rather small, very dully marked and with all hyaline spots small; in *P. m. vincenti* Bell and Comstock 1948 from St Vincent hyaline spots are larger, though still small; and in *P. m. angasi* Godman and Salvin 1886 from Dominica and St Lucia they are as well developed as in continental *P. mercurius*, but the underside ground colour is very dark, even darker than in *P. m. jamaicensis*. *P. mercurius* is a strong flyer, but not too difficult to take whilst visiting flowers such as *Lantana*, of which it is very fond. RANGE: Mexico to Argentina. TL: French Guiana.

Early stages. The caterpillar is variously described as honey-coloured mixed with dark brown, or very dark olive-green. It has a red lateral stripe and a very robust red head, and lives in a leaf shelter. Food plants include *Muellera moniliformis* (in Brazil), *Derris eliptica*, *Cassia* and tree-like Papilionaceae.

PROTEIDES MAYSI Lucas 1856   *Mays' Giant Skipper*   **Pl. 21**

Description. Fw ♂ 23–27 mm, ♀ 30 mm. Upperside glossy dark brown, the base of the forewing and (when fresh) most of the hindwing covered with slightly lighter long hair scales; forewing with *one very small, or twin, hyaline spots at mid-costa and just before apex.* Underside ground colour purplish, forewing unmarked, *hindwing with short silver discal bar*, of varying width, not reaching costa or inner margin, and broader in the female than in the male.

Distribution. Confined to Cuba: Santiago de Cuba, Holguin, etc. TL Cuba.

Early stages. Not known.

EPARGYREUS ZESTOS Geyer 1832   *Zestos Skipper*   **Pl. 21**

Description. Fw ♂ 23–25 mm, ♀ 27–28 mm. Upperside in both sexes rich ochreous brown; forewing with transverse series of *four translucent brassy spots, from mid-costa to space 1b, usually conjoined*; a similar but smaller spot near base of space 3, and a subapical group of three very much smaller spots; hindwing unmarked, its basically darker ground colour heavily obscured by long ochreous hair-scales. Underside like upperside, but hindwing underside sprinkled with ochreous scales that tend to indicate a broad transverse light brown band; ground colour rather more purplish in female than in male.

Distribution. Bahamas (Nassau), Virgin Isles (St Thomas), St Kitts, Guadeloupe, Dominica, Martinique, St Lucia, St Vincent, Barbados, and probably on the other Lesser Antilles. Not reported from any of the Greater Antilles. RANGE: Florida, C. America and Lesser Antilles. TL: Surinam.

Early stages. Not known. The few caterpillars of *Epargyreus* that are known are conspicuously coloured in green and black, with red prolegs, and feed on leguminous trees and shrubs.

EPARGYREUS ANTAEUS Hewitson 1867

Jamaican Silver-spotted Skipper **Pl. 21**

Description. Fw ♂ 25–26 mm, ♀ 27–28 mm. Upperside exactly like that of *Epargyreus zestos* Geyer. Underside ground colour more purplish; hindwing with dazzling white transverse *band* which is *twice as wide in the lower half* (towards anal angle) *as in upper half.*

Distribution. Jamaica only, where it appears to be local rather than rare. Flies high. TL: Jamaica.

Early stages. Not known.

EPARGYREUS SPANNA Evans 1952

Haitian Silver-spotted Skipper **Pl. 21**

Description. Fw ♀ 34 mm; ♂ not known. Like *Epargyreus zestos* Geyer but the spots of the transverse band on the forewing relatively smaller, and *white band* on underside of hindwing *narrowing evenly* from just below costa (where it is divided) towards anal angle.

Distribution. The only known specimen was collected on 'St Domingo' (Dominican Republic) about 1850. RANGE: Hispaniola. TL: San Domingo.

POLYGONUS LEO Gmelin 1790 *Hammock Skipper* **Pl. 21**

Description. Fw ♂ 13–16 mm, ♀ 14–18 mm. Upperside blackish in both sexes with faint purplish flush when fresh; forewing with bifid spot in cell, a rectangular spot in space 2 and in space 3, and three very small subapical spots, all translucent pearly white; hindwing with at most faint shadowy indications of underside markings showing through. *Underside* paler, the ground colour of the apical half of the forewing and all the hindwing much paler, *pinkish purple to greenish; two parallel darker bands*; margin darkened especially around anal angle.

Distribution. *Polygonus leo* is represented in the West Indies by three subspecies: *P. leo savignyi* Latreille 1824 from Cuba, the Bahamas, Virgin Isles, St Kitts and Montserrat has a strong purplish sheen on the upperside and prominent dark bands on the hindwing underside; in *P. leo hagar* Evans 1952 from Jamaica the upperside gloss is almost or quite lacking and the dark bands on the hindwing underside are hardly differentiated from the ground colour; *P. leo ishmael* Evans 1952 from Haiti differs markedly in having the ground colour of the hindwing underside grey-green. RANGE: southern U.S.A. to Argentina. TL: America.

Early stages. The caterpillar has been described as somewhat mottled yellow-green with a roughened appearance, yellow prolegs and a narrow yellow lateral line. The very large head is shown in an unpublished figure of the Jamaican caterpillar as dirty white with a black mark on the crown. In Cuba it is said to be black; in Porto Rico lemon-yellow. It feeds on dogwood (*Piscidia erythrina* and *P. piscipula*) and, at any rate in Cuba, on *Lonchocarpus.*

Note. *Polygonus leo* derives its popular name from its predilection for shady trails in Hardwood Hammocks. Pitches on the undersides of leaves when resting.

POLYGONUS MANUELI Bell and Comstock
Manuel's Skipper   Pl. 21

Description. Fw ♂ 22 mm, ♀ 23 mm. Upperside as in *Polygonus leo*, but the purple gloss more bluish and restricted to the wing bases, the translucent white spots smaller. Underside ground colour browner, with considerable purple gloss; on the hindwing underside the *prominent black subbasal spot is lacking or very small*, the inner dark band is most prominent against the costa (in *P. leo* it is weakest there), and the ground colour between the bands in space 1c is distinctly ochreous.

Distribution. *P. manueli* is essentially a continental species. It is represented in the West Indies by *P. manueli punctus* Bell and Comstock 1948, which is described above and is confined to the Lesser Antilles: St Kitts, Guadeloupe, Dominica, St Lucia, St Vincent (TL) and no doubt other islands. RANGE: southern U.S.A. to Argentina. TL: Brazil.

Early stages. Nothing is known of the early stages of the Caribbean subspecies. In Brazil the full grown caterpillar is 'half green, half yellow, with a patchy look, the dorsal area enclosed by light stripes; head flat, light red and glossy, darker behind and with black eye-spots on the crown. Food plant *Muellera moniliformis* (Leguminosae)' (Miles Moss).

CHIOIDES CATILLUS Cramer 1779
Jamaican Long-tail Skipper   Pl. 21

Description. Fw ♂ and ♀ 24–28 mm. The yellowish translucent cell-spot on the forewing largely or completely overlaps the similar square spot in space 2 below it. On the underside of the forewing the dark velvety subapical triangular spot is sharply defined; on the hindwing underside the subbasal *dark band is outwardly edged, and surrounded towards the costa, by light grey scaling* which also occurs along the outer margin. The tail, which is about 15 mm long, is uniformly dark brown. The antennal club is white beneath, and the hindwing outer margin very straight.

Distribution. The above description is based on *Chioides catillus churchi* Bell and Comstock 1948, which is the only subspecies of this variable and wide ranging species to occur in the West Indies. It is confined to Jamaica where it is widespread but not particularly common. RANGE: southern U.S.A. to Argentina. TL: S. America.

Early stages. The fully grown caterpillar (in Mexico) is rather squat, the body pale greenish yellow with a faint dorso-lateral yellow line on each side, densely sprinkled with minute black dots, ventral surface darker green than the back, legs all orange; head large, vertex scarlet merging into red below and with a frontal Y-shaped black mark, the very narrow black neck and prothoracic collar separated by a bright orange band. Food plant *Tephrosia* sp.

CHIOIDES VINTRA Evans 1952
St Vincent Long-tail Skipper   Pl. 22

Description. Fw ♂ and ♀ 21–23 mm. Upperside uniformly dark brown, fringes barely chequered, tail relatively short, curved and not expanded at its tip (not spatulate); forewing with 5 to 8 (♀) small or very small white translucent spots, viz., 3 subapically in an even row, a more or less dumb-bell shaped spot on space 3 and a minute spot at cell-end always present; in addition there may be a minute spot at mid-costa and another in space 2; and in the female the last

1. Papilio machaonides   *Machaonides Swallowtail*   p. 148
Two of the yellow bands on the forewing run diagonally, not parallel to the outer margin.
♂ Porto Rico.

2. Papilio polyxenes   *American Black Swallowtail*   148
Hindwing yellow band wide and filling distal half of cell; an eyespot at anal angle.
♂ Cuba.

3. Papilio palamedes   *Palamedes Swallowtail*   148
Hindwing yellow band not entering cell; no eye-spot at anal angle.
♂ Florida.

4. Papilio troilus   *Spice Bush Swallowtail*   149
On the underside the spots forming the submarginal band are yellow on the forewing, red on the hindwing.
♂ Florida.

5. Papilio thersites   *False Androgeus Swallowtail*   149
♂ with clear yellow submarginal crescents on hindwing upperside and postdiscal blue crescents in spaces 2 to 5; ♀ with wide yellow discal band on forewing upperside.
5a ♂, 5b ♀, Jamaica.

6. Papilio androgeus   *Androgeus Swallowtail*   150
♂ with narrow dusky submarginal crescents on hindwing upperside and no blue crescents in spaces 2 to 5; ♀ forewing without yellow band.

20

1. **Papilio homerus**   *Homerus Swallowtail*   p. 150
   The largest Caribbean Swallowtail, and confined to Jamaica.
   ♂ Rio Grande Valley, Jamaica. June.

2. **Papilio aristor**   *Scarce Haitian Swallowtail*   151
   The two convergent rows of isolated pale spots in the subapical
   region of the forewing are diagnostic.
   ♀ Turgeau, Port au Prince, Haiti. July.

3. **Papilio oxynius**   *Cuban Black Swallowtail*   151
   Forewing with a series of white rectangular marginal spots
   between the veins, but no other markings.
   ♂ Guantanamo, Cuba.

4. **Papilio pelaus**   *Prickly Ash Swallowtail*   151
   Forewing with single diagonal white band from mid-costa to
   anal angle.
   ♂ Jamaica.

5. **Papilio caiguanabus**   *Poey's Black Swallowtail*   152
   Forewing with straight row of yellow submarginal spots close to
   the margin.
   ♂ Cuba.

6. **Eurytides celadon**   *Cuban Kite Swallowtail*   152
   Middle pair of transverse pale bands in forewing cell expanded
   to form a broad U-shaped mark; discal line on underside of
   hindwing red from costa to vein 7 only.
   ♀ Cuba.

7. **Eurytides zonaria**   *Haitian Kite Swallowtail*   153
   Middle lines in forewing cell very narrow and widely separated
   by a black bar; discal line on hindwing underside red-centred as
   far as vein 4.
   ♀ Haiti.

8. **Eurytides marcellinus**   *Jamaican Kite Swallowtail*   153
   Third and fourth lines in forewing cell fused and forming an
   extension of the discal band; discal line on hindwing underside
   red and continuous from costa to space 3.
   ♂ Jamaica.

of these may span the space from vein 2 to vein 3 and be accompanied by a very small spot in space 1b. On the underside of the forewing the dark triangular subapical mark is well defined against the rather powdery grey ground colour which extends to the whole of the hindwing; the darker markings on the underside of the hindwing consist of a basal and subbasal group of four roughly rectangular spots followed by a *postdiscal band which, starting broad but not well defined from the distal half of costa, gradually tapers away towards the inner margin* and is partially paralleled by a similar submarginal band.

Distribution. Apparently confined to St Vincent and Grenada. RANGE: Lesser Antilles. TL: St Vincent.

Early stages. Not known.

Note. *Chioides vintra* was originally described as a subspecies of *C. catillus*, but it is so distinct in appearance and morphology that such an association seems unjustified. It bears a great resemblance to *Urbanus obscurus* Hewitson (p. 164) with which it flies and possibly has a mimetic association. The characters of the forewing spotting, the tail, and the markings of the underside of the hindwing will readily separate it.

CHIOIDES IXION Ploetz 1881 *Ixion Skipper* Pl. 21

Description. Fw ♂ and ♀ 27–28 mm. Like *C. catillus* but a larger and more heavily built insect. Forewing translucent cell-spot separate from or only overlapping a corner of the spot in space 2; hindwing outer margin markedly rounded. On the underside of the forewing the apical area is variegated and the triangular subapical costal spot not sharply isolated; *hindwing pattern very confused*, the *darker discal markings edged silver*, no silver markings in postdiscal area but some silvery dusting towards apex.

Distribution. Confined to Haiti. TL: Haiti.

Early stages. Not known.

CHIOIDES MARMOROSA Herrich-Schaeffer 1865
Marbled Skipper Pl. 21

Description. Fw ♂ 24 mm. Upperside dull brown, the fringes faintly chequered in paler brown. *Forewing translucent spots almost white*, much smaller than in *C. catillus*, almost linear in space 2, a little wider in space 3, reduced to a point in space 1b, and in the cell to a dot against the anterior margin. Underside markings of hindwing and of apex of forewing very much as in *Chioides ixion* but redder and with less silver.

Distribution. Known only from Cuba, and seemingly very rare. TL: Cuba.

Early stages. Not known.

AGUNA ASANDER Hewitson 1867 *Aguna Skipper* Pl. 21

Description. Fw ♂ and ♀ 25–26 mm. The stubby laterally projecting lobe that takes the place of the usual long hindwing tail is characteristic of this species. Upperside ground colour medium brown, with faint brassy reflections on thorax and at wing bases. Translucent spots of forewing band only separated by the veins and subequal in size, subapical spot in space 6 far removed beyond those in spaces 7, 8 and 9. Underside ground colour purplish, forewing markings as on the upperside, *hindwing with a white transverse stripe* from mid-costa to vein 1b.

Distribution. *Aguna asander* throughout most of its range has the ground colour of the underside of the hindwing heavily powdered with silvery grey scales. In the two subspecies that occur in the West Indies this powdering is absent or restricted to the sides of the white band. In *A. asander haitensis* Mabille and Boullet 1912 the translucent spots are yellow; in *A. asander jasper* Evans 1952, from Jamaica, they are smaller and white. The species is not known elsewhere in the West Indies. RANGE: Mexico to Argentina. TL: Amazons.

Early stages. Not known. In the Argentine Republic the caterpillar is said to feed on Leguminosae, but it has not been described.

URBANUS PROTEUS Linnaeus 1758
Common Long-tail Skipper   **Pl. 21**

Description. Fw ♂ 21–24 mm, ♀ 22–26 mm. The *iridescent green hair scales* of the head, thorax and abdomen, the hindwing and the base of the forewing, readily distinguish this common species. The female is always larger than the male and has larger translucent spots, and also nearly always has a translucent spot in space 4 of the forewing, which is usually lacking in the male.

Distribution. Throughout the West Indies, slightly smaller, darker and with smaller forewing spots in the Lesser Antilles than elsewhere. The West Indian subspecies is *U. proteus domingo* Scudder 1872 (TL: Haiti). RANGE: U.S.A. to Argentina. TL: 'America'.

Early stages. The full grown caterpillar is yellowish green, with a speckled appearance, and has a light yellow lateral stripe, a narrower dark dorsal stripe, the posterior segments touched with red or orange; head reddish to orange, or brown, prolegs the same. The precise colour appears to vary a good deal from place to place, especially in respect of the head and anal segments. Food plants include peas and beans, on which the caterpillar is a minor pest, and many other plants.

URBANUS DORANTES Stoll 1790   *Dorantes Skipper*   **Pl. 21**

Description. Fw ♂ and ♀ 21–23 mm. Upperside ground colour uniformly rather dark brown, *cilia lightly chequered*; hindwing tail 9–10 mm long. Forewing *translucent spots small*, spot in space 2 often linear in male, always broader in female; spot in space 1b present in both sexes. Hindwing underside ground colour faintly purplish grey, against which the dark transverse bands stand out conspicuously; outer margin almost as dark as the bands.

Distribution. *Urbanus dorantes* occurs in the West Indies in two subspecies. *U. dorantes cramptoni* Comstock 1944, described above and illustrated on Plate 21 occurs in Hispaniola, Porto Rico and the Virgin Islands (St Thomas) (TL: Porto Rico) but not elsewhere. *U. dorantes santiago* Lucas 1857 is confined to the island of Cuba; it differs markedly on the underside of the hindwing, the ground colour between the dark bands being so dark, and the outer margin so broadly pale grey, that the general appearance is quite altered. It seems remarkable that *U. dorantes* is so far unknown from Jamaica. It has recently reached Andros Island in the Bahamas, presumably from Florida where it is common. RANGE: southern U.S.A. to Argentina. TL: Surinam.

Early stages. In the West Indies the caterpillar seems to be pale green or yellowish, with the first segment and the thoracic shield orange in front, fuscous behind, the head black and very rough. Food plants beans. In Brazil the full grown caterpillar is described as pinkish, with a black dorsal line, a large sepia head and a row of sepia arrow-shaped marks along the side.

URBANUS OBSCURUS Hewitson 1867
Stub-tailed Skipper   **Pl. 22**

Description. Fw ♂ and ♀ 19–23 mm. Upperside ground colour dark brown; fringes only faintly chequered; tail 6–7 mm, i.e. much shorter than in *U. dorantes*. Forewing translucent spots very small (may be entirely lacking in male); no spot in space 1b, spot in space 2 absent in male but usually present in female. Hindwing underside pattern as in *U. dorantes cramptoni*, but less well marked, the *outer dark transverse band not so close to the outer margin*.

Distribution. Throughout the Lesser Antilles from St Kitts and Antigua to Barbados and Grenada. May be confused with *Chioides vintra* (p. 159) on the upperside, but readily separable by the pattern of the markings on the underside of the hindwing. It is sometimes regarded as a subspecies of the wide ranging *Urbanus dorantes*, with which it is obviously closely related, though clearly distinct. RANGE: Lesser Antilles. TL: Guadeloupe.

Early stages. The caterpillar (in St Lucia) when fully grown is yellowish brown, heavily speckled with minute black dots; a fine black dorsal line and narrow cream-coloured interrupted lateral line; neck red, head very dark brown. Found on *Hyptis pectinata*.

Note. Three other species of *Urbanus* have been reported to occur on Jamaica, *Urbanus tellus* Huebner 1821, *Urbanus tanna* Evans 1952 and *U. albimargo* Mabille 1875. In each case the record is based on a single specimen, and in no case is the species recorded from any other West Indian island. Unless confirmed by further captures it seems best to ignore these records. *U. tellus* and *U. tanna* are characterised by a narrow translucent bar running from forewing mid-costa to just beyond vein 2 near the anal angle; they can only be distinguished by dissection of the male genitalia. *U. albimargo* has a similar line, but the hindwing margin and the tail are white.

POLYTHRIX OCTOMACULATA Sepp 1848
Eight Spot Skipper   **Pl. 21**

Description. Fw ♂ and ♀ 19–23 mm. Upperside ground colour rather pale smooth greyish brown; forewing translucent spots arranged in the pattern common to the whole group of related species, but rather small. On the underside the pale inner margin of the forewing is characteristic. Hindwing *tail curved*.

Distribution. In the West Indies *P. octomaculata* occurs only in Haiti, in the subspecies *decussata* Ménétriés 1855, which differs from the mainland subspecies figured in that the forewing spot in space 2 is minute, that in space 3 absent. RANGE: Mexico to Argentina. TL Surinam.

Early stages. Nothing is known of the early stages of the species in Haiti. The caterpillar of the typical Amazonian subspecies is nearly white and has numerous tiny longitudinal streaks of grey and a very faint lateral line; head very flat, yellow, patterned in pale mauve or light red. It feeds on *Pterocarpus draco*, *P. indicus* and *Muellera moniliformis*, all Leguminosae.

ASTRAPTES TALUS Cramer 1777   *Guaraguao Skipper*   **Pl. 21**
Description. Fw ♂ and ♀ 23–30 mm. Upperside ground colour medium brown; head, thorax, abdomen, basal third of forewing and most of hindwing clothed in *vivid green hair-scales*; the translucent spot in space 2 of forewing, forming part of the usual chain of spots, anvil-shaped; adjoining spot in space 3

roughly square. On the underside the palpi and thorax and a large part of the hindwing are green, but only the extreme base of the forewing.

Distribution. Cuba. Hispaniola. Jamaica. Porto Rico and St Vincent. Not common. RANGE: Mexico to Argentina. TL: Surinam.

Early stages. The caterpillar is black, the segments divided by a thin transverse dirty yellow line; head grey, with a median black stripe; prolegs red. Food plant (in Surinam) Taytay (*Paullinia*); in Cuba it feeds on *Guarea guara* (Yamao) also known as Guaraguao.

ASTRAPTES ANAPHUS Cramer 1777   *Roy's Skipper*   Pl. 21

Description. Fw ♂ and ♀ 24–27 mm. Upperside warm brown, the hair-scales on head, thorax and wing bases faintly yellowish; *hindwing fringes cream coloured*, the darker bands positioned as in other species of the genus but a good deal more conspicuous. Underside similar, the dark bands more prominent, the postdiscal band on the hindwing often bordered with a diffuse band of yellow scales that sometimes extends almost to the outer margin.

Distribution. Local in Jamaica, mainly in the east; apparently widespread in Cuba, e.g. Santiago, Holguin, etc.; Haiti (Port au Prince) and Dominican Republic; Dominica and St Vincent; all in subspecies *A. anaphus anausis* Godman and Salvin 1896 (TL: St Vincent). Typical *A. anaphus* Cramer occurs throughout most of South America and has an extensive yellow area at the anal angle of the hindwing. A third subspecies, *A. anaphus anoma* Evans 1952, occurs in Trinidad. RANGE: Mexico to Argentina. TL: Surinam.

Early stages. In Brazil the caterpillar is 'plain yellow with a big round head which is brown and has prominent eye-spots. Food plant a creeping wild bean'.

ASTRAPTES CASSANDER Fabricius 1793
Dismal Skipper   Pl. 21

Description. Fw ♂ 26 mm, ♀ 33 mm. Upperside uniformly dull dark brown, only the *thorax and extreme wing bases relieved by dull greyish blue hair-scales*. Forewing rather paler than hindwing and with two faint slightly darker transverse bands on both surfaces. Hindwing underside uniformly chocolate-brown. Palpi grey-brown beneath.

Distribution. Known only from Cuba and the Isle of Pines. A fast flying woodland species. TL: Cuba.

Early stages. Not known.

ASTRAPTES XAGUA Lucas 1857   *Blue-backed Skipper*   Pl. 21

Description. Fw ♂ 25 mm, ♀ 28 mm. Upperside dark brown, almost black, the head, thorax, abdomen and the bases of both wings vivid iridescent sky blue. *Underside* ground colour not quite so dark, the *iridescent blue confined to the base of the forewing in the cell and space 2*, and terminating level with a white spot on the costa; palpi and thorax buff.

Distribution. Cuba: Santiago, Holguin, Guantanamo, as *A. xagua xagua*. In Hispaniola it is replaced by *A. xagua christyi* Sharpe 1899, which is distinguished by having a chain of narrow translucent spots that form a boundary to the iridescent blue on the forewing and run from the costa to just below vein 2. RANGE: Cuba and Hispaniola. TL: Cuba.

Early stages. Not known.

ASTRAPTES HABANA Lucas 1857
Cuban Giant Blue Skipper

Pl. 21

Description. Fw ♂ and ♀ 25–28 mm. Upperside black; thorax and abdomen (but not the head) basal two-thirds of forewing and most of the disc of the hindwing brilliant bright blue; cilia white on whole of hindwing but only near anal angle on forewing. *Underside* rather uniformly warm dark brown *with no blue scaling*; forewing with lighter rectangular area at cell-end; both wings with purple-tinted white marginal borders about 2 mm wide, but wider in spaces 2 and 3 of forewing.

Distribution. *Astraptes habana habana*, described above, is confined to Cuba, where it would seem to be widely distributed and not uncommon: Santiago, Holguin, Guantanamo, Sierra Maestra, etc. It is replaced on Hispaniola by *A. h. heriul* Mabille and Boullet 1912, which differs in having the pale underside borders greatly reduced, darker, and much less well defined, and the lighter brown ground colour crossed by indistinct darker bands. *A. habana* is very similar to *Astraptes xagua* on the upperside, but easily distinguished by its brown head, white hindwing fringe and absence of blue scaling on the underside. It is often treated as a subspecies of the continental *A. alardus* Stoll 1790, which has upper wing bases on the upperside and very much wider pale borders on the underside. RANGE: Cuba and Hispaniola. TL: Cuba.

Early stages. The caterpillar is olive-green, the first segment straw-coloured and with a black band posteriorly, covered with numerous yellow dots that are paler below the spiracular line; a fine yellow lateral line widens and darkens towards the rear; all legs bright red; spiracles white; head orange, the sutures, mouth and antennal origins black. Food plant piñon (*Erythina*, Leguminosae).

ASTRAPTES JAIRA Butler 1870
Jamaican Astraptes Skipper

Pl. 21

Description. Fw ♂ and ♀ 24–27 mm. Upperside rather cold greyish brown; *head, thorax, a small area at the base of the forewing and a much larger area on the hindwing covered with rather dull blue-green hair-scales*; forewing sometimes with faint traces of darker bands especially towards the apex; hindwing fringes white-tipped. Underside warmer brown; both wings with faint darker brown bands; thorax and part of abdomen with blue-green hair-scales and a few also at wing bases.

Distribution. Widespread in Jamaica. Not known elsewhere. Flight rapid, but not too difficult to take when settled on foliage. TL: 'West Indies', *recte* Jamaica.

Early stages. Caterpillar bright rather mottled green, freckled with yellow-green dots, lateral line greenish yellow, head black with two large orange spots near the jaws, terminal body segments also with two orange spots, first thoracic segment with a red-edged black chitinous shield. Caterpillars are said to be gregarious but to rest solitarily in leaf shelters. Food plant *Vigna* (Leguminosae).

AUTOCHTON CELLUS Boisduval and LecConte 1883
Gold-banded Skipper

Pl. 22

Description. Fw ♂ and ♀ 22–24 mm. Upperside dark brown; forewing glistening transverse *yellow band slightly translucent*; fringes chequered on both wings but more strongly on hindwing. Underside pattern as on upperside but those areas that are plain brown on upperside are mottled with red-brown and, on postdiscal area of hindwing, with grey-brown.

Distribution. Cuba, Holguin. The only specimen known from Cuba, the male figured on Plate 22, may be no more than a vagrant from the mainland. Confirmation of its occurrence is needed before it can be accepted as an indigenous species. RANGE: southern U.S.A. and Mexico. TL: N. America.

Early stages. The caterpillar, in North America, is yellowish green, much spotted with yellowish dots and with a broad clear yellow lateral line; head brown, with a pair of yellow 'eye-spots'. Food plant Hog Peanut (*Falcata* or *Amphicarpa pitcheri*).

AUTOCHTON NEIS Geyer 1832
Trinidad White-banded Skipper

Description. Fw ♂ and ♀ 18–21 mm. Upperside dark brown, fringes not chequered; head dark green; forewing markings as in *A. cellus* but *band pearly translucent white*; hindwing without markings. Underside lighter brown, hindwing with two evenly spaced rather wide darker brown bands, the outer one outwardly bordered with cream scales towards the anal angle.

Fig. 18. *Autochton neis.* ♂ Atoyac, Vera Cruz, Mexico, May.

Distribution. Taken at Stoney Hill, St Andrew, Jamaica, 29th July 1891 by C. B. Taylor, but not reported since from Jamaica. The species is not known from any other West Indian island, but is more likely to occur than *A. cellus*, perhaps in the Lesser Antilles, as it is a common species in Trinidad and Central America. RANGE: Mexico to southern Brazil. TL: Brazil.

Early stages. Caterpillar when fully fed is grey, paler along the sides and with a pale dorsal stripe; head large and brown. Food plant (in Brazil) *Miconia* (Melastomaceae).

COGIA CALCHAS Herrich-Schaeffer 1869   *Calchas Skipper*

Description. Fw ♂ and ♀ 16–21 mm. Upperside evenly dull brown, the fringes faintly chequered; forewing usually with a row of three very small subapical spots; hindwing, in male only, with a short reddish brown hair pencil near the wing base. *Underside ground colour mottled purplish brown and grey-brown; palpi conspicuously white*.

Distribution. An unlikely insect to occur in the islands. Said to have been taken once at Kingston, Jamaica, possibly as a vagrant or accidental importation. The record needs confirmation. Occurs commonly on the mainland from Central America to Guiana and Trinidad. RANGE: Mexico to Argentina. TL: not stated.

Fig. 19. *Cogia calchas.* ♂ Atoyac, Vera Cruz, Mexico. April.

Early stages. The caterpillar is stumpy, yellowish, and covered with fine white dots. Food plants Malicia (*Schrankia* sp.) and Anil (*Indigofera* sp.).

NISONIADES BESSUS Moeschler 1876   *Bessus Skipper*   **Pl. 22**
Description. Fw ♂ and ♀ 17–19 mm. Upperside very *dark slightly glossy brown*, with ill-defined faintly paler bands and spots; forewing with *three minute subapical spots*, hindwing without markings. Underside similar but rather paler and not glossy.
Distribution. *N. bessus* has a distribution like that of the preceding species, *Cogia calchas*, and its chance of occurring in the islands is about the same. The only record is from Jamaica and rests on a single male of the typical subspecies, which is common in Trinidad and southwards in South America. RANGE: Mexico to Argentina. TL: Surinam.
Early stages. Not known.

BURCA STILLMANI Bell and Comstock 1948
Stillman's Skipper   **Pl. 22**
Description. Fw ♂ 14–16 mm, ♀ 17–18 mm. Male upperside blackish brown; forewing *with costal fold but no sex brand on inner margin*, three very small subapical spots, fringes slightly paler; hindwing without markings. Underside ground colour paler, some slight rusty red scaling near forewing apex and discal area of hindwing; hindwing with intricate pattern of indistinct dark bands, a small greyish white mark at cell-end sometimes present. Female similar, but paler above, and underside with scattered red scaling towards apex of forewing and on disc of hindwing. Palpi creamy white beneath, thorax grey, in both sexes.
Distribution. Dominican Republic: near Monte Christi and at Montserrat, February to July. Haiti, Port au Prince, July. Confined to Hispaniola. TL: Dominican Republic.
Early stages. Not known.

BURCA CONCOLOR Herrich-Schaeffer 1864
Lesser Burca Skipper   **Pl. 22**
Description. Fw ♂ 14–15 mm, ♀ 14–16 mm. Male upperside black, forewing without costal fold but with *sex brand on inner margin composed of three parallel*

but staggered rows of androconia, postdiscal area slightly paler; hindwing with only the faintest suggestion of darker discal markings; underside similar. Female upperside dark brown with lighter discal and postdiscal bands on both wings, those on forewing the brighter; underside similar. Palpi beneath dark brown in both sexes.

Distribution. Cuba, in the same localities as *B. braco*, from which it is readily separable by its smaller size, much more brightly marked female and lack of costal fold and hindwing sex-mark in the male, also the dark palpi and lack of rusty red scaling beneath. RANGE: only known from Cuba. TL: Cuba.

Early stages. Not known.

BURCA BRACO Herrich-Schaeffer 1864
Cuban Burca Skipper   **Pl. 22**

Description. Fw ♂ and ♀ 17–22 mm. Male upperside uniformly sooty dark brown; forewing with faintest trace of three subapical dots; distal third with faint bronze reflections in certain lights; costal fold present and also an ill-defined dark patch of androconial scales (brand) midway along the inner margin; hindwing with lanceolate patch of modified scales on vein 7 towards the margin; underside uniformly dark brown. Female upperside lighter brown; forewing margin broadly paler, apical spots well developed and a similar spot present near base of space 3; hindwing obscurely banded with dark grey-brown; underside ground colour dark *red-brown at forewing apex and on all hindwing*, the darker bands on the hindwing more prominent than on the upperside. Palpi white beneath in both sexes.

Distribution. Cuba: Santiago, Holguin, Matanzas, Tanamo, Baracoa, etc. Bahamas: Nassau. RANGE: Bahamas, Cuba and C. America. TL: Cuba.

Early stages. Not known.

Note. *Burca cubensis* Skinner 1913, known only from a female taken at Yberia, near Baracoa, Cuba, appears to be an exceptionally large female of *B. braco* rather than a distinct species.

BURCA HISPANIOLAE Bell and Comstock 1948
Haitian Burca Skipper

Description. Fw ♂ 15–16 mm, ♀ 17–18 mm. Male upperside ground colour dark brown, not sooty black; forewing with well-marked *large patch of dark androconia on inner margin*; *no costal fold*; three minute subapical spots and a faintly paler postdiscal band; hindwing with several faintly darker roughly rectangular markings and scattered grey scales in the postdiscal area; no glandular patch on vein 7. Underside uniformly lighter brown with extensive

Fig. 20. *Burca hispaniolae*. ♀ Dominican Republic.

scattering of yellow-grey scales, markings less well indicated than on upperside. Female upperside ground colour grey-brown, forewing hyaline spots larger · and augmented by one each in cell, space 2 and space 3; base and disc darker brown as far as these spots; hindwing pattern as in *B. braco* (Plate 22) but brighter; underside with the hindwing upperside pattern outlined only in darker scales on underside. Palpi creamy white in both sexes.

Distribution. Haiti: Port au Prince, Fond Parisien, St Marc, Frères, Pétion-ville, etc. Dominican Republic: Manzanilla Bay, Santiago, etc. RANGE: His-paniola. TL: Haiti.

Early stages. Not known.

CABARES POTRILLO Lucas 1857   *Potrillo Skipper*   **Pl. 22**

Description. Fw ♂ and ♀ 18–20 mm. Upperside dark brown, forewing translucent spots all very small and surrounded by slightly darker brown; *spot in cell sickle-shaped but sometimes broken*; hindwing unmarked. Underside ground colour lighter brown; forewing darker towards apex and in basal area; hindwing with two darker bands of which the inner is broken above the cell, enlarged and displaced outwardly.

Distribution. Cuba, Hispaniola and Jamaica; not reported from Porto Rico. A lowland species frequenting undergrowth, and slow-flying. RANGE: southern Texas to Colombia. TL: Cuba.

Early stages. Not known.

ANTIGONUS NEARCHUS Latreille 1817
Velvet Skipper   **Pl. 22**

Description. Fw ♂ 24 mm, ♀ 25 mm. Male patterned in velvety light and dark brown, both wings very angular. Underside lighter purplish brown, pattern as on the upperside. Female similar but much paler above, the underside ground colour pale yellow.

Distribution. A wide-ranging handsome species reputed to occur in Jamaica, but the record needs confirmation. RANGE: Mexico to Argentina. TL: S. America.

Early stages. Nothing is known of the early stages of this species or of *A. erosus* (below).

Note. A smaller similar species of *Antigonus*, *A. erosus* Huebner 1812, with a similar distribution, has been reported to occur in Grenada, 'St Georges', but in all probability came from St Georges County, Trinidad, where the species, like *A. nearchus*, is common. The male of *A. erosus* is slate-grey on the upperside, the female mottled medium brown with small hyaline discal spots that are usually lacking in the male; underside rather light brown. Both sexes have the angular wings of *A. nearchus*.

ACHLYODES THRASO Jung 1792   *Jung's Dusky Wing*   **Pl. 22**

Description. Fw ♂ 21–25 mm, ♀ 24–28 mm. Upperside *velvety dark brown, forewing apex slightly falcate* above the very convex outer margin, a conspicuous paler crescent-shaped costal mark towards apex; a postdiscal mark towards inner margin, and sometimes two or three similar small discal *spots all paler*; hindwing with a discal group of similar spots; female not so dark as male. Underside ground colour brown, but lightly grey-washed towards the hind margin, both wings crossed by a continuous slightly paler discal band and sometimes a fainter postdiscal band as well.

Distribution. *A. thraso* is represented in the West Indies by four distinct sub-species. *A. thraso sagra* Evans 1952, described above and figured on Plate 22, occurs in Hispaniola, Porto Rico and St Thomas. The Jamaican subspecies, *A. thraso mithridates* Fabricius 1793, is darker, very dark beneath and with ill-defined markings on the upperside. *A. thraso minor* Comstock 1944 is a smaller, lighter brown well-marked race known only from Dominica. In the Cuban *A. thraso papinianus* Poey 1832 the upperside ground colour is distinctly greyish with very well-defined markings, and the outer margin on the hindwing under-side is broadly washed with grey. A common species. RANGE: southern U.S.A. to Argentina. TL: not stated.

Early stages. The fully grown caterpillar is light grey-blue on the back, shading to greenish laterally, with a bright yellow stripe above the spiracles composed of numerous short dashes; head large, flat and flesh-coloured, roughened. Food plants orange and lime, in folded leaves.

TIMOCHARES RUPTIFASCIATA Ploetz 1884
Broken-barred Dusky Wing **Pl. 22**

Description. Fw ♂ and ♀ 19–20 mm. Upperside ground colour dusky rather light brown, hindwing paler than forewing. *Both wings with irregular discal, postdiscal and submarginal bands of darker squarish spots,* those of forewing discal band much the largest and more or less united; submarginal spots the smallest; all hindwing dark spots roughly equal in size, those of submarginal band merging into the dark marginal band. Underside ground colour paler; forewing discal band obsolescent; hindwing submarginal band often divided lengthwise into two narrower parallel bands of smaller spots. Palpi large, dark, and very hairy.

Distribution. The Jamaican subspecies, described above, has been named *runia* by Evans (1952). It is the only known Caribbean race and differs from the typical *T. ruptifascia* of the mainland in being darker and having the dark spots of the palbs better separated. Widespread but not common, local. RANGE: Mexico and Jamaica. TL: 'S. America', *recte* Mexico.

Early stages. The caterpillar's head is broad and flat with a dark brown border that expands at the crown, mottled ivory and olive green; first segment light green, remainder blue-green sprinkled with many yellow dots, a yellow dorso-lateral line from 3rd segment to tail is accompanied by an orange spot on each segment. Food plant a malpighiaceous vine (in Mexico).

GRAIS STIGMATICUS Mabille 1883 *Grais Skipper* **Pl. 22**

Description. Fw ♂ and ♀ 23 mm. Upperside rather pale dull grey-brown; forewing with a darker bar across cell-end which unites broadly with the broken postdiscal band towards the base of space 2; hindwing with similar discal and postdiscal bands neither of which reaches the inner margin. Under-side paler, yellowish, markings as on upperside, but *hindwing inner marginal area devoid of markings and anal area without black marginal spot.*

Distribution. In the West Indies *Grais stigmaticus* is known only from Jamaica, where it occurs as a distinct subspecies *Grais stigmaticus juncta* Evans 1952, described above and illustrated on Plate 22. Typical *Grais stigmaticus* of the mainland is a larger rather paler insect in which the discal and postdiscal bands on the forewing upperside do not unite, the spots forming these bands on both wings are smaller and on the hindwing underside more often than not there is an ill-defined black anal spot; it could be a distinct species. RANGE: Mexico to Argentina. TL: Brazil.

Early stages. Not known.

ANASTRUS SEMPITERNUS Butler and Druce 1872
Dillon's Dusky Wing   **Pl. 22**

Description. Fw ♂ and ♀ 22–24 mm. Very like *Timochares ruptifasciata* but larger and forewing more pointed. Upperside ground colour dark brown, pattern of markings also very similar but less distinct, the forewing discal band widely interrupted at the cell and the submarginal bands on both wings merged with the dark margin. *Underside* similar but ground colour paler towards inner margin of forewing, *forewing apex always with a quite small yellowish apical spot* which is sometimes just discernible on the upperside as well.

Distribution. Jamaica and Hispaniola. Not common but widely distributed. Frequents lowland bush and grasslands and is rather shy. The Caribbean subspecies *Anastrus sempiternus dilloni* Bell and Comstock 1948 differs strikingly from typical *A. sempiternus* of C. America in lacking the blue flush on the underside of the hindwing; it is only doubtfully distinct from the S. American *A. s. simplicior* Moeschler 1876. RANGE: Mexico to Brazil. TL: Costa Rica.

Early stages. The caterpillar is dull green, the anterior segments a little paler; head orange, sprinkled with black and notched; body with faint darker dorsal line and a yellow spot on 7th and 11th segments through which the 'heart' can be seen pulsating. Food plant guava, *Psidium guajava*, the caterpillar curling the leaf edges to form a shelter.

GESTA GESTA Herrich-Schaeffer 1863
Common Dusky Wing   **Pl. 22**

Description. Fw ♂ and ♀ 15–16 mm. Upperside dark brown, very like *Chiomara mithrax* but smaller and with narrower forewings, the *discal markings on the upperside of the forewing diagonal rather than transverse* and better defined; a single (sometimes double) minute subapical spot, and, on the hindwing upperside, the middle dusky band much the broadest. On the underside the pattern of markings is the same but less well defined. The female tends to lack the faint purplish tint of the male.

Distribution. Occurs widely in the typical subspecies, *Gesta gesta gesta*, in Cuba, Hispaniola and Jamaica, always without the white hindwing fringes that characterise many continental subspecies, especially in Brazil. A butterfly of open country, where it flies low and often settles on the ground with its wings spread flat. Not a strong flier. RANGE: Mexico to Argentina. TL: Cuba.

Early stages. The full grown caterpillar's head is broader than the thoracic segments, deep orange and pilose with a pattern of relatively large round sepia spots; body spindle-shaped, greyish green, densely sprinkled with white dots, orange tinted on the back and underneath, yellow below the spiracles and with an orange lateral line above them. Food plant *Cassia*.

OULEUS FRIDERICUS Geyer 1832   *Geyer's Skipper*   **Pl. 22**

Description. Fw ♂ and ♀ 13–14 mm. Upperside very dark brown, almost black, *forewing with a double row, hindwing a single row of* paler square *postdiscal spots*. Underside lighter brown; hindwing postdiscal area below vein 5 washed with greyish yellow.

Distribution. Reported to occur in Jamaica, but the record is almost certainly unreliable. The specimens on which it was based belong to subspecies *trina* Evans 1952 which flies in Trinidad. RANGE: Mexico to Argentina. TL: Surinam.
Early stages. Not known.

CHIOMARA ASYCHIS Stoll 1780
St Vincent Grizzled Skipper   Pl. 22

Description. Fw ♂ and ♀ 15–18 mm. Upperside black, with numerous white markings most of which on the forewing upperside are clouded with brown or bluish scales; forewing with a square spot in the cell and, below it on about the centre of the inner margin, a large spot from which an irregular band extends to mid-costa; three very small white subapical spots and *a submarginal row of small white lunules enclosed in the black border*; hindwing with a large discal white patch that does not extend into the basal half of cell; an irregular postdiscal series of which the largest spots by far are in spaces 4 and 5; faint white lunules in the black marginal area. Upperside markings repeated below, but white marks larger and not clouded, hindwing almost wholly white with grey markings.

Distribution. *Chiomara asychis vincenta* Evans 1952, the subspecies described above, is known only from St Vincent; of the many subspecies of *C. asychis* it is the one closest to typical *C. asychis* of the Guianas. Most other races are lighter in colour and more mottled. On St Lucia, Grenada and the Grenadines it is replaced by *C. asychis grenada* Evans 1952 in which the white markings of the upperside are larger, brighter and not clouded with brown or bluish scales, the submarginal lunules bolder (especially on the Grenadines), and the discal white area on the upperside of the hindwing extends well into the cell. The species has not been reported from any other West Indian islands. RANGE: Mexico to Argentina. TL: Surinam.

Early stages. In the neighbourhood of Para, Brazil, the caterpillar can be found on the leaves of a straggling creeper belonging to the Malpighiaceae. It is plain green.

CHIOMARA MITHRAX Moeschler 1878
Cuban Dusky Wing   Pl. 22

Description. Fw ♂ and ♀ 17–20 mm. Male upperside velvety dark brown; forewing purple-tinted, *a transverse row of dark spots near wing base*, a very ill-defined row of postdiscal spots becoming light brown towards the costa, and a light brown submarginal line; hindwing with three concentric wide ill-defined darker bands. Female upperside paler and markings better defined. Underside ground colour smooth purplish brown, forewing with wide paler margin enclosing submarginal band of ground colour, hindwing as above.

Distribution. The only West Indian records are from Cuba where it is evidently decidedly rare. Cuban specimens are indistinguishable from those of the mainland, which suggests that the insect is a relatively recent arrival there, or sporadic in its occurrence. RANGE: Mexico to Argentina. TL: Colombia.

Early stages. Not known.

EPHYRIADES ZEPHODES Huebner 1825
Haitian Dusky Wing

Description. Fw ♂ 21 mm, ♀ 22 mm, but both very variable in size. Male upperside silky jet black without markings, but *forewing with massive costal fold* extending two-thirds of the way to the apex and enclosing cream-coloured androconia; underside uniformly brown, with only the inner marginal area of forewing paler. Female upperside dull brown; forewing upperside with narrow subbasal, broad discal, and less well defined macular postdiscal bands; a curved series of small hyaline spots in spaces 3 to 9 and *two large spots, in cell and space 2, with their inner edges in line*; hindwing upperside with short curved mark at cell-end and narrow postdiscal band of reddish brown; underside similar but forewing inner margin almost white.

Fig. 21. *Ephyriades zephodes*. ♀ Tortola, British Virgin Isles, September.

Distribution. Apparently widespread and fairly common in Cuba and Hispaniola, less common in Porto Rico, the Virgin Isles, St Thomas and St Bartholomew. Recorded from Jamaica but the record not yet confirmed. RANGE: C. America to Brazil. TL: not stated.

Early stages. See *Ephyriades arcas* (below).

EPHYRIADES ARCAS Drury 1773   *Hairy Dusky Wing*

Description. Fw ♂ 18 mm, ♀ 20 mm. Male indistinguishable from *E. zephodes* except by the presence of *a very small white dot near the apex of the cell on the underside of the forewing*, otherwise only by the characters of the male genitalia. Female separable by the fact that the *spot in space 2* on the forewing extends farther towards the wing base than does the *spot above it in the cell*, i.e. they are *not strictly in line* as they are in *E. zephodes*.

Distribution. *E. arcas arcas*, as described above, certainly occurs in St Kitts, Antigua and St Eustatius. Its mainland subspecies, *E. arcas philemon* Fabricius 1775, which is larger and lacks the small cell spot on the forewing underside, occurs in Jamaica, St Thomas and Cuba. RANGE: C. America to Brazil. TL: St Kitts.

Early stages. The caterpillar has a heart-shaped head which when full grown is light yellow with darker yellow markings, body grey-green and spattered with numerous small bright yellow dots which, becoming confluent along the sides, form two pairs of lateral lines. Food plants *Stigmaphyllon ligulatum*, *Malphigia fulcata* and *Ceiba pentandra*.

Note. When this description of the caterpillar was written it was not realised that *E. arcas* of those days consisted of two species which are now known as *E. arcas* and *E. zephodes* and, as both appear to occur in Porto Rico (although this is by no means certain) it is uncertain to which species the caterpillar described belongs. That two species are involved is evident from a study of the male genitalia. So little reliable material is, however, available that at present it is not possible to plot their distributions with certainty.

EPHYRIADES BRUNNEA Herrich-Schaeffer 1864
Jamaican Dusky Wing   **Pl. 23**

Description. Fw ♂ 21 mm, ♀ 22 mm. Very similar to *Ephyriades zephodes*, but male not so black and the forewing with *a circle of very small hyaline spots in the apical third* (except in subspecies *dominicensis*), and the costal fold reaching little more than half way along costa. Female ground colour more lilac, the dark bands rather better defined, the hyaline spots in cell and space 2 narrow and not markedly larger than the others; spot in space 3 equidistant between those in space 2 and space 4, not nearer 3 as in *E. zephodes*. Underside like the upperside.

Distribution. *E. brunnea brunnea*, as described above, is found in the Bahamas and is widespread in Cuba. In Jamaica it is replaced by *E. b. jamaicensis* Moeschler 1878, which is a larger insect (forewing 24–25 mm) with more pointed wings and the apical circlet of spots in the male reduced to two or three only; in the female, however, the hyaline spots are relatively larger. *E. b. dominicensis* Bell and Comstock 1948 (TL: Dominica) differs in that the male entirely lacks apical spots. A fast-flying species with a fondness for logwood thickets. RANGE: Florida to Dominica; Honduras (?). TL: Cuba.

Early stages. The fully grown caterpillar of the Jamaican subspecies is pale green dotted with yellow points producing a yellow-green effect, a dark green dorsal line flanked by two faint pale yellow dorso-lateral lines below which runs a grey lateral line. The well-defined neck is grey, the mottled head black marked with orange that later is replaced by red. Has been found feeding on garden cherry, *Prunus* sp.

ERYNNIS ZARUCCO Lucas 1857   *Zarucco Dusky Wing*   **Pl. 23**

Description. Fw ♂ and ♀ 21 mm. Upperside rather shiny dark brown. Male with costal fold to just beyond mid-point of costa. Upperside in both sexes with very little definite pattern, but more marked in female than in male. Forewing with *four minute subapical hyaline spots and a fifth in space* 3; a dark diagonal postdiscal shadow followed by faint submarginal grey sagittate marks and a marginal series of very small pale dots; basal half of wing with pale brown wavy line in space 2 but little else; hindwing almost uniformly dark brown. Underside dark brown with an incomplete series of faint submarginal, and sometimes marginal spots. Fringes brown.

Distribution. Typical *Erynnis zarucco* occurs in Cuba: Matanzas, Soledad, Holguin, Guantanamo, Santiago, etc. Haiti. Also in south-eastern U.S.A. Elsewhere on the mainland replaced by *E. zarucco funeralis* Scudder and Burgess 1870 in which the fringes are white. RANGE: southern U.S.A. to Argentina. TL: Cuba.

Early stages. The caterpillar feeds on Leguminosae, e.g. *Baptista* and, in Cuba, *Sesbanea grandiflora*. It has a black head covered with whitish pubescence, body light green and so densely sprinkled with whitish hair as to give it a greyish

Plate 21   **HESPERIIDAE**   *Scale:* × ⅔

1. **Phocides pigmalion**   *Mangrove Skipper*   p. 156
   ♂ Haiti. The only blue-banded Skipper in the West Indies.

2. **Phocides perkinsae**   *Miss Perkins' Skipper*   156
   ♂ Jamaica. Hindwing with faint yellow shades

3. **Proteides mercurius**   *Mercury Skipper*   156
   ♂ Rio Yuma district, Dominican Republic. November. Hindwing
   underside with roughly wedge-shaped area of white scales.

4. **Proteides maysi**   *Mays' Giant Skipper*   157
   ♂ Santiago, Cuba. Hindwing with short silver discal bar.

5. **Epargyreus zestos**   *Zestos Skipper*   157
   ♂ Dominica. Hw underside light and dark red-brown.

6. **Epargyreus antaeus**   *Jamaican Silver-spotted Skipper*   158
   ♀ Jamaica. Underside only.

7. **Epargyreus spanna**   *Haitian Silver-spotted Skipper*   158
   ♀ Dominican Republic. Underside only. Upperside as in *E. zestos*;
   shape of silver band specific.

8. **Polygonus leo**   *Hammock Skipper*   158
   ♂ *P. l. ishmael*, Haiti. Hindwing underside grey-green.

9. **Polygonus manueli**   *Manuel's Skipper*   159
   ♂ Dominica. Hindwing underside purple-brown.

10. **Chioides catillus**   *Jamaican Long-tail Skipper*   159
    ♂ Long Mt, Jamaica. Straight line on hindwing underside.

11. **Chioides ixion**   *Ixion Skipper*   162
    ♂ Haiti. Hindwing underside central white spot.

12. **Chioides marmorosa**   *Marbled Skipper*   162
    ♂ Holguin, Cuba. Forewing hyaline spots white.

13. **Aguna asander**   *Aguna Skipper*   162
    ♂ Haiti. White stripe includes a short black line.

14. **Urbanus proteus**   *Common Long-tail Skipper*   163
    ♂ Haiti. Long tails and thick clothing of green hair-scales.

15. **Urbanus dorantes**   *Dorantes Skipper*   163
    ♂ *U. d. cramptoni*, Haiti. Spots small, tails rather short.

16. **Polythrix octomaculata**   *Eight Spot Skipper*   164
    ♂ Para. The eight spots are the hyaline spots on the forewing.

17. **Astraptes talus**   *Guaraguao Skipper*   164
    ♂ Dominican Republic. Upperside with vivid green scaling.

18. **Astraptes anaphus**   *Roy's Skipper*   165
    ♂ Haiti. Fringes of hindwing yellowish.

19. **Astraptes cassander**   *Dismal Skipper*   165
    ♂ Cuba. Thoracic hair-scales dull grey-blue.

20. **Astraptes xagua**   *Blue-backed Skipper*   165
    ♂ Santiago, Cuba. Base of forewing vivid blue above and below.

21. **Astraptes habana**   *Cuban Giant Blue Skipper*   166
    ♂ Lomo de Tornote, Dominican Republic. No blue on underside.

22. **Astraptes jaira**   *Jamaican Astraptes Skipper*   166
    ♂ Newcastle, Jamaica. Underside with some green scaling.

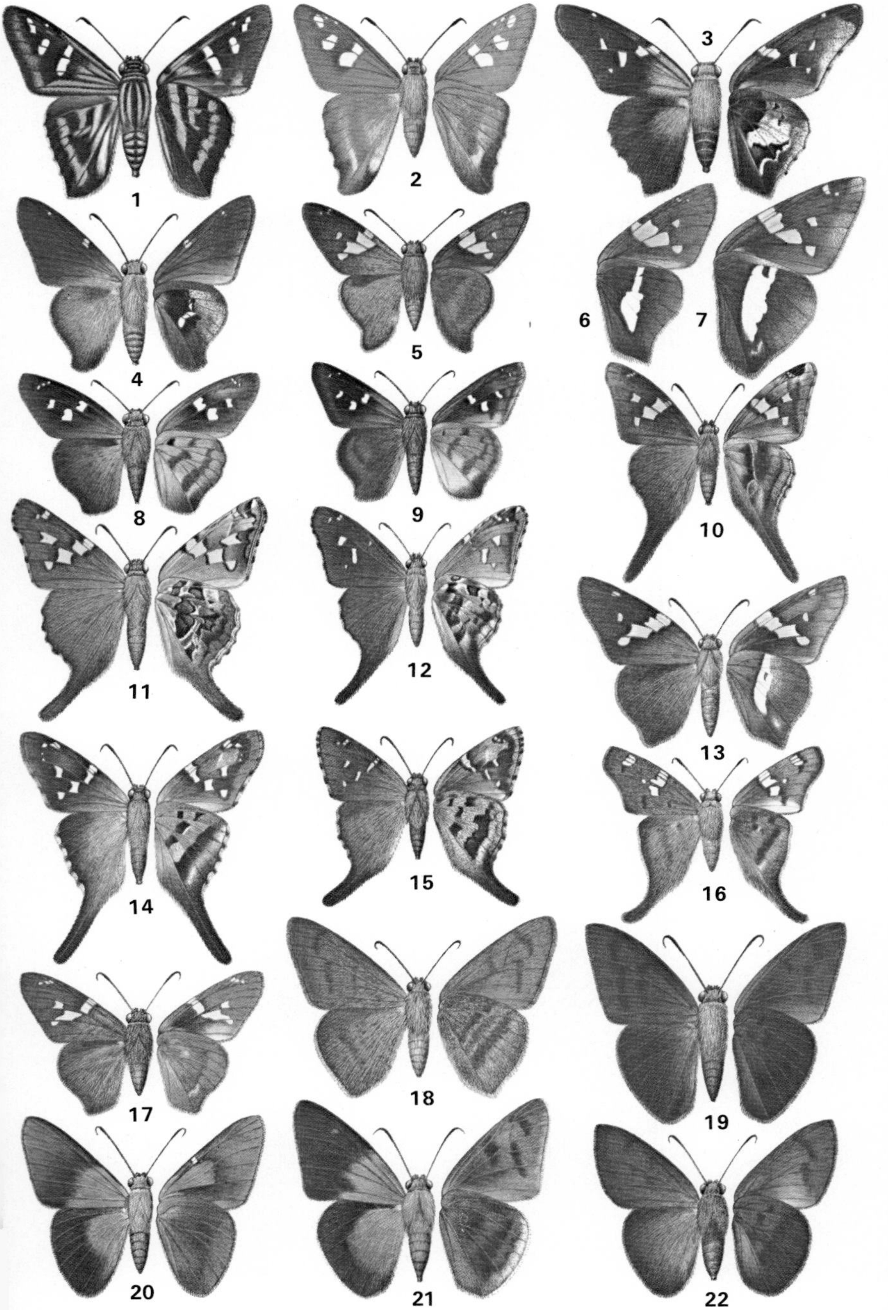
1
2
3
4
5
6
7
8
9
10
11
12
13
14
15
16
17
18
19
20
21
22

22

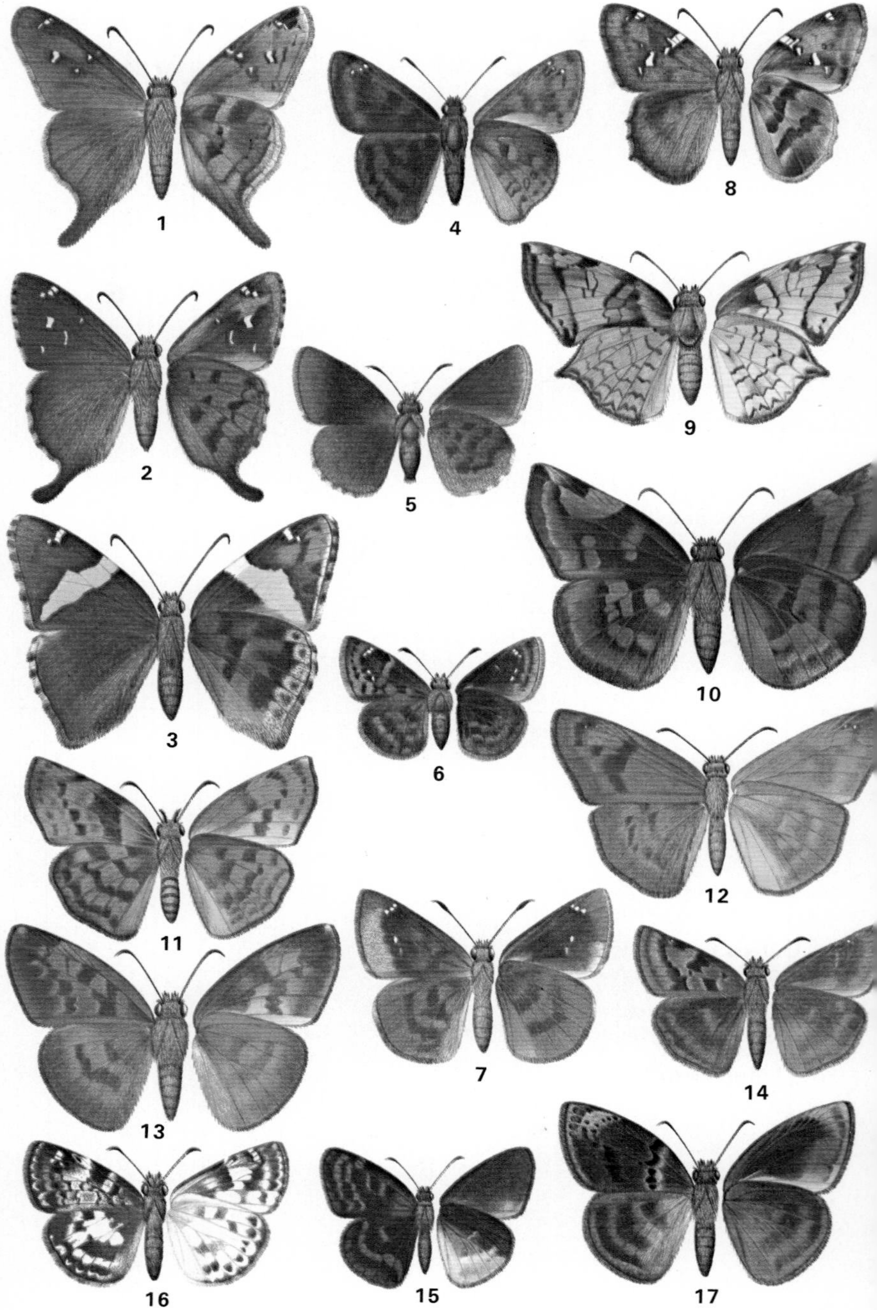

1. **Chioides vintra** *St Vincent Long-tail Skipper*   p. 159
   ♂ St Vincent. Dark markings in space 7 reach costa.

2. **Urbanus obscurus** *Stub-tailed Skipper*   164
   ♂ St Vincent. Dark markings in space 7 do not reach costa.

3. **Autochton cellus** *Gold-banded Skipper*   166
   ♂ Holguin, Cuba. Forewing with distinctive yellow band.

4. **Nisoniades bessus** *Bessus Skipper*   168
   ♂ St Ann's, Trinidad. Almost black; apical spots minute.

5. **Burca stillmani** *Stillman's Skipper*   168
   ♂ Rio Yague, S. of Monti Christi, Dominican Republic. Smooth dark brown with chequered fringes.

6. **Burca concolor** *Lesser Burca Skipper*   168
   ♀ Cuba. Dark markings against a yellow-brown background.

7. **Burca braco** *Cuban Burca Skipper*   169
   ♀ Santiago, Cuba. Hindwing background bright red-brown.

8. **Cabares potrillo** *Potrillo Skipper*   170
   ♂ Santiago, Cuba. Fw cell with narrow hook-shaped marking.

9. **Antigonus nearchus** *Velvet Sipper*   170
   ♀ Manzanilla, Trinidad. Wings very angular.

10. **Achlyodes thraso** *Jung's Dusky Wing*   170
    ♂ Dominican Republic. Purplish markings distinctive.

11. **Timochares ruptifasciata** *Broken-barred Dusky Wing*   171
    ♀ Jamaica. Hindwing underside with concentric wavy lines.

12. **Grais stigmaticus** *Grais Skipper*   171
    ♂ Jamaica. Peculiarly featureless.

13. **Anastrus sempiternus** *Dillon's Dusky Wing*   172
    ♂ Dominican Republic. Similar; markings obscure.

14. **Gesta gesta** *Common Dusky Wing*   172
    ♂ Jamaica. Fw dark markings bordered with scattered grey scales.

15. **Ouleus fridericus** *Geyer's Skipper*   172
    ♂ St Ann's, Trinidad. Postdiscal spots faintly purplish.

16. **Chiomara asychis** *St Vincent Grizzled Skipper*   173
    ♂ St Vincent. Hindwing upperside with large white discal patch.

17. **Chiomara mithrax** *Cuban Dusky Wing*   173
    ♂ Brazil. Fw with black dots within subapical band.

B.W.I.   M appearance; a yellow dorso-lateral line runs from the fourth to the last segment and towards the back of each segment there is an orange spot; legs green.

HELIOPETES ARSALTE Linnaeus 1758
Common White Skipper   **Pl. 23**

Description. Fw ♂ and ♀ 16–20 mm. Upperside white, costal fold very narrow, both wings with veins marked with black for a short distance inwards from the margin and a fine marginal line; *forewing apex with a variable amount of black clouding* and a series of antemarginal white points; hindwing fringes conspicuously chequered. Underside white, but some veins outlined in black.

Distribution. It is doubtful whether this species is really established anywhere in the West Indies. The only records are from Jamaica, where a male was taken very many years ago, and La Vega in the Dominican Republic, in 1925. Both may have been in respect of vagrants. The butterfly is a common insect on the mainland of America. RANGE: Mexico to Argentina. TL: 'Indiis'.

Early stages. Not known.

PYRGUS OILEUS Linnaeus 1767
Tropical Chequered Skipper   **Pl. 23**

Description. Fw ♂ and ♀ 13–16 mm. Upperside ground colour black, *overlaid with long hair-scales which are white in the male, brown in the female*, and with a complicated pattern of small angular white spots; fringes chequered. On the underside the forewing upperside markings are repeated below, but on the hindwing a marbled effect is produced by series of very irregular discal and postdiscal dark spots of varying intensity on a white or light brown background. The costal fold on the male forewing is outlined by white lines but otherwise is not at all obvious. The differing shades of underside ground colours suggest seasonal variations.

Distribution. *Pyrgus oileus* occurs in the West Indies in two subspecies readily distinguished by a seemingly trivial character, namely the presence (in *P. o. oileus*) of a narrow dark brown spot about 2 mm long on the middle of the costa of the hindwing on the underside. This spot is lacking in *P. o. orcus* Stoll 1780. This character is so constant that it may mean that two species rather than subspecies are involved. *P. o. oileus* ranges from the southern United States through Cuba, Hispaniola, Jamaica and Porto Rico to Montserrat; *P. o. orcus* is essentially South American but extends along the chain of the Lesser Antilles at least as far as Dominica. In most places the species is so common as to be almost a nuisance. RANGE: southern U.S.A. to Argentina. TL: 'Algeria', *recte* U.S.A.

Early stages. The full grown caterpillar is light yellowish green, blotched here and there with darker green, first segment smaller than the rest and dark brown, a pulsating narrow dorsal line is green, the intersegmental membranes yellow, head black and much larger than first thoracic segment; head and body pubescent. Food plants *Sida rhombifolia* (Broomweed), *Malvastium* and various Malvaceae.

PYRGUS CRISIA Herrich-Schaeffer 1864
Cuban Chequered Skipper   **Pl. 23**

Description. Fw ♂ and ♀ 11 mm. Upperside *black, with numerous scattered small white spots on both wings*; fringes chequered black and white. On the underside the forewing markings are as on the upperside, but on the hindwing the white markings are so enlarged that the surface of the wing appears white relieved only by a complicated pattern of black lines. The male has a costal fold on the forewing.

Distribution. Cuba and Haiti, rare. Said to occur also in Porto Rico. RANGE: Cuba and Haiti. TL: Haiti.

Early stages. Not known.

PYRRHOCALLES ANTIQUA Herrich-Schaeffer 1863
Great Tawny Skipper   **Pl. 23**

Description. Fw ♂ 24–25 mm, ♀ 28–30 mm. Upperside *bright tawny*; forewing outer *margin broadly black*, separated from a similar black patch at cell-end by a crescent of small tawny spots; a dark shade centrally in space 1b; hindwing upperside costal and outer margins similarly broadly black. Underside similar but margins not so dark; hindwing with tawny cell-spot and circle of tawny discal spots beyond.

Distribution. Occurs in three well-marked subspecies that could with some justification be regarded as species. *P. a. antiqua* (described above) is widespread in the Dominican Republic and Porto Rico. *P. a. eleutherae* Bates 1934 (TL: Eleuthera Island, Bahamas) differs in that the ground colour of the underside is purple-grey and devoid of markings. In *P. a. orientis* Skinner 1920 (TL: Cuba) on the upperside of the forewing the black cell-bar is joined to the dark margin which is much wider (7 mm on vein 2) than in the other subspecies, and the black shade in space 1b is poorly developed. RANGE: Bahamas, Cuba and Hispaniola. TL: 'Cuba', *recte* Haiti.

Early stages. Not known.

PYRRHOCALLES JAMAICENSIS Schaus 1902
Schaus's Tawny Skipper

Description. Fw ♂ and ♀ 22–24 mm. Very similar to *Pyrrhocalles antiqua* (above) but slightly *smaller and with more sharply defined black markings*. Forewing upperside black border only 4–5 mm wide along vein 2; black shade in space 1b bold and overlapping base of vein 2; small tawny spots often present in space 3 and sometimes space 4; hindwing black border projecting across end of cell. The underside differs conspicuously in lacking the circlet of tawny discal spots characteristic of *P. antiqua*; instead, the outer half of the wing is sharply distinguished from the basal half by being smoothly paler tawny.

Distribution. Jamaica; apparently widespread and not uncommon. RANGE and TL: Jamaica.

Early stages. Not known.

PERICHARES PHILETES Gmelin 1790   *Dolores Skipper* **Pl. 23**
Description. Fw ♂ and ♀ 24–26 mm. Upperside medium brown, fringes white and narrowly chequered black at the ends of the veins. Male distinguishable by presence of grey crescent-shaped sex brand on forewing that lies across the base of space 2 and extends into space 1b. Forewing with hyaline crescent-shaped

mark at cell-end, a smaller one in space 2 and a rectangular spot in space 3, all smaller in male than in the female, which also has an extra spot in space 1b; hindwing without markings. Underside markings like those of upperside, but forewing apex and whole of *hindwing clouded with purplish and darker brown: tip of abdomen bright orange.*

Distribution. A common insect in Cuba, Hispaniola, Jamaica and Porto Rico, in the typical subspecies *P. philetes philetes*, and very constant. Rather crepuscular in habit, resting by day in shady forest paths. Several continental subspecies have been described, with overlapping characters and distributions. RANGE: C. America to S. Brazil. TL: Jamaica.

Early stages. The fully grown caterpillar is shining green, laterally greenish yellow shading to transparent green and pale bluish beneath, a greenish yellow dorsal line not well defined, and a chalky white blotch beneath on segment 4; head rather small, heart-shaped, pale, minutely speckled with black. Food plants include sugar cane, Indian corn, bamboo and various grasses.

PHERAEUS UNIA Butler 1870   *Square Spot Skipper*

Description. Fw ♂ and ♀ 14 mm. Upperside dark brown, almost black; forewing upperside with a small square hyaline spot at the base of space 2 and space 3 and a dot in space 5; hindwing upperside devoid of markings. Underside of forewing like upperside; underside of hindwing also brown except spaces 2 to 6 which are dull ochreous and contain black rectangular spots that are inwardly capped white in spaces 2 and 3, *very large, double and outwardly white capped in spaces 4 and 5,* small in space 6, smaller still and less obvious in space 1b.

Fig. 22. *Pheraeus unia.* ♂ Dominican Republic. × 1½.

Distribution. A very beautiful little species only known from the Dominican Republic and apparently very rare. TL: San Domingo.

Early stages. Not known.

VETTIUS FANTASOS Stoll 1780   *Opal Skipper*   **Pl. 23**

Description. Fw ♂ and ♀ 14–15 mm. Upperside dark brown, fringes on hindwing and near anal angle of forewing yellow. Forewing upperside with a row of three small hyaline spots just beyond cell-end, a similar spot towards the base of space 3 and another much larger one in space 2; a small yellowish spot on vein 1; hindwing with a short yellowish horizontal discal bar. Underside forewing with an additional rectangular white spot in space 4+5; *hindwing white, veins rust-red,* a dark brown patch at cell-end extends via the base of space 5 and vein 5 to form a marginal patch which then curves back to form a *large dark mark that reaches to the anal angle* and along the inner margin.

Distribution. *V. fantasos* has been reported from Jamaica on the evidence of a single male taken prior to 1849. As it has never been reported there since then it seems improbable that it is really indigenous to that island. It has not been taken elsewhere in the West Indies either, but it is a comparatively common species on the mainland. RANGE: Mexico to Brazil. TL: Surinam.

Early stages. Not known.

SYNAPTE MALITIOSA Herrich-Schaeffer 1865
The Drab
Pl. 23

Description. Fw ♂ and ♀ 15–16 mm. Upperside dull medium brown, the *male only with a tapering dull fulvous stripe* from middle of inner margin to base of space 3. Underside similar, with a slight yellowish sandy tint, the forewing stripe much fainter, hindwing with a short broad but very indefinite dark bar at the end of the cell.

Distribution. *S. malitiosa malitiosa* occurs only in Cuba, where it appears to be moderately common. On the mainland other subspecies occur, notably *S. m. pericles* Moeschler, a much brighter insect which is common in northern South America and in Trinidad and Tobago. Frequents low-growing bushes. RANGE: Mexico to Brazil. TL: Cuba.

Early stages. Not known.

CYMAENES TRIPUNCTUS Herrich-Schaeffer 1865
Three Spot Skipper
Pl. 23

Description. Fw ♂ and ♀ 14–15 mm. A dull brown rather insignificant little Skipper, the forewing particularly pointed in the male. Forewing upperside with a line of three very small subapical spots (some of which may be absent), a larger spot in space 2 and another in space 3, all hyaline, rarely a faint spot centrally on vein 1 but no cell-spot; hindwing without markings. Underside ground colour paler, except disc of forewing; hindwing with curved discal row of faint paler spots in spaces 2 to 6.

Distribution. A common butterfly in Cuba, the Cayman Isles, Hispaniola, Jamaica, Porto Rico and the Virgin Isles, rare in the Bahamas and apparently absent from the Lesser Antilles. Can easily be confused with *Lerodea eufala* (p. 196), but the length of the antennae distinguishes it: less than half the length of costa in *L. eufala*, more than half as long in *C. tripunctus*. *Lerodea eufala* is also paler brown. Caribbean *C. tripunctus* are all referable to the typical subspecies. The wide-ranging continental subspecies, *C. t. theogenis* Capronnier 1874 (TL: Brazil), is slightly larger and has more clearly defined markings. RANGE: southern U.S.A. to Brazil. TL: Cuba.

Early stages. Caterpillars have been found feeding on Guinea Grass. When full grown the head is white, pilose, with a central V-shaped mark and side bars of brown, the body is presumably some shade of green.

RHINTHON CUBANA Herrich-Schaeffer 1865

Bath Skipper　　　　　　　　　　　　　　　　　　　　　　**Pl. 23**

Description. Fw ♂ 21 mm, ♀ 19 mm. *Head and thorax greenish.* Forewing pointed in male and with a narrow pearly grey sex stripe midway along vein 1, rounded in female. Upperside rather sooty dark brown, but paler below vein 5 on the hindwing; forewing *hyaline spots clear white, large (3 mm long) in space 2,* a little shorter and longitudinally divided in the cell (especially in the male), much smaller in space 3; the three very small subapical spots staggered; costa coppery towards base; hindwing with two, sometimes three small round pale discal spots, in spaces 2 to 4. Underside similar but ground colour with faintly slate-grey appearance.

Distribution. Cuba and Jamaica (e.g. near Bath), decidedly rare, and only in the typical subspecies. RANGE: Mexico to Ecuador. TL: Cuba.

Early stages. Not known.

RHINTHON BUSHI Watson 1937　*Bush's Skipper*

Description. Fw ♂ 18 mm. Male upperside dark brown. Head and palpi above bright green; palpi orange beneath, thorax and base of abdomen bright green. Forewing upperside apical spots semihyaline and yellowish white in space 1b (on vein 1), space 2 (subquadrate and larger than the others), space 3 (the smallest) and in the cell; hindwing upperside without markings. Underside paler brown, costal and inner marginal areas dark fulvous; base blackish; inner margin fuscous; forewing markings as on upperside with the addition of *greenish yellow streaks above the cell* and beyond the fourth subapical spot; *hindwing with two large silvery white spots below the cell*; an irregular white spot in cell more or less ringed with orange; an orange spot beyond it and another in space 7. Female unknown.

Fig. 23. *Rhinthon bushi.* ♂ Paradis, Dominican Republic, August.

Distribution. Paradis, Dominican Republic, only a single male known. RANGE: Dominican Republic. TL: San Domingo.

Early stages. Not known.

HOLGUINIA HOLGUIN Evans 1955　*Tollin's Skipper*　**Pl. 23**

Description. Fw ♂ and ♀ 18 mm. Upperside black, both wings with white hyaline spots; forewing with two quite small separate spots in cell, **three sub-apical** spots in spaces 6 to 8 and a fourth in space 4 all equally small; three

larger spots in spaces 3, 2 and 1b of which the middle one is the largest and
connected by a dash below vein 1 to the spot in space 1b; hindwing with a small
yellowish spot in cell and a discal row of three small white spots in spaces 2, 3
and 4. The underside markings are as on the upperside, but the apex of the forewing and the whole of the *hindwing* are *densely covered with bright emerald green
scales*; hindwing discal spots increased to five in number.

Distribution. Known only from Holguin in Cuba. RANGE and TL: Cuba.
Early stages. Not known.

OARISMA NANUS Herrich-Schaeffer 1865
Pygmy Skipper   **Pl. 23**

Description. Fw ♂ and ♀ 8 mm. The smallest West Indian Skipper. Upperside
bright fulvous, including the fringes. Outer half of forewing and inner margin
broadly fuscous; hindwing costal margin fuscous, vein 1a wholly, veins 2, 3 and 4
partly black. Underside rather paler fulvous, *veins* below and beyond cell on
forewing and all *on hindwing black.*

Distribution. Known only from Cuba, where it is widespread and common.
RANGE and TL: Cuba.
Early stages. Not known, but the caterpillar almost certainly feeds on grasses
like its allies.

OARISMA STILLMANI Bell and Comstock 1948
Haitian Pygmy Skipper

Description. Fw ♂ and ♀ 10 mm. A little larger than *Oarisma nanus* from Cuba
and with the dusky borders of the forewing upperside not quite so wide. Male
at once distinguished by the possession of a *black sex-brand* between veins 2
and 3.

Fig. 24. *Oarisma stillmani.* ♂ near Monte Christi, Dominican Republic, March. × 1¼.

Distribution. All known specimens have been taken near Monte Christi,
Dominican Republic, in March. RANGE and TL: Haiti.
Early stages. Not known.

POLITES BARACOA Lucas 1857   *Baracoa Skipper*   **Pl. 23**
Description. Fw ♂ 10–11 mm, ♀ 10–14 mm. Upperside ground colour rather
dull yellow; forewing outer margin with even black border about 2 mm wide, a
narrow dark sagittate mark from cell-end, and a narrow shade from wing base to
anal angle along vein 1 and passing through the short linear black sex-brand at
the base of space 2 that extends into space 1b; hindwing darker brown but with a
scattering of yellow scales. Underside similar, but the *hindwing usually with a*

curved discal band of faint grey spots. In the female the upperside is darker, and the brand is replaced by a dark patch that extends to the wing base.

Distribution. The typical subspecies is widespread and common in Cuba. In Haiti and the Dominican Republic it is replaced by *P. baracoa loma* Evans 1955, the male of which is easily distinguished by its longer and more prominent sex-brand. The continental subspecies *P. b. myus* French 1885 is nearer to the Cuban subspecies but darker, especially on the upperside. RANGE: Florida, Cuba and Hispaniola. TL: Cuba.

Early stages. Caterpillar purplish buff, a narrow dorsal line and a pair of similar but wider lateral lines are dark brown, the paler areas between the lines irregularly spotted with dark brown; head dull yellow with two white stripes and a pair of ocellar spots. Food plants grasses.

POLITES DICTYNNA Godman and Salvin 1896
Lesser Whirlabout   **Pl. 23**

Description. Fw ♂ and ♀ 14 mm. Upperside golden-yellow, very similar to *Hylephila phylaeus,* but forewing apex rather more rounded and *black border continuous* and not formed of a series of wedges as in that species. Male sex-brand intensely black, replaced in the female by a simple dark shade. Underside in both sexes uniformly yellow except for black shades at anal angle, along inner margin and at the base of forewing.

Distribution. St Vincent, Grenada, Grenadines and St Kitts, and probably on other islands of the Lesser Antilles. A very distinct species sometimes treated as a subspecies of the continental *Polites vibex.* RANGE: Lesser Antilles. TL: St Vincent.

Early stages. Not known.

WALLENGRENIA OTHO Abbot and Smith 1797
Broken Dash Skipper   **Pl. 23**

Description. Fw ♂ 13–15 mm, ♀ 12–15 mm. Upperside medium to dark brown with bronze overtones; body hair-scales bronze-green; forewing orange-yellow between the cell and the costa as far as space 6; wedge-shaped spots of same colour at base of space 3 and immediately below in space 2 and also adjacent to the *short velvety black sex-brand at the base of space* 2; *below the brand lies a round patch of exceptionally large shining grey scales* from which extends a double streak of similar but smaller and darker scales almost to the outer margin; hindwing costal area almost black; fringes orange or grey, shading to brown apically; on forewing underside the orange areas are more extensive, the inner margin and anal area dark grey, apex yellow-green; hindwing all yellow-green. In the female the upperside is wholly dark brown except for the small orange spots in space 1b (linear), space 2 (square and the largest), space 3 (a dash) and spaces 6 and 7 (specks); underside like the male.

Distribution. A common and very variable species. The subspecies described above, *W. otho druryi* Latreille 1824 (TL: Haiti), is common in Haiti and the Dominican Republic and occurs sparingly in Porto Rico, St Thomas and Tortola. To the north flies *W. o. misera* Lucas 1857 on Cuba and the Bahamas; in the male it has lost all trace of orange on the upperside except for an occasional faint mark at the base of space 2, though the female has very small spots, sometimes almost white, in spaces 2, 3, 6 and sometimes 7; underside dark grey to brown; fringes grey. *W. o. vesuria* Ploetz 1883 from Jamaica moves in the opposite direction, being much brighter, with more extensive orange markings, the disc of the hindwing mostly orange and the underside yellow-green as in *W. o. druryi*. *W. o. ophites* Mabille 1878 inhabits the whole chain of the Lesser Antilles: *bright fulvous with restricted black markings* in both sexes, the male sex-brand very prominent. These four subspecies have been regarded as good species by many authors, which they may well be. There is no experimental evidence in favour of one view or the other. RANGE: U.S.A. to Argentina. TL: Georgia.

Early stages. The caterpillar is pale green, roughened along the back, profusely mottled with darker green, dorsal line dark green tapering at either end, yellow-green spiracular band expanding over the back beyond the seventh segment, where the body becomes tinged with pink, two faint subspiracular lines; head chocolate-brown. Food plants coarse grasses, sugar cane, rice, etc.

HYLEPHILA PHYLAEUS Drury 1773   *Fiery Skipper*   **Pl. 23**
Description. Fw ♂ 14–17 mm, ♀ 15–17 mm. Sexes rather different. Male upperside golden-orange, both *wings bordered with a series of black wedges based on the outer margin*; the forewing on the upperside has a conspicuous isolated black sex-brand across the base of spaces 1b and 2 outwardly bordered with a lunule of glistening grey scales; a narrow rectangular dark spot just beyond the cell; on the hindwing the costal and inner marginal areas are darkened; underside yellow, very sparsely marked. Female basically similar but the dark markings always more extensive and sometimes reducing the orange areas to a few small apical and discal spots on the forewing above and discal spots only on hindwing.

Distribution. Throughout the West Indies, usually common and quite variable. The brightest males and females are found in the Bahamas. In Cuba and Jamaica the males are less fiery, the females darker. The darkest females seem to occur in the Lesser Antilles. No subspecies have been described in the Caribbean area. RANGE: Canada to Argentina. TL: Antigua.

Early stages. The caterpillar feeds on grasses. It is pale green, mottled with darker green, and has a dark green dorsal line and a pale lateral stripe; head dark brown.

ATALOPEDES MESOGRAMMA Latreille 1823
Striped Skipper   **Pl. 24**
Description. Fw ♂ 18 mm, ♀ 20 mm. Upperside warm medium brown, fringes orange below vein 2 of forewing; forewing with scimitar-shaped *sex-brand very black at either end, grey in between*, and with an area of bronze-green upstanding scales on its outer edge; orange-tawny opaque spots in spaces 1a, 1b and 2 (ill-defined), in space 3 (triangular) and in spaces 4, (5), 6, 7 and 8 (very small and square); hindwing with streaky orange discal markings; underside dark brown, markings yellow, those on forewing in spaces 1a, 1b and 2 forming a single large patch; *hindwing with an almost straight yellow band* from mid-costa to vein 1b and a yellow cell-spot; anal angle yellow. Female upperside blackish brown, forewing spots white and hyaline except spot on vein 1, spot in base of space 2 large and square; hindwing with two or three short tawny discal streaks; underside as in male, but hindwing band and cell-spot white.

Distribution. Common and widespread in Cuba and also present in the Bahamas at least on Providence Island. Replaced in Haiti and no doubt in the Dominican Republic by *A. mesogramma apa* Comstock 1944 which is slightly smaller and much brighter, most of the forewing between the costa and the sex-brand being filled with orange-tawny, which also is more extensive in space 1a and on the disc of the hindwing; in the female the spot on vein 1 always tawny. RANGE: Bahamas to Hispaniola. TL: Cuba.

Early stages. Not known.

ATALOPEDES CARTERI Evans 1955   *Carter's Skipper*

Description. Fw ♂ and ♀ 14 mm. Like a dwarf *Atalopedes mesogramma* Latreille. Much smaller and darker, the *discal markings on the hindwing not streaks but spots*. On the underside of the forewing markings in spaces 1a, 1b and 2 restricted, and on the hindwing the broad yellow (♂) or white (♀) band is reduced to a thread or broken chain of very small spots.

Fig. 25. *Atalopedes carteri.* ♂ Nassau Island, Bahamas, October. × 1¼.

Distribution. Known only from Providence Island in the Bahamas, where it flies with *A. mesogramma*. RANGE: Bahamas. TL: Nassau.

Early stages. Not known.

ATALOPEDES NABOKOVI Bell and Comstock 1948
Nabokov's Skipper

Description. Fw ♂ 20 mm, ♀ 18 mm. Male upperside orange fulvous; forewing veins all black, costa dark brown in basal half, apex and outer margin pale brown fading into orange ground colour; two very small spots in spaces 4 and 5; sex brand as in *A. mesogramma*; marginal line black, fringes orange; hindwing veins not so dark. Underside similar, paler, forewing with faint subapical spots, hindwing yellowish and with *traces of an angled discal band of small pale*

a   b

Fig. 26. *Atalopedes nabokovi. Left,* ♂ Thomazeau, Haiti, September; *right,* ♀ Fond Parisien, Haiti, February.

spots. Female upperside forewing light brown; fulvous spots in spaces 1 to 5; three very small subapical spots and another in the cell-end extending basad along both edges of the cell; fringes brown; hindwing orange fulvous, costal and outer margins broadly brown, a few pale discal spots; underside pattern very similar but hindwing with discal band of six white spots sharply angled on vein 6.

Distribution. Only known from Haiti: Thomazeau and Fond Parisien. A much brighter insect than *Atalopedes mesogramma*, more like the North American *Atalopedes campestris*. TL: Thomazeau.

Early stages. Not known.

PARACHORANTHUS MAGDALIA Herrich-Schaeffer
Cuban Dwarf Skipper   Pl. 24

Description. Fw ♂ and ♀ 10–11 mm. Upperside golden-brown, sometimes lightly suffused dusky brown; forewing with dusky outer border 1–2 mm wide. Male with *narrow black straight sex brand* from origin of vein 3 to vein 1 along outer edge of cell; female with dusky outer marginal border extending along inner margin to base of wing; hindwing costal border broadly black, outer margin with thin black line. Underside uniformly yellow-brown, except basal area of forewing, which is almost black.

Distribution. Only in Cuba, but apparently widespread: San Christobal, Holguin, Sierra Maestra, etc. RANGE and TL: Cuba.

Early stages. Not known.

CHORANTHUS VITELLIUS Fabricius 1793
V-mark Skipper   Pl. 24

Description. Fw ♂ and ♀ 14–15 mm. Upperside light golden-yellow, slightly glistening in the male; *male without sex brand*; forewing with dark border about 2–3 mm wide from which short *very fine rays run basad along the veins*; a black V-shaped mark at upper outer angle of cell with some black shading beyond, a dark longitudinal line centrally in cell with some black shading below it; hindwing costal border broadly black, the border continuing narrowly along the outer margin and expanding again broadly at anal angle, where it is divided by a yellow streak in space 1c. Underside plain yellow, except for the black shade at the base of the forewing.

Distribution. Recorded only from Porto Rico, St Thomas and Tortola Island in the West Indies. RANGE: Florida to St Thomas. TL: 'American Islands'.

Early stages. The fully grown caterpillar is 'robin's egg blue' in appearance, the first three and last three segments more yellow-green, dorsal line darker, spiracles yellow; head rough dull yellow, black behind and round the edges, and with two broad straight vertical lines. Feeds by night on the older sugar cane leaves and rests by day in folded leaf shelters.

CHORANTHUS HAITENSIS Skinner 1920
Haitian V-mark Skipper

Description. Fw ♂ and ♀ 14–15 mm. Exactly like *Choranthus vitellius* except for the fact that the male does have a very *delicate linear black sex brand*, which is interrupted by vein 2.

Fig. 27. *Choranthus haitensis*. ♂ Dominican Republic.

Distribution. Known only from Haiti where it clearly replaces *C. vitellius.*
TL: Haiti.
Early stages. The caterpillar is known to attack sugar cane, but has not been described.

CHORANTHUS RADIANS Lucas 1857   *Rayed Skipper*   **Pl. 24**
Description. Fw ♂ 14–15 mm, ♀ 14–16 mm. Upperside golden-yellow, slightly glistening in the male, which has a *linear black sex brand* from vein 1 to vein 3; forewing outer margin broadly dark brown (2 mm in male to 4 mm in female), the inner edge forming projections basad between the veins, which are larger in the female than the male; basal half of hindwing dusky, costa broadly black, outer border narrower but with more prominent projections. Underside dusky, disc of forewing yellow, *all veins yellow*; a broad yellow stripe in space 1c of hindwing.
Distribution. Confined to Cuba, but occurring in two rather distinct forms with few intermediates. Form *radians*, the typical form described above, seems to predominate in western Cuba, e.g. at Habana, Matanzas, etc. In eastern Cuba the darker form *ammonia* Ploetz 1883 from Santiago and Guantanamo, in which on the underside the yellow veins are often obliterated by the dusky ground colour, predominates. As both forms occur at Holguin it may be that the differences are only seasonal, in which case the dark form would probably be the summer form. On the other hand, it may be that two distinct species are involved. RANGE and TL: Cuba.
Early stages. The caterpillar has been reared on grasses, but has not been described.

CHORANTHUS RICHMONDI Miller 1965
Bahaman Rayed Skipper
Description. Fw ♀ 16 mm. Upperside dark fuscous; forewing with darker patch near the cell-end, discal area thinly dusted with fulvous scales; hindwing with basal hair-scales and poorly defined discal area both fulvous. Underside fuscous, forewing basally darker, but apex, margin and postdiscal areas thickly dusted with fuscous and green scales; hindwing similar, *no discal markings and veins not pale.* Male not known.
Distribution. Known only from Great Guana Cay and Bitter Guana Cay, Exuma Islands, Bahamas. Very close to *Choranthus radians*, especially the form *ammonia* of eastern Cuba. RANGE: Bahamas. TL: Exuma Islands.

CHORANTHUS LILLIAE Bell 1931
Miss Perkins' Branded Skipper   **Pl. 24**
Description. Fw ♂ and ♀ 17–18 mm. Male upperside tawny; forewing with

wide black inwardly *slightly dentate outer marginal border*; all veins black; a rather broad black sex brand joined to a large square black area beyond the cell that is only separated from the black border by a row of three very small tawny subapical spots; hindwing black border widest along costal margin and at anal angle. Female upperside dark brown except for three rusty ill-defined discal spots. Underside in the male with forewing markings much as on upperside, in female with the discal markings forming a band; *hindwing dark rusty brown*, sometimes with faint traces of a paler discal band.

Distribution. Jamaica only; especially in St Thomas and Trelawny counties, local and rather scarce. TL: Bath, Jamaica.

Early stages. Not known.

CHORANTHUS BORINCONUS Watson 1937
Watson's Choranthus

Description. Fw ♂ and ♀ 16–20 mm. Very like the Jamaican *Choranthus lilliae*, which it seems to represent. Upperside *tawny areas lighter in colour*, the *forewing band in the male continuous from costa to vein 1b*, not interrupted by black patch beyond cell-end and as broad as the black border; some rusty streaks in the subapical area. Female forewing dark brown, as in *C. lilliae*, the spots of the discal band rusty yellow, the spot in space 1b double; hindwing unmarked. On the underside the forewing markings are as on the upperside, the male hindwing bronze, the female rusty brown with paler streaks near the inner margin. Head, palpi and thorax above green.

Fig. 28. *Choranthus borinconus.* ♂ Porto Rico, November.

Distribution. Porto Rico only. TL: Adjuntas.

Early stages. The fully grown caterpillar resembles that of *C. vitellius* but differs in that the 'four curving bands on the front of the head are dark brown ventrally, fading to dull orange above, only the thoracic half-collar black'. Food plant *Areca catechu*, the betel palm.

PARATRYTONE BATESI Bell 1935 *Bates's False Choranthus*

Description. Fw ♂ and ♀ 17–20 mm. Upperside dark brown; forewing with three subapical orange-fulvous *spots*, others, *larger and semihyaline, in bases of spaces 3 and 2*, all paler in female and more hyaline; an orange streak in space 1b; male with prominent oblique greyish black-edged sex-brand from near base of vein 3 to vein 1; hindwing orange-fulvous, bordered broadly on costa with black, narrowly elsewhere. On the underside the forewing is patterned as above but the whole apical area and a basal streak are bright green, hindwing

a   b

Fig. 29. *Paratrytone batesi. Left,* ♂; *right,* ♀ La Selle Mountains, Haiti, 6–7,000 ft., September.

also bright green, the male with a discal band of three black spots, the female with five silvery spots.

Distribution. Only known from the La Selle Mountains of Haiti at 5000–7500 ft. RANGE and TL: Haiti.

Early stages. Not known.

EUPHYES SINGULARIS Herrich-Schaeffer 1865
Butler's Branded Skipper   **Pl. 24**

Description. Fw ♂ 18 mm, ♀ 18–20 mm. Upperside smooth *deep bronze-brown,* costa and inner margin of forewing and almost all of hindwing clothed in *long greenish ochreous hair-scales*; male forewing with very dark grey sex-brand intensely black at proximal end, not divided by vein 2, rather wide; no hyaline spots; female forewing with round hyaline spots at base of space 2 and space 3 (small). Underside uniformly greyish ochreous, inner marginal area of forewing in male grey and space 2 pale ochreous towards the base, female with large pale area in space 1b below the hyaline spot in space 2.

Distribution. The Jamaican subspecies, *E. singularis insolata* Butler 1878, described above, is local and rather rare but widespread. The typical subspecies is confined to Cuba and is distinctly rare; the male is a good deal darker than the male of *insolata*, and the female is distinguished by the considerable enlargement of the hyaline spots on the forewing and the presence of a broad white area below them on the underside in space 1b. Recently taken at El Yungue, Porto Rico, in July. RANGE: Cuba to Porto Rico. TL: Cuba.

Early stages. Not known.

EUPHYES CORNELIUS Latreille 1824
Cornelius Skipper   **Pl. 24**
syn. *insulaepinorum* Holland 1916

Description. Fw ♂ and ♀ 18 mm. Upperside rather silky dark brown. The *sex-brand of the male consists of two separate dark grey ovals*, the lower of which, in space 1b, is intensely black proximally, the whole *surrounded by an area of blacker scales*. Upperside of both wings usually without markings, but forewing sometimes with a minute pale dot at the base of space 3 and another at the base of space 6; fringes for the most part grey; female forewing with small white hyaline spots in spaces 2, 3, 6 and 7, rarely in spaces 4 and 5. Underside uniformly silky greenish dark brown; male usually with two minute discal spots on the hindwing; female with a series of four or five, a pale grey area towards the anal angle, and the hyaline spots more prominent than on the upperside.

Distribution. *Euphyes cornelius cornelius*, described above, seems to be wide-spread and common in the Isle of Pines, and Cuba especially in eastern pro-vinces. In the Bahamas, at any rate on Nassau Island, it is replaced by the sub-species *agra* Evans 1955 in which the hyaline spots of the forewing are reduced, those of the hindwing absent. RANGE: Bahamas to Isle of Pines. TL: Cuba.
Early stages. Not known.

ASBOLIS CAPUCINUS Lucas 1856   *The Monk*   Pl. 24

Description. Fw ♂ 22–23 mm, ♀ 23–27 mm. Upperside dark brown, *hindwing almost black*, especially in the male; fringes of hindwing and anal angle of fore-wing white. *Male with delicate white sex-brand* curving from base of space 3 towards middle of inner margin; female forewing usually with pale shade filling base of space 2 and sometimes with a similar longitudinally divided shade in space 1b. Underside rusty ochreous with markings of upperside repeated and a little stronger; basal half of forewing and a broad wedge parallel to the inner margin on hindwing sooty black.
Distribution. Cuba only: Santiago, Havana, Holguin, San Cristoban, Soledad, etc. A widespread and very distinct species somewhat reminiscent of the species of the genus *Astraptes*. RANGE and TL: Cuba.
Early stages. Not known.

CALPODES ETHLIUS Stoll 1782   *The Canna Skipper*   Pl. 24

Description. Fw ♂ 23–25 mm, ♀ 23–27 mm. Upperside dark brown, both wings, but especially the hindwings, clothed basally with long ochreous hair-scales; forewing cell with a single hyaline spot at lower outer angle; *hindwing with* a characteristic *straight discal row of three bold hyaline spots*. Underside the same, but ground colour rather more coffee coloured.
Distribution. Throughout the West Indies with the apparent exception of the Virgin Islands. A powerful flier and common especially in gardens where Cannas are grown, on which the caterpillar feeds. RANGE: southern U.S.A. to Argentina. TL: Surinam.
Early stages. The fully grown caterpillar is translucent pale greenish grey, the pulsating dorsal vessel showing up as a darker line, sides inclining to white, legs green; head heart shaped, pale brownish grey to orange, with a black mark on the vertex and another on either side. Food plant *Canna*, on which it is sometimes a pest.

PANOQUINA SYLVICOLA Herrich-Schaeffer 1865
Sugar Cane Skipper   Pl. 24

Description. Fw ♂ and ♀ 19–20 mm. Upperside dark brown; forewing with white hyaline spots in space 2 (the largest and triangular), 3, 4, 6 and 7 (all small), centrally on vein 1 and in cell adjacent to the large spot in space 2, long and narrow in the male (2–3 mm), shorter (1 mm) in female; hindwing without markings. Underside forewing like the upperside, the same in both sexes; *hindwing with a row of small blue spots in spaces* 1c *to* 7 parallel to and rather close to the outer margin; ground colour uniformly brown in the male but flushed blue in the female over the anterior half.
Distribution. Cuba, Cayman Isles, Hispaniola, Jamaica, Porto Rico, St Kitts, St Lucia, Guadeloupe, Martinique, Antigua, Montserrat, Dominica and no doubt other islands, common. Not reported from the Bahamas. In Porto Rico

Plate 23   HESPERIIDAE

1. **Ephyriades brunnea**   *Jamaican Duksy Wing*   p. 175
   1a ♂, 1b ♀, Cuba. Forewing with circle of hyaline spots near apex.

2. **Erynnis zarucco**   *Zarucco Dusky Wing*   175
   ♂ Matanzas, Cuba. July. Obscure dark forewing bands rather wavy.

3. **Rhinthon cubana**   *Bath Skipper*   182
   ♂ Tobago. Forewing with twin hyaline cell spots.

4. **Heliopetes arsalte**   *Common White Skipper*   178
   ·♂ Trinidad. December. Male with very narrow costal fold.

5. **Pyrgus oileus**   *Tropical Chequered Skipper*   178
   ♂ Sierra Maestra, Cuba. The commonest skipper.

6. **Pyrgus crisia**   *Cuban Chequered Skipper*   179
   ♂ La Lisa, Cuba. Smaller and much darker than *P. oileus*.

7. **Pyrrhocalles antiqua**   *Great Tawny Skipper*   179
   ♂ *P. a. antiqua,* Haiti. Singled out by its large size and fiery colour.

8. **Oarisma nanus**   *Pygmy Skipper*   183
   ♂ Holguin, Cuba. Veins on underside of hindwing intensely black.

9. **Perichares philetes**   *Dolores Skipper*   179
   ♂ St Christobal, Cuba. Curved cell-spot and sex brand.

10. **Vettius fantasos**   *Opal Skipper*   180
    ♂ French Guiana. Underside pattern unmistakable.

11. **Synapte malitiosa**   *The Drab*   181
    ♂ Rio Cano, Cuba. Hw underside with light and dark shadows.

12. **Cymaenes tripunctus**   *Three Spot Skipper*   181
    ♂ Grand Cayman. July. No hyaline spot in forewing cell.

13. **Polites baracoa**   *Baracoa Skipper*   183
    ♂ Haiti. Male sex brand black linear and angled.

14. **Polites dictynna**   *Lesser Whirlabout*   184
    ♂ St Vincent. Clear golden, the inner edge of black borders even.

15. **Wallengrenia otho**   *Broken Dash Skipper*   185
    15a ♂ *W. o. druryi,* Haiti. Upperside very dusky.
    15a ♂ *W. o. ophites,* St Lucia. December. Upperside bright ochreous.

16. **Hylephila phylaeus**   *Fiery Skipper*   185
    16a ♂ Sierra Maestra, Cuba. Borders of black wedges.
    16b ♀ Grand Cayman. June. Black wedges enlarged and fused.

17. **Holguinia holguin**   *Tollin's Skipper*   182
    ♂ Holguin, Cuba. Underside of hindwing brilliant green.

23

1. **Atalopedes mesogramma**   *Striped Skipper*   p. 185
   ♂ Haiti. Hindwing underside with broad yellow stripe.

2. **Parachoranthus magdalia**   *Cuban Dwarf Skipper*   187
   ♂ Sierra Maestra, Cuba. September. Uniformly golden brown.

3. **Choranthus vitellius**   *V-mark Skipper*   187
   ♂ Porto Rico. Black border projects in space 1c.

4. **Choranthus radians**   *Rayed Skipper*   188
   ♂ Cuba. Black border fills spaces 1a and 1b.

5. **Choranthus lilliae**   *Miss Perkins' Branded Skipper*   188
   ♂ Bath, Jamaica. Costa of hindwing upperside very broadly black.

6. **Euphyes singularis**   *Butler's Branded Skipper*   190
   ♂ Port au Prince, Haiti. Sex brand large but not conspicuous.

7. **Euphyes cornelius**   *Cornelius Skipper*   190
   ♂ Holguin, Cuba. Almost black above and below.

8. **Asbolis capucinus**   *The Monk*   191
   ♂ Holguin, Cuba. Very dark, but sex brand cream coloured.

9. **Calpodes ethlius**   *The Canna Skipper*   191
   ♂ Barbados. Hindwing with horizontal row of translucent spots.

10. **Panoquina sylvicola**   *Sugar Cane Skipper*   191
    ♂ Sierra Maestra, Cuba. Chain of blue spots close to margin.

11. **Panoquina nero**   *Haitian White-barred Skipper*   194
    ♂ Haiti. White band on dark brown hindwing underside.

12. **Panoquina fusina**   *Hewitson's White-barred Skipper*   194
    ♀ *P. fusina jumbo*, Jamaica. White band on purplish ground colour.

13. **Panoquina corrupta**   *Cuban White-barred Skipper*   195
    ♂ Holguin, Cuba. Distinctive white band on hindwing underside.

14. **Panoquina ocola**   *Ocola Skipper*   195
    ♂ Florida. Hindwing underside without markings.

15. **Panoquina panoquinoides**   *Obscure Skipper*   195
    ♂ Rum Point, Grand Cayman. May. Hyaline spots yellow.

16. **Nyctelius nyctelius**   *Nyctelius Skipper*   196
    ♂ St Vincent. Hindwing underside with round black spot costa.

17. **Lerodea eufala**   *Eufala Skipper*   196
    ♂ Cuba. Forewing with twin hyaline spots at cell-end.

18. **Saliana esperi**   *Cuban Saliana Skipper*   196
    ♂ Cuba. Hindwing underside outer half chestnut.

B.W.I.   N

the females lack the blue flush on the underside of the hindwings and the ground colour above and below is lighter brown than in typical *sylvicola*. This form has been named *woodruffi* Watson 1937. Similar specimens occur in the Cayman Isles, Jamaica, Haiti and elsewhere and on St Kitts both forms occur. *Woodruffi* would seem to be a recurrent variety rather than a true subspecies. Dominican *P. sylvicola* are indistinguishable from Cuban specimens. RANGE: southern U.S.A. to Argentina. TL: Cuba.

Early stages. The fully grown caterpillar is light green, like the underside of a cane-sugar leaf, with pale intersegmental yellow transverse lines and four pale dorsal lines, sprinkled with darker green dots, lateral line white, body bluish underneath; head large and green. Food plants include sugar cane, rice, bamboo, Johnson and Pimento Grass, etc. Often a pest of sugar cane.

PANOQUINA NERO Fabricius 1798
Haitian White-barred Skipper   **Pl. 24**
syn. *belli* Watson 1937

Description. Fw ♂ and ♀ 22–23 mm. Very like *Panoquina corrupta* but considerably larger and with the white band on the underside of the hindwing parallel-sided, only about 1 mm wide and delicately cut by the veins. Could also be confused with *P. sylvicola* but is again much larger, the *spots on the underside of the hindwing forming a band rather than a loose chain*, and farther from the outer margin.

Distribution. Hispaniola and Porto Rico. Widespread but not common. RANGE: Haiti to Porto Rico. TL: Haiti.

Early stages. Fully grown caterpillar light green, dotted with darker green and with paler transverse and longitudinal lines; head green and with two narrow purplish stripes. Food plants rice, sugar cane, bamboo and grasses.

PANOQUINA FUSINA Hewitson 1877
Hewitson's White-barred Skipper   **Pl. 24**

Description. Fw ♀ 28 mm. Female upperside dark brown, hyaline spots of forewing white, spot on vein 1 hemispherical, small spot in cell as in *P. sylvicola*; underside ground colour purplish except basal two-thirds of the forewing and inner marginal area (broadly) of hindwing; *hindwing band of even width, white, but ragged* and terminating abruptly just below vein 2, where it bends towards the extremity of vein 1b. Male not known (see below).

Distribution. 'Jamaica'. There is considerable doubt as to where the race of *P. fusina* described above and named *P. fusina jumbo* by Evans in 1955 really came from. The name is based on two females collected very many years ago and labelled 'Jamaica'. Unless the insect has become extinct in Jamaica it seems improbable that so large an insect should not have been seen there since. Of the several continental subspecies of *P. fusina*, these supposed Jamaican specimens most closely resemble the typical Brazilian *P. fusina fusina*. RANGE: Texas to S. Brazil. TL: S. America.

Early stages. In Brazil the fully grown caterpillar is grey-green, with a pair of subdorsal yellowish stripes on either side and grey beneath; head large, grey, rimmed black and with a vertical black frontal stripe and a curved black stripe on each cheek. (Described from Miles Moss's unpublished coloured figure.)

PANOQUINA CORRUPTA Herrich-Schaeffer 1865
Cuban White-barred Skipper   **Pl. 24**

Description. Fw ♂ and ♀ 18–19 mm. Upperside very dark brown, almost black; forewing hyaline spots arranged as in the other species of the genus, but cell-spot very small or absent, and spot on vein 1 inclined to be opalescent rather than hyaline. On the underside of the hindwing there is a highly characteristic bold *white band starting near apex and broadening till it ends about the middle of space* 1c, its course faintly visible on the upperside of the wing.

Distribution. Only in Cuba, principally in the east, e.g. Santiago, Holguin, etc., and in the Isle of Pines. RANGE and TL: Cuba.

Early stages. Not known.

PANOQUINA OCOLA Edwards 1863   *Ocola Skipper*   **Pl. 24**

Description. Fw ♂ and ♀ 18–19 mm. Very similar to *Panoquina sylvicola* from which it differs in the following respects: slightly smaller, upperside ground colour rather more ochreous brown, *no spot in forewing cell, spot on vein* 1 *often yellowish*; on the underside the veins in the apical area of the forewing and on the whole of the hindwing are lined ochreous; the discal spots on the hindwing if present are very faint, barely differentiated from the ground colour and a little farther from the outer margin. Sexual dimorphism in the wing markings is much less than in *P. sylvicola*.

Distribution. Cuba, Hispaniola, Jamaica and Porto Rico but always rather sporadic. RANGE: southern U.S.A. to Argentina. TL: Florida.

Early stages. The caterpillar has been reared on sugar cane and on *Hymenachne amplexicaulis* in Porto Rico but has not been distinguished from the caterpillar of *P. sylvicola*.

PANOQUINA PANOQUINOIDES Skinner 1892
Obscure Skipper   **Pl. 24**

Description. Fw ♂ and ♀ 13–14 mm. Upperside slightly glistening dark ochreous brown. The *forewing spots in the male yellowish, not hyaline*, small, at the base of space 2, 3, 6 and 7, the last two very small; no spot in space 8; *in the female these spots are* much *paler and semihyaline*, and there is also a faint spot on vein 1. Underside similar, the veins standing out, hindwing with single bluish spots in spaces 2, 3 and 6.

Distribution. Cayman Isles and Jamaica, local. Probably a recent arrival from Florida and likely to turn up in Cuba as well. In Grenada and the Grenadines there occurs subspecies *eugeon* Godman and Salvin 1896. It differs most obviously from typical *panoquinoides* in lacking the bluish white spots on the underside of the hindwing and in having a well-marked yellow spot on vein 1 on the upperside of the forewing. It could well be a distinct species. RANGE: southern U.S.A. to Brazil. TL: Florida.

Early stages. Fully grown caterpillar reddish brown, with a dark dorsal line and thin dark lateral lines, the anal segments and the underneath darker brown; head black and white; prothoracic shield white. Food plant Bahama grass, *Cynodon dactylon* and sugar cane, the caterpillar hiding by day in a rolled-up leaf shelter.

NYCTELIUS NYCTELIUS Latreille 1824

Nyctelius Skipper **Pl. 24**

Description. Fw 16 mm (♂) to 20 mm (♀). Upperside dark brown, the base of the forewing and much of the disc of the hindwing clothed with greenish ochreous hair-scales; forewing with two very small spots in cell, three subapical spots; the spot at base of space 2 usually square, spot on vein 1, if present, opaque and yellow; hindwing ochreous between the veins on the disc. Underside mottled grey and dark brown; forewing with extensive white patch in space 1b; *hindwing with round black spot centrally in space 7*, a broad dark transverse discal band and a darkened outer margin and anal area.

Distribution. Throughout the West Indies and generally common. *N. nyctelius nyctelius* is essentially the mainland subspecies, the underside grey to purplish in general tone, the fringes greyish, the palpi almost white. In Dominica and St Lucia (and indeed elsewhere sporadically) there occurs a much darker form, the general underside colour dark purplish, the fringes almost rust coloured and the palpi ochreous. This has been named *N. nyctelius agari* Dillon 1948, but seems only doubtfully to be a true subspecies. RANGE: Central America to S. Brazil. TL: Brazil.

Early stages. The fully grown caterpillar (in Porto Rico) is bluish grey transversely shadowed with pale grey, prothoracic collar black and reaching laterally to the spiracles; head dirty yellow with a central black stripe and a black lateral stripe on each cheek. It feeds at night on coarse-leaved grasses and also on sugar cane, but is a much less important pest of cane than *Panoquina sylvicola*.

LERODEA EUFALA Edwards 1869 *Eufala Skipper* **Pl. 24**

Description. Fw ♂ and ♀ 14–15 mm. Upperside drab grey-brown, forewing noticeably more rounded in the female than the male. Forewing with a row of three very small subapical spots, *a pair of similar spots well separated at the cell-end*, another at base of space 3, and a seventh and largest at base of space 2; in the female there is also very rarely an eighth spot on vein 1; hindwing unmarked. Underside more greyish brown, only the basal area of forewing blackish brown, the hindwing usually with a paler stripe along vein 1b in space 1c and the faintest indications of pale grey discal spots.

Distribution. Only in Cuba, Jamaica and possibly Hispaniola, not common. A rather insignificant little butterfly often confused with *Cymaenes tripunctus* (p. 191), which is slightly larger, is warmer brown, has longer antennae and never has the twin spots at the forewing cell-end characteristic of *Lerodea eufala*. *C. tripunctus* male also has black modified scales on the forewing forming a patch that occupies the base of space 2 and a streak along vein 1; *L. eufala* has no sex-brand. RANGE: southern U.S.A. to Argentina. TL: Florida.

Early stages. The fully grown caterpillar is bright grass green, with darker mid-dorsal and supraspiracular lines, the former bordered with yellow patches, and with transverse yellow lines between the segments, a white subspiracular line. Food plants grasses, sugar cane, etc.

SALIANA ESPERI Evans 1955 *Cuban Saliana Skipper* **Pl. 24**

Description. Fw ♂ 20–21 mm. Upperside dark brown, the hyaline spots rather large; no spot in forewing space 4 but the cell-spot bold and comma-shaped; hindwing with small square spot in space 4 and sometimes a much smaller one below it in space 3. On the underside the forewing is marked as on the upperside but the ground colour is rusty red, with the basal half of the costal area ochreous; on the hindwing the *basal half is very pale dirty brown, outer half deep chestnut*, costal and inner marginal areas broadly grey.

Distribution. Cuba, rare. Not known from any other island, but present in Trinidad and Tobago. The description given above applies only to the Cuban race. Typical *Saliana esperi* of the mainland differs in always having a spot in space 4 of the forewing and the basal half of the hindwing underside pale yellow to creamy white. RANGE: Mexico to Brazil. TL: Ecuador.

Early stages. Not known.

In the preparation of the following Distribution Table certain rather arbitrary decisions had to be taken for the sake of simplicity. As a result it should be noted that, in the Table,

N. America includes Mexico
Mainland includes S. and Central America
The Bahamas include Turks Island
Cuba includes the Isle of Pines
The Virgin Isles include Anegada, Tortola, St Thomas and St Croix
The Leeward Islands include Anguilla, Barbuda, St Kitts, Antigua, Nevis, Montserrat, Guadeloupe and Dominica, i.e. the Lesser Antilles north of 15° N. latitude
The Windward Islands include Martinique, St Lucia, St Vincent, Grenada and Barbados

Distribution within the Lesser Antilles is given in much greater detail in the recently published work of Pinchon and Enrico (see Bibliography).

● indicates a resident species, whether permanent or temporary, i.e. for several generations

V indicates a visitor, whether a frequent migrant, a chance vagrant, or accidental

? indicates a very doubtful record

	N. America	Bermuda	Bahamas	Cuba	Cayman Isles	Hispaniola	Jamaica	Porto Rico	Virgin Isles	Leeward Isles	Windward Isles	Trinidad	Mainland
DANAIDAE 9 species													
Danaus plexippus	●	●	●	●	●	●	●	●	●	●	●	●	●
,, eresimus	●		●	●	●	●	●	●	●	●	V	●	●
,, gilippus	●		●	●		●	●				V	●	●
,, cleophile						●	●	?					
Anetia briaria				●		●							
,, pantherata				●		●							
,, jaegeri						●							
,, cubana				●									
Lycorea ceres				●		●	●	●				●	●
ITHOMIIDAE 2 species													
Greta diaphana						●	●						
,, cubana				●									

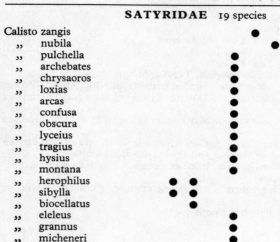

SATYRIDAE 19 species

	N. America	Bermuda	Bahamas	Cuba	Cayman Isles	Hispaniola	Jamaica	Porto Rico	Virgin Isles	Leeward Isles	Windward Isles	Trinidad	Mainland
Calisto zangis							●						
,, nubila								●					
,, pulchella						●							
,, archebates						●							
,, chrysaoros						●							
,, loxias						●							
,, arcas						●							
,, confusa						●							
,, obscura						●							
,, lyceius						●							
,, tragius						●							
,, hysius						●							
,, montana						●							
,, herophilus			●	●									
,, sibylla			●	●									
,, biocellatus				●									
,, eleleus						●							
,, grannus						●							
,, micheneri						●							

NYMPHALIDAE 58 species

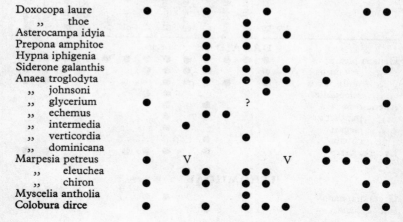

	N. America	Bermuda	Bahamas	Cuba	Cayman Isles	Hispaniola	Jamaica	Porto Rico	Virgin Isles	Leeward Isles	Windward Isles	Trinidad	Mainland
Doxocopa laure	●			●								●	●
,, thoe						●							
Asterocampa idyia				●				●					
Prepona amphitoe				●		●							
Hypna iphigenia				●		●							
Siderone galanthis				●		●		●					●
Anaea troglodyta				●			●	●		●			
,, johnsoni							●						
,, glycerium	●					?							●
,, echemus				●	●								
,, intermedia				●									
,, verticordia						●							
,, dominicana										●			
Marpesia petreus	●		V						V	●	●	●	●
,, eleuchea			●	●		●	●						
,, chiron	●			●		●	●					●	●
Myscelia antholia				●		●							
Colobura dirce	●			●		●	●					●	●

	N. America	Bermuda	Bahamas	Cuba	Cayman Isles	Hispaniola	Jamaica	Porto Rico	Virgin Isles	Leeward Isles	Windward Isles	Trinidad	Mainland
Historis acheronta	●			●		●	●	?				●	●
,, odius	●			●		●	●	●		●	●	●	●
Hamadryas feronia	●					V	●	●			V	●	●
,, februa	●			●		●	●	●				●	●
,, amphinome	●			V								●	●
Mestra dorcas							●						
,, cana											●	●	●
Dynamine egaea	●			●			●						
,, mylitta	●			●									
Archimestra teleboas						●							
Lucinia sida				●									
,, cadma							●						
Eunica tatila				●		●	●	●					
,, monima	●			●		●	●					●	●
,, heraclitus				●									
Adelpha abyla							●						
,, gelania						●	●						
,, iphicla	●											●	●
Hypolimnas misippus	●	●				●	●			●	●	●	●
Junonia coenia	●	●	●	●									
,, evarete			●	●	●	●	●	●	●	●	●	●	●
Anartia jatrophae	●		●	●	●	●	●	●	●	●	●	●	●
,, amathea												●	●
,, lytrea							●						
,, chrysopelea				●			?						
Biblis hyperia	●			●		●	●		●	●	●	●	●
Siproeta stelenes				●		●	●	●	●			●	●
Atlantea pantoni				●									
,, perezi				●									
,, tulita								●					
Antillea pelops				●		●	●	●	●				
,, proclea							●						
Phyciodes frisia			●	●		●	●						
,, phaon	●			●	●								
Vanessa cardui	●	V	V	V		V	V	V		V	V	V	
,, virginiensis	●			V		V	V	V					●
,, atalanta	●	V		V		V	V						
Hypanartia paullus				●		●	●	●					
Euptoieta hegesia			●	●	●	●	●	●				●	
,, claudia	●						●						●

HELICONIIDAE 6 species

	N. America	Bermuda	Bahamas	Cuba	Cayman Isles	Hispaniola	Jamaica	Porto Rico	Virgin Isles	Leeward Isles	Windward Isles	Trinidad	Mainland
Heliconius charitonius	•			•	•	•	•	?	•	•			•
Eueides melphis	•			•		•		?					
Dryas iulia	•		•	•		•	•	•	•	•	•	•	•
Dione juno												•	•
„ vanillae	•	•	•	•		•	•	•	•	•	•	•	•
Philaethria dido				?		?						•	•

LIBYTHEIDAE 3 species

	N. America	Bermuda	Bahamas	Cuba	Cayman Isles	Hispaniola	Jamaica	Porto Rico	Virgin Isles	Leeward Isles	Windward Isles	Trinidad	Mainland
Libytheana motya				•									
„ terena						•	•	•					
„ fulvescens										•			

RIODINIDAE 1 species

	N. America	Bermuda	Bahamas	Cuba	Cayman Isles	Hispaniola	Jamaica	Porto Rico	Virgin Isles	Leeward Isles	Windward Isles	Trinidad	Mainland
Apodemia carteri			•	•									

LYCAENIDAE 31 species

	N. America	Bermuda	Bahamas	Cuba	Cayman Isles	Hispaniola	Jamaica	Porto Rico	Virgin Isles	Leeward Isles	Windward Isles	Trinidad	Mainland
Eumaeus atalus	•		•	•									
Pseudolycaena marsyas											•	•	•
Thereus bourkei						•							
Allosmaitia coelebs				•		•	?	•					
„ piplea											•		
Cyanophrys crethona						•							
Chlorostrymon simaethis	•		•	•		•	•	•	•	•	•	•	•
„ maesites	•		•	•		•	•				•	•	•
Nesiostrymon celida						•		•					
Strymon bazochii				•		•	•	•				•	•
„ martialis	•		•	•		•							
„ toussainti						•							
„ rufofusca	•										•		
„ acis			•	•		•	•	•					
„ bubastus	•					•			•	•	•	•	
„ columella	•			•		•	•	•		•			•
„ christophei						•							
„ limenia				•		•							
Electrostrymon angerona										•	•		
„ angelia			•	•		•	•	•					
„ dominicana										•			
„ pan						•							

	N. America	Bermuda	Bahamas	Cuba	Cayman Isles	Hispaniola	Jamaica	Porto Rico	Virgin Isles	Leeward Isles	Windward Isles	Trinidad	Mainland
Leptotes cassius	●		●	●	●	●	●	●	●	●	●	●	●
,, perkinsae							●						
Hemiargus hanno	●			●	●	●	●	●	●	●	●	●	●
,, ammon			●	●	●								
,, thomasi	●					●			●				
,, dominica							●						
Pseudochrysops bornoi						●							
Brephidium exilis	●		●	●	●								●
,, pseudofea	●												

PIERIDAE 50 species

	N. America	Bermuda	Bahamas	Cuba	Cayman Isles	Hispaniola	Jamaica	Porto Rico	Virgin Isles	Leeward Isles	Windward Isles	Trinidad	Mainland
Ascia josephina						●	●	●					●
,, menciae						●							
,, monuste	●			●	●	●	●	●	●	●	●	●	●
Appias drusilla	●			●	●	●	●	●	●	●	●	●	●
,, punctifera							●	●	●				
Pontia protodice	●			V									●
Pieris rapae	●	●											
Melete salacia				●									
Eurema euterpiformis				●									
,, nise	●						●						●
,, chamberlaini			●										
, larae			●	●									
,, leuce						●							
,, venusta										●	●	●	●
,, daira	●			●		●					●	●	●
,, elathea				●	●	●	●	●			●	●	●
,, lisa		●	●	●	●	●	●	●	●	●	●	●	●
,, lucina				●									
,, priddyi						●							
,, albula	●									●	●		●
,, amelia				●									
,, portoricensis								●					
,, pyro						●							
,, messalina			●	●	●	●	●						
,, dina	●		●	●		●	●						
,, adamsi							●						
,, gratiosa											●	●	●
,, boisduvaliana	●			●									●
,, proterpia	●			●		●	●						●

	N. America	Bermuda	Bahamas	Cuba	Cayman Isles	Hispaniola	Jamaica	Porto Rico	Virgin Isles	Leeward Isles	Windward Isles	Trinidad	Mainland
Eurema nicippe	●		●	●	●	●	●	●					
,, nicippiformis						●							
Nathalis iole	●			●		●	●						●
Kricogonia lyside	●			●		●	●	●					
,, cabrerai				●									
Zerene cesonia	●			●		●							
Anteos maerula	●			●		●		●				●	●
,, clorinde	●			●								●	●
Phoebis avellaneda				●									
,, philea	●			●		●		?				●	●
,, argante	●			●		●	●					●	●
,, agarithe	●			●		●	●	●		●	●	●	●
,, sennae	●	●	●	●	●	●	●	●	●	●	●	●	●
,, editha						●							
Aphrissa trite	●					●	●			●	●		
,, orbis				●									
,, neleis			●	●									
,, godartiana							●	●	?				
,, statira	●			●		●	●	●			●	●	●
Dismorphia spio						●	●	●					
,, cubana				●									

PAPILIONIDAE 22 species

	N. America	Bermuda	Bahamas	Cuba	Cayman Isles	Hispaniola	Jamaica	Porto Rico	Virgin Isles	Leeward Isles	Windward Isles	Trinidad	Mainland
Parides gundlachianus				●									
Battus zetides						●							
,, polydamas	●		●	●	●	●	●	●	●	●	●	●	●
,, devilliersi			●	●									
Papilio thoas	●			●			●					●	●
,, cresphontes	●	V	V	●									
,, aristodemus	●			●	●	●		?					
,, andraemon			●	●			●	●					
,, machaonides						●		●					
,, polyxenes	●			●									●
,, palamedes	●			V									
,, troilus	●			V									
,, thersites							●						
,, androgeus	●			●			●				●	●	●
,, homerus							●						
,, aristor						●							
,, oxynius				●									
,, pelaus				●		●	●	●					

	N. America	Bermuda	Bahamas	Cuba	Cayman Isles	Hispaniola	Jamaica	Porto Rico	Virgin Isles	Leeward Isles	Windward Isles	Trinidad	Mainland
Papilio caiguanabus				●									
Eurytides celadon				●									
" zonaria						●							
" marcellinus							●						

HESPERIIDAE 92 species

	N. America	Bermuda	Bahamas	Cuba	Cayman Isles	Hispaniola	Jamaica	Porto Rico	Virgin Isles	Leeward Isles	Windward Isles	Trinidad	Mainland
Phocides pigmalion	●		●	●			●					●	
" perkinsae				●									
Proteides mercurius	●					●				●	●		
" maysi				●									
Epargyreus zestos				V						●	●		
" antaeus							●						
" spanna						●							
Polygonus leo	●		●	●		●	●	●					●
" manueli	●										●	●	
Chioides catillus	●						●					●	
" vintra													
" ixion													
" marmorosa				●									
Aguna asander						●	●						
Urbanus proteus	●		●	●	●	●	●	●		●	●	●	●
" dorantes	●		●					●			●		●
" obscurus										●			
" tellus	●						?						
" tanna	●						?						
" albimargo						?	?						●
Polythrix octomaculata	●											●	●
Astraptes talus	●			●		●	●	●		●	●	●	●
" anaphus	●			●			●			●			●
" cassander				●									
" xagua				●			●						
" habana				●			●						
" jaira							●						
Autochton cellus	●			V									
" neis	●						V	V				●	●
Cogia calchas	●						V	V				●	●
Nisoniades bessus	●						V						
Burca stillmani						●							
" concolor				●									
" braco			●	●									
" hispaniolae						●							

	N. America	Bermuda	Bahamas	Cuba	Cayman Isles	Hispaniola	Jamaica	Porto Rico	Virgin Isles	Leeward Isles	Windward Isles	Trinidad	Mainland
Cabares potrillo	●			●		●	●						
Antigonus nearchus	●			●		●	?					○	●
Achlyodes thraso	●			●		●	●	●	●	●			●
Timochares ruptifasciata	●			●		●	●					●	●
Grais stigmaticus	●						●					●	●
Anastrus sempiternus	●					●	●					●	●
Gesta gesta	●			●		●						●	●
Ouleus fridericus	●						V						●
Chiomara asychis	●										●		●
,, mithrax				●		●							●
Ephyriades zephodes				●		●	●						
,, arcas				●		●		●	●	●			
,, brunnea	●		●			●							
Erynnis zarucco	●			●		●							
Heliopetes arsalte	●			●		V	V						●
Pyrgus oileus	●			●	●	●	●	●	●			●	●
,, crisia				●		●	?						
Pyrrhocalles antiqua			●	●		●							
,, jamaicensis							●						
Perichares philetes	●					●						●	●
Pheraeus unia												●	●
Vettius fantasos	●						?					●	●
Synapte malitiosa				●								●	●
Cymaenes tripunctus	●		●	●	●	●	●	●				●	●
Rhinthon cubana	●			●		●						●	●
,, bushi				●									
Holguinia holguin				●									
Oarisma nanus				●									
,, stillmani				●									
Polites baracoa	●			●									
,, dictynna								●		●			
Wallengrenia otho	●			●		●	●	●		●			●
Hylephila phylaeus	●	●		●	●	●	●	●	●	●	●	●	●
Atalopedes mesogramma	●		●	●	●	●							●
,, carteri				●									
,, nabokovi						●							
Parachoranthus magdalia				●									
Choranthus vitellius	?							●	●				?
,, haitensis						●							
,, radians					●								
,, richmondi				●									
,, lilliae						●							

	N. America	Bermuda	Bahamas	Cuba	Cayman Isles	Hispaniola	Jamaica	Porto Rico	Virgin Isles	Leeward Isles	Windward Isles	Trinidad	Mainland
Choranthus borinconus								●					
Paratrytone batesi						●							
Euphyes singularis				●			●						
„ cornelius			●	●									
Asbolis capucinus				●									
Calpodes ethlius	●	●	●	●		●	●	●	●	●	●	●	●
Panoquina sylvicola	●			●		●	●	●	●	●	●	●	●
„ nero				●			●	●					
„ fusina	●						?					●	●
„ corrupta				●									
„ ocola	●			●	●	●						●	●
„ panoquinoides	●			●	●	●					●	●	●
Nyctelius nyctelius	●		●	●	●	●	●	●	●	●	●	●	●
Lerodea eufala	●					●	●					●	●
Saliana esperi				●								●	●

Families represented, 11; species, 293.

General works

BARCANT, M. 1970. *Butterflies of Trinidad and Tobago.* Collins, London. Fully illustrated, except Hesperiidae, and with a wealth of life history information.

GODMAN, F. D. and SALVIN, O. 1879–1901. *Biologia Centrali-Americana.* 3 vols. London. A work of basic systematic and faunistic importance.

GOSSE, P. H. 1851. *A Naturalist's Sojourn in Jamaica.* London.

FORD, E. B. 1945. *Butterflies.* Collins, London. Primarily concerned with the butterflies of Great Britain, but in fact an admirable introduction to the study of any group of butterflies.

KLOTS, A. B. 1951. *A Field Guide to the Butterflies of N. America east of the Great Plains.* Houghton Mifflin, Boston. An exceptional work and very necessary to the study of the butterflies of the West Indies.

LONGSTAFF, G. B. 1912. *Butterfly Hunting in Many Lands.* Longman and Green, London. A fund of unusual information.

MOSS, A. MILES. 1949. 'Biological Notes on some Hesperiidae of Para and the Amazon.' *Acta zool. Lilloana,* 7:27. Extensive information on larvae, pupae and food plants.

SEITZ, A. (Editor). 1907–24. *Macrolepidoptera of the World. Vol. 5, American Fauna.* The only work covering the whole of the American fauna. Profusely illustrated. Compiled by a number of authors of varying ability. Expensive.

WILLIAMS, C. B. 1930. *The Migration of Butterflies.* Oliver and Boyd, Edinburgh and London. The standard work on the subject.

Faunistic works

a. General

CLENCH, HARRY 1964. 'Synopsis of West Indian Lycaenidae with remarks on their zoogeography.' *Journal of Research in Lepidoptera,* 1963, 2:247.

COMSTOCK, W. P. and HUNTINGTON, E. I. 1943. 'Lycaenidae of the Antilles.' *Annals New York Academy of Sciences,* 45:49.

SCOTT, J. A. 1971. 'List of Antillean Butterflies.' *Journal of Research in Lepidoptera,* 9:249.

b. The Islands

Antilles Françaises

PINCHON, R. and ENRICO, P. 1969. *Faune des Antilles Françaises. Les Papilions.* Fort de France, Martinique. Includes a detailed distribution table covering all the Lesser Antilles.

Bahamas

RINDGE, F. H. 1955. 'The butterflies of the Bahama Islands.' *American Museum Novitates,* No. 1715.

Barbados

PEARCE, E. J. 1969. 'The Butterflies of Barbados.' *Journal of the Barbados Museum,* 33:76.

B.W.I.   o

Bermuda
OGILVIE, L. 1928. 'Insects of Bermuda.' *Department of Agriculture*, Bermuda.

Cayman Islands
CARPENTER, G. D. HALE and LEWIS, C. B. 1943. 'Lepidoptera from the Cayman Islands.' *Annals of the Carnegie Museum*, 29:371.

Cuba
BATES, D. MARSTON. 1935. 'The Butterflies of Cuba.' *Bull. Mus. Comp. Zoology, Harvard*, 78:63. Excellent, but out of print.

GUNDLACH, J. 1881. *Contribución a la Entomologia Cubana*, and Supplement, 1891.

TORRE Y CALLEJAS, S. L. 1954. 'Annotated List of the Butterflies of Cuba.' *Journal of the New York Entomological Society*, 62.

Dominica
GODMAN, F. D. and SALVIN, O. 1884. 'Rhopalocera . . . in Dominica.' *Proc. zoological Society of London*, 1884:314.

Dominican Republic, *see* Hispaniola.

Grenada, *see* St Vincent.

Guadeloupe, *see* Antilles Françaises.

Haiti
WOLCOTT, G. N. 1927. 'Entomologie d'Haiti.' Department of Agriculture, Port au Prince, Haiti. Mostly concerned with crop pests. See Hispaniola.

Hispaniola
HALL, ARTHUR. 1925. 'List of the Butterflies of Hispaniola.' *Entomologist*, 58:161.

Jamaica
BROWN, F. M. and HEINEMAN, B. 1972. *Jamaica and its Butterflies*. E. W. Classey, London. Very complete study. All species illustrated in colour.

Martinique, *see* Antilles Françaises.

Pines, Isle of
HOLLAND, W. J. 1916. 'Lepidoptera of the Isle of Pines.' *Annals of the Carnegie Museum*, 10:487.

Porto Rico
COMSTOCK, W. P. 1944. 'Insects of Porto Rico and the Virgin Isles. Rhopalocera.' *New York Academy of Sciences.* 12:421.

St Kitts
HALL, ARTHUR. 1936. 'The Butterflies of St Kitts.' *Entomologist*, 69:274.

St Vincent
GODMAN, F. D. and SALVIN, O. 1896. 'Butterflies . . . St Vincent, Grenada.' *Proc. zoological Society of London*, 1896:513.

Virgin Islands, *see* Porto Rico

Taxonomy

(Specialist papers on the classification of particular groups)

Hesperiidae
EVANS, W. H. 1951–55. *Catalogue of American Hesperiidae*. British Museum (N.H.), London.

MILLER, L. D. 1965. 'Review of the West Indian *Choranthus*.' *Journal of Research in Lepidoptera*, 4:259.

Lycaenidae

NABOKOV, V. 1945. 'Notes on neotropical Lycaenidae . . .' *Psyche*, 52:1.
CLENCH, HARRY. See Faunistic,. General.

Nymphalidae

FIELD, W. D. 1971. 'Butterflies of the genus *Vanessa*'. *Smithsonian Contributions to Zoology*, No. 84.
MUNROE, E. G. 1951. 'The genus *Junonia* in the West Indies.' *American Museum Novitates*, No. 1498.
RILEY, N. D. 1926. '*Colaenis* and *Dione*, a revisional note.' *Entomologist*, 59: 240.

Papilionidae

JORDAN, KARL. 1907–9. Papilionidae *in* Seitz, Macrolepidoptera World 5.
ROTHSCHILD, W. and JORDAN, K. 1906. 'A revision of the American Papilios.' *Novitates Zoologicae* 13, No. 3. Facsimile Reprint, California Academy of Sciences, 1967.

Pieridae

BROWN, F. M. 1929. 'Revision of the genus *Phoebis*.' *American Museum Novitates*, No. 368
BROWN, F. M. 1931. 'Revision of the genus *Aphrissa*.' *American Museum Novitates*, No. 454.
KLOTS, A. B. 1928, 1929. 'Revision of the genus *Eurema*.' Part 1, *J. New York Entomological Society*, 36:61; Part 2, *Entom. Americana*, 9:99.

Satyridae

MICHENER, CHARLES. 1943. 'Review of the genus *Calisto*.' *American Museum Novitates*, No. 1236.
MUNROE, E. G. 1950. 'The systematics of *Calisto*.' *Journal New York Entomological Society*, 58:211.

Zoogeography

BOND, JAMES. 1963. 'Derivation of the Antillean Avifauna.' *Proc. Academy Natural Sciences,* Philadelphia, 115:79.
KHUDOLEY, K. M. and MEYERHOFF, A. A. 1971. 'Paleogeography and Geological History of the Greater Antilles.' *Mem. geol. Soc. America*, 129.
SCOTT, J. A. 1972. 'Biogeography of the Antillean Butterflies.' *Biotropica*, 4:32.
See also: BROWN and HEINEMAN *under* Jamaica.
        CLENCH, HARRY *under* Faunistic, General.

Index of English Names

Numerals in **bold** type refer to plates

Index of Scientific Names

Names in Roman type are synonyms

90°
80°
FLORIDA
Grand Bahama I.
Great Abaco I.
New Providence I.
BAHAMA
ISLANDS
Eleuthera I.
Cat I.
Nassau
Andros Islands
Exuma I.
Rum
Long I.
Acklin I.
25°
GULF OF MEXICO
Straits of Florida
Habana
Channel of Yucatan
CUBA
Zapata Pen.
GREATER
Isle of Pines
YUCATAN
20°
Isla Cozumel
Little Cayman
Grand Cayman
Cayman Brac
Santiago de Cuba
JAMAICA
Gona
Kingston
Swan Is.
Islas de la Bahia
CARIBBEAN
15°
HONDURAS
NICARAGUA
Old Providence
St. Andrew
10°
COSTA RICA
Panama Canal
PANAMA
PACIFIC OCEAN
COLOMBI